JONES & BARTLETT
CDX

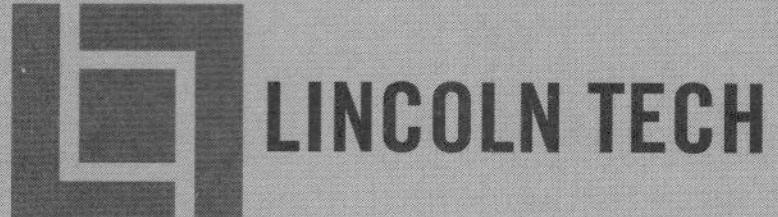

Lincoln Technical Institute

Medium/Heavy Truck Lab Manual *Volume 4*

JONES & BARTLETT
LEARNING

World Headquarters
Jones & Bartlett Learning
5 Wall Street
Burlington, MA 01803
978-443-5000
info@jblearning.com
www.jblearning.com

Jones & Bartlett Learning books and products are available through most bookstores and online booksellers. To contact Jones & Bartlett Learning directly, call 800-832-0034, fax 978-443-8000, or visit our website, www.jblearning.com.

Substantial discounts on bulk quantities of Jones & Bartlett Learning publications are available to corporations, professional associations, and other qualified organizations. For details and specific discount information, contact the special sales department at Jones & Bartlett Learning via the above contact information or send an email to specialsales@jblearning.com.

Production Credits
General Manager: Douglas Kaplan
Executive Publisher—CDX and Electrical: Vernon Anthony
Managing Editor—CDX Automotive: Amanda J. Mitchell
Editorial Assistant: Jamie Dinh
Vendor Manager: Tracey McCrea
Senior Marketing Manager: Brian Rooney
Manufacturing and Inventory Control Supervisor: Amy Bacus
Composition: B-books, Ltd.
Cover Design: Stephanie Torta
Rights & Media Specialist: Robert Boder
Media Development Editor: Shannon Sheehan
Cover Image: © Masekesam/Shutterstock
Printing and Binding: McNaughton & Gunn
Cover Printing: McNaughton & Gunn

ISBN: 978-1-284-11186-6

6048

Printed in the United States of America

21 10 9 8

Contents

Diesel Engines, DT101

CONTENTS

Diesel Engines: General 1

Student/intern information:

Name__________ Date__________ Class__________

Vehicle used for this activity:

Year__________ Make__________ Model__________

Odometer__________ VIN __________

Time off__________

Time on__________

Total time__________

Learning Objective / Task	CDX Tasksheet Number	2014 NATEF Priority Level	2014 NATEF Reference Number
• Inspect fuel, oil, Diesel Exhaust Fluid (DEF) and coolant levels, and condition; determine needed action.	H026	P-1	1A1
• Identify engine fuel, oil, coolant, air, and other leaks; determine needed action.	H027	P-1	1A2
• Listen for engine noises; determine needed action.	H028	P-3	1A3
• Observe engine exhaust smoke color and quantity; determine needed action.	H029	P-2	1A4

Materials Required

- Vehicle with possible engine concern
- Vehicle manufacturer's service information
- Manufacturer-specific tools depending on the concern
- Vehicle lifting equipment if applicable

Some Safety Issues to Consider

- Diagnosis of this fault may require test driving the vehicle on the school grounds or on a hoist, both of which carry severe risks. Attempt this task only with full permission from your supervisor/instructor and follow all the guidelines exactly.
- Caution: If you are working in an area where there could be "brake dust" present (may contain asbestos, which has been determined to cause cancer when inhaled or ingested), ensure you wear and use all OSHA-approved asbestos protective/removal equipment.
- Lifting equipment such as vehicle jacks and stands, vehicle hoists, and engine hoists are important tools that increase productivity and make the job easier. However, they can also cause severe injury or death if used improperly. Make sure you follow the manufacturer's operation procedures. Also make sure you have your supervisor/instructor's permission to use any particular type of lifting equipment.
- Comply with personal and environmental safety practices associated with clothing; eye protection; hand tools; power equipment; proper ventilation; and the handling, storage, and disposal of chemicals/materials in accordance with federal, state, and local regulations.
- Always wear the correct protective eyewear and clothing and use the appropriate safety equipment, as well as fender covers, seat protectors, and floor mat protectors.
- Make sure you understand and observe all legislative and personal safety procedures when carrying out practical assignments. If you are unsure of what these are, ask your supervisor/instructor.

Performance Standard

0–No exposure: No information or practice provided during the program; complete training required

1–Exposure only: General information provided with no practice time; close supervision needed; additional training required

2–Limited practice: Has practiced job during training program; additional training required to develop skill

3–Moderately skilled: Has performed job independently during training program; limited additional training may be required

4–Skilled: Can perform job independently with no additional training

Student/intern information:

Name__________________ Date__________ Class______________

Vehicle used for this activity:

Year__________ Make__________________ Model______________

Odometer________________ VIN ______________________

TASK Inspect fuel, oil, Diesel Exhaust Fluid (DEF) and coolant levels and condition; determine needed action. NATEF 1A1

Time off________

Time on________

Total time________

CDX Tasksheet Number: H026

1. Inspect fuel, oil, and coolant levels, and condition.
2. Research the procedure and specifications to identify the engine oil type and quantity in the appropriate service information.
   a. Recommended type of engine oil: ________________
   b. Recommended engine oil quantity: ________________
3. Research the procedure and specifications to identify the engine coolant type and quantity in the appropriate service information.
   a. Recommended type of engine coolant: ________________
   b. Recommended engine coolant quantity: ________________
4. Using a clean, clear plastic container, drain off a sample of the diesel fuel from the fuel tank(s).
   a. Ensure there is no fuel spillage.
   b. Visually inspect the sample for any contaminations (e.g., water).
      Note: In case of poor running conditions or catastrophic failure, it may be necessary to send the sample out to an independent lab to check the fuel.
      i. List your observations:
      ii. Within manufacturer's specifications: Yes: ______ No: ______
      iii. Determine any necessary action(s):
   c. If directed by your instructor, arrange for the fuel sample to be tested in accordance with industry standards.
5. Check the engine oil level as outlined in the appropriate service information.
   a. Within manufacturer's specifications: Yes: ______ No: ______
      Note: The manufacturer's specifications may state that the oil level should be between the low and high marks on the dipstick.
   b. Determine any necessary action(s):

c. Using a clean, clear plastic container, drain off a sample of the diesel engine oil.
d. If directed by your instructor, arrange for the engine oil sample to be tested in accordance with industry standards.

6. Check the coolant levels.
   a. Within the manufacturer's specifications: Yes: _______ No: _______
      Note: The manufacturer's specifications may indicate that the level should be between the high and low marks on the coolant reservoir.
   b. Determine any necessary action(s):
      ____
      ____
   c. Using a clean, clear plastic container, drain off a sample of the engine coolant from the radiator.
   d. Inspect the sample for any contaminations (e.g., oil).
      i. Within manufacturer's specifications: Yes: _______ No: _______
         Note: The manufacturer's specifications may or may not have information on observing contamination in the coolant.
      ii. Determine any necessary action(s):
         ____
         ____
         ____
         ____
         ____
   e. If directed by your instructor, arrange for the coolant sample to be tested in accordance with industry standards.
7. Check the DEF.
   a. List the DEF level: ______________________________
   b. List the DEF condition: ______________________________
   c. Determine any necessary action(s):
      ____
      ____
8. Discuss the findings with your instructor.

Performance Rating

CDX Tasksheet Number: H026

☐	☐	☐	☐	☐
0	1	2	3	4

Supervisor/instructor signature ______________________________ Date__________

Student/intern information:

Name_______________ Date_______________ Class_______________

Vehicle used for this activity:

Year_______________ Make_______________ Model_______________

Odometer_______________ VIN _______________

TASK Identify engine fuel, oil, coolant, air, and other leaks; determine needed action.

NATEF 1A2

Time off_______________

Time on_______________

Total time_______________

CDX Tasksheet Number: H027

1. Research the procedure for checking and identifying the main causes of engine fuel leaks in the appropriate service information.
   a. List, or print off and attach to this sheet, all possible causes for engine fuel leaks:

2. Research the procedure for checking and identifying the main causes of engine oil leaks in the appropriate service information.
   a. List, or print off and attach to this sheet, all possible causes for engine oil leaks:

3. Research the procedure for checking and identifying the main causes of engine coolant leaks in the appropriate service information.
   a. List, or print off and attach to this sheet, all possible causes for engine coolant leaks:

4. Research the procedure for checking and identifying the main causes of air and other leaks in the appropriate service information.
   a. List, or print off and attach to this sheet, all possible causes of air intake and other air filter related problems and leaks:

5. Given a suitable vehicle, inspect for any engine oil, fuel, coolant, or air leaks.
   a. List your observations:

   b. Determine any necessary action(s):

Performance Rating

CDX Tasksheet Number: H027

☐ 0 ☐ 1 ☐ 2 ☐ 3 ☐ 4

Supervisor/instructor signature _______________ Date_______________

Student/intern information:

Name____________________ Date__________ Class________________

Vehicle used for this activity:

Year__________ Make____________________ Model________________

Odometer____________________ VIN ____________________

TASK Listen for engine noises; determine needed action. NATEF 1A3

Time off__________

Time on__________

Total time__________

CDX Tasksheet Number: H028

1. Start the engine.
2. Check engine starting/operation for any unusual noises and vibrations.
   a. List any usual noises from the engine (if any).

   b. Are there any vibrations coming from the engine? Yes: _____ No: _____
      i. If yes, record where they are coming from:

3. Shut the engine down.
4. Referencing the appropriate service information, record your recommendations to identify the source of the abnormal engine noises and vibrations:

5. Discuss your findings and recommendations with your instructor.

Performance Rating

CDX Tasksheet Number: H028

☐ 0 ☐ 1 ☐ 2 ☐ 3 ☐ 4

Supervisor/instructor signature ____________________ Date__________

Student/intern information:

Name____________________ Date__________ Class________________

Vehicle used for this activity:

Year__________ Make____________________ Model________________

Odometer____________________ VIN ____________________

TASK Observe engine exhaust smoke color and quantity; determine needed action.

NATEF 1A4

Time off__________

Time on__________

Total time__________

CDX Tasksheet Number: H029

1. Start the engine.
2. Check the exhaust smoke.
   a. With the engine running:
      i. Record the idle rpm: ____________________
      ii. Record the governed rpm: ____________________
      iii. Record the color of the exhaust smoke from the stack: ____________________
      iv. Record the quantity of smoke coming from the exhaust (e.g., short bust, then cleared; longer bust, then cleared; large amount after start up and at idle):

      ____

3. Shut the engine down.
4. Referencing the appropriate service information, record your recommendations to rectify the source of the abnormal exhaust smoke.

   ____

   ____

   ____

   ____

   ____

5. Discuss your findings and recommendations with your instructor.

Performance Rating

CDX Tasksheet Number: H029

☐	☐	☐	☐	☐
0	1	2	3	4

Supervisor/instructor signature ____________________________ Date__________

Diesel Engines: General 2

Student/intern information:

Name________________ Date________ Class____________

Vehicle used for this activity:

Year________ Make________________ Model____________

Odometer______________ VIN ________________

Time off________

Time on________

Total time________

Learning Objective / Task	CDX Tasksheet Number	2014 NATEF Priority Level	2014 NATEF Reference Number
• Identify causes of no cranking, cranks but fails to start, hard starting, and starts but does not continue to run problems; determine needed action.	H030	P-1	1A5
• Identify engine vibration problems.	H032	P-2	1A7

Materials Required

- Vehicle with possible engine concern
- Vehicle manufacturer's service information
- Manufacturer-specific tools depending on the concern
- Vehicle lifting equipment if applicable

Some Safety Issues to Consider

- Diagnosis of this fault may require test driving the vehicle on the school grounds or on a hoist, both of which carry severe risks. Attempt this task only with full permission from your supervisor/instructor and follow all the guidelines exactly.
- Caution: If you are working in an area where there could be "brake dust" present (may contain asbestos, which has been determined to cause cancer when inhaled or ingested), ensure you wear and use all OSHA-approved asbestos protective/removal equipment.
- Lifting equipment such as vehicle jacks and stands, vehicle hoists, and engine hoists are important tools that increase productivity and make the job easier. However, they can also cause severe injury or death if used improperly. Make sure you follow the manufacturer's operation procedures. Also make sure you have your supervisor/instructor's permission to use any particular type of lifting equipment.
- Comply with personal and environmental safety practices associated with clothing; eye protection; hand tools; power equipment; proper ventilation; and the handling, storage, and disposal of chemicals/materials in accordance with federal, state, and local regulations.
- Always wear the correct protective eyewear and clothing and use the appropriate safety equipment, as well as fender covers, seat protectors, and floor mat protectors.
- Make sure you understand and observe all legislative and personal safety procedures when carrying out practical assignments. If you are unsure of what these are, ask your supervisor/instructor.

Performance Standard

0–No exposure: No information or practice provided during the program; complete training required

1–Exposure only: General information provided with no practice time; close supervision needed; additional training required

2–Limited practice: Has practiced job during training program; additional training required to develop skill

3–Moderately skilled: Has performed job independently during training program; limited additional training may be required

4–Skilled: Can perform job independently with no additional training

Student/intern information:

Name_______________ Date_______________ Class_______________

Vehicle used for this activity:

Year_______________ Make_______________ Model_______________

Odometer_______________ VIN_______________

TASK Identify causes of no cranking, cranks but fails to start, hard starting, and starts but does not continue to run problems; determine needed action. NATEF 1A5

Time off_______________

Time on_______________

Total time_______________

CDX Tasksheet Number: H030

1. Reference the appropriate service information for the common causes for a "no crank" situation.
   a. List, or print off and attach to this sheet, all possible causes for "no crank" (the engine will not turn over using the starter motor):
   b. Determine what action will be required for "no crank":
2. Given a suitable vehicle that has been set up to serve as an example of a "no-crank" condition, determine the cause of the "no crank" condition. The vehicle has been "bugged" with a fault to prevent the engine from starting.
   a. List the customer concern:
   b. Diagnose the cause of the concern. List the steps you took, results of those tests, and cause of the concern.
   c. Determine any necessary action(s):
3. Reference the appropriate service information for the common causes for a "cranks but fails to start" situation (the engine will run but takes longer than usual to start).
   a. List, or print off and attach to this sheet, all possible causes for "cranks but fails to start":
   b. Determine what action will be required for "cranks but fails to start":

4. Reference the appropriate service information for the common causes for a "hard starting" situation (the engine will run but takes longer than usual to start).
    a. List, or print off and attach to this sheet, all possible causes for "hard starting":

    ____
    ____
    ____

    b. Determine what action will be required for "hard starting":

    ____
    ____
    ____

5. Reference the appropriate service information for the common causes for a "starts but does not continue to run problem" situation.
    a. List all possible causes for "starts but does not continue to run problem":

    ____
    ____
    ____

    b. Determine what action will be required for "starts but does not continue to run problem":

    ____
    ____
    ____

6. Discuss the findings with your instructor.

Performance Rating

CDX Tasksheet Number: H030

☐	☐	☐	☐	☐
0	1	2	3	4

Supervisor/instructor signature ______________________ Date__________

Student/intern information:

Name________________ Date________ Class____________

Vehicle used for this activity:

Year________ Make________________ Model____________

Odometer______________ VIN ____________________

TASK Identify engine vibration problems. NATEF 1A7

Time off________

Time on________

Total time________

CDX Tasksheet Number: H032

1. Reference the appropriate service information for the common causes for an engine's possible "vibration" problems.
   a. List, or print off and attach to this sheet, all possible causes for an engine's possible "vibration" problems:

2. List how the causes of engine vibrations can be located:

3. List what must be done to correct engine vibration problems:

4. Discuss the findings with your instructor.

Performance Rating

CDX Tasksheet Number: H032

☐ 0 ☐ 1 ☐ 2 ☐ 3 ☐ 4

Supervisor/instructor signature ________________ Date________

Diesel Engines: Cylinder Head and Valve Train 1

Student/intern information:

Name__________ Date__________ Class__________

Vehicle used for this activity:

Year__________ Make__________ Model__________

Odometer__________ VIN __________

Time off__________

Time on__________

Total time__________

Learning Objective / Task	CDX Tasksheet Number	2014 NATEF Priority Level	2014 NATEF Reference Number
• Remove, clean, inspect for visible damage and replace cylinder head(s) assembly.	MHT01	N/A	N/A
• Clean and inspect threaded holes, studs and bolts for serviceability; determine needed action.	MHT02	N/A	N/A
• Inspect cylinder head for cracks/damage; check mating surfaces for warpage; check condition of passages; inspect core/expansion and gallery plugs; determine needed action.	H034	P-2	1B1
• Disassemble head and inspect valves, guides, seats, springs, retainers, rotators, locks, and seals; determine needed action.	H035	P-3	1B2
• Measure valve head height relative to deck and valve face-to-seat contact; determine needed action.	H036	P-3	1B3
• Inspect injector sleeves and seals; measure injector tip or nozzle protrusion; determine needed action.	H037	P-3	1B4
• Inspect valve train components; determine needed action.	H038	P-1	1B5

Materials Required

- Vehicle with possible engine concern
- Vehicle manufacturer's service information
- Manufacturer-specific tools depending on the concern
- Vehicle lifting equipment if applicable

Some Safety Issues to Consider

- Diagnosis of this fault may require test driving the vehicle on the school grounds or on a hoist, both of which carry severe risks. Attempt this task only with full permission from your supervisor/instructor and follow all the guidelines exactly.
- Caution: If you are working in an area where there could be "brake dust" present (may contain asbestos, which has been determined to cause cancer when inhaled or ingested), ensure you wear and use all OSHA-approved asbestos protective/removal equipment.
- Lifting equipment such as vehicle jacks and stands, vehicle hoists, and engine hoists are important tools that increase productivity and make the job easier. However, they can also cause severe injury or death if used improperly. Make sure you follow the manufacturer's operation procedures. Also make sure you have your supervisor/instructor's permission to use any particular type of lifting equipment.

- Comply with personal and environmental safety practices associated with clothing; eye protection; hand tools; power equipment; proper ventilation; and the handling, storage, and disposal of chemicals/materials in accordance with federal, state, and local regulations.
- Always wear the correct protective eyewear and clothing and use the appropriate safety equipment, as well as fender covers, seat protectors, and floor mat protectors.
- Make sure you understand and observe all legislative and personal safety procedures when carrying out practical assignments. If you are unsure of what these are, ask your supervisor/instructor.

Performance Standard

0–No exposure: No information or practice provided during the program; complete training required

1–Exposure only: General information provided with no practice time; close supervision needed; additional training required

2–Limited practice: Has practiced job during training program; additional training required to develop skill

3–Moderately skilled: Has performed job independently during training program; limited additional training may be required

4–Skilled: Can perform job independently with no additional training

Student/intern information:

Name____________________ Date__________ Class____________________

Vehicle used for this activity:

Year__________ Make____________________ Model____________________

Odometer____________________ VIN ____________________

◀◀ TASK Remove, clean, and inspect for visible damage and replace cylinder head(s) assembly.

Non-NATEF

Time off__________

Time on__________

Total time__________

CDX Tasksheet Number: MHT01

1. Research the procedure and specifications for removing and installing the cylinder head(s) in the appropriate service information.

   a. Does this vehicle use TTY head bolts? Yes: _____ No: _____

   b. List or print off and attach any special tools required for this task:

   c. List or print off and attach any special precautions required for this task:

   d. List or print off and attach the cylinder head bolt detorquing sequence for removing the head bolts:

   e. List or print off and attach the torque procedure for installing the head bolts:

   f. Method specified for lifting the cylinder head/s off of the block:

2. Following the specified procedure, remove the cylinder head/s from the engine. List any difficulties you had performing this procedure.
   Note: Be very careful not to damage or scratch the head surface as this could cause a leak. Lay the head down on shop towels, and only use nonmetallic scrapers on aluminum or plastic surfaces.

3. Perform an initial visual inspection of the following items for any irregularities:
   a. Head gasket: ______
   b. Head surface: ______
   c. Valves: ______
   d. Valve springs and retainers: ______
   e. Rocker arms or cam followers: ______
   f. Cylinder walls and top of the pistons: ______

4. Following the specified procedure, clean and visually inspect the cylinder head/s for cracks and surface finish; check passage condition. List your observations:
   ______
   ______
   ______

5. Determine any necessary actions:
   ______
   ______
   ______

6. Have your instructor verify removal of the head, and review your answers: ______

7. Ask your instructor if he or she wants you to reinstall the head, or move on to the next tasksheet. List the answer here: ______

8. If your instructor directed you to reinstall the cylinder head(s), follow the specified procedure to install the head gasket(s) and cylinder head(s). Make sure you follow the specified procedure and sequence for tightening down the head bolts. Failure to do so could cause the gasket to fail.
   ______
   ______
   ______

9. List any difficulties you experienced during the installation procedure:
   ______
   ______
   ______

10. Discuss the findings with your instructor.

Performance Rating

CDX Tasksheet Number: MHT01

☐ 0 ☐ 1 ☐ 2 ☐ 3 ☐ 4

Supervisor/instructor signature ______ Date______

Student/intern information:

Name________________ Date________ Class____________

Vehicle used for this activity:

Year________ Make________________ Model____________

Odometer________________ VIN ________________

TASK Clean and inspect threaded holes, studs and bolts for serviceability; determine needed action. Non-NATEF

Time off________

Time on________

Total time________

CDX Tasksheet Number: MHT02

1. Visually inspect all threaded holes in the cylinder head for the following conditions. List your observations:

   a. Broken off fasteners:

   b. Stripped threads:

   c. Cross-threaded threads:

   d. Side of threaded hole broken out:

   e. Heavily rusted/corroded:

   f. Other:

2. Visually inspect all threaded studs, nuts and bolts from the cylinder head for the following conditions. List your observations:

   a. Broken off:

   b. Stripped threads:

   c. Cross-threaded threads:

d. Stretched/necked down:

____

____

e. Heavily rusted/corroded:

____

____

f. Other:

____

____

3. Using a thread pitch gauge, identify the correct tap/s needed to clean the threaded holes in the cylinder head.

4. With your instructor's permission, use the taps to clean the threaded holes in the cylinder head. **Note:** Make sure that the tap you selected fits the threads properly. You should be able to start the tap by hand, and it should turn with a tap handle easily and smoothly. If not, stop and ask your instructor for assistance.

5. Ask your instructor which method they would like you to use to clean the threads on the bolts and studs you will be reusing. Check the appropriate answer below:

   a. Wire wheel: _______

   Note: this can be dangerous. Make sure your instructor has trained you on how to perform this safely if they choose this method.

   b. Die: _______

   c. Other (list method): _______________________________

6. After cleaning the fasteners and threaded holes, determine any necessary action/s:

____

____

____

7. Discuss the findings with your instructor.

Performance Rating

CDX Tasksheet Number: MHT02

☐	☐	☐	☐	☐
0	1	2	3	4

Supervisor/instructor signature _______________________________ Date_______

Student/intern information:

Name____________________________________ Date____________ Class________________________

Vehicle used for this activity:

Year______________ Make_____________________________________ Model______________________

Odometer______________________________ VIN ____

◀◀ TASK Inspect cylinder head for cracks/damage; check mating surfaces for warpage; check condition of passages; inspect core/expansion and gallery plugs; determine needed action.

NATEF 1B1

Time off__________

Time on__________

Total time__________

CDX Tasksheet Number: H034

1. Determine the type of crack detention process(es) that your workshop utilizes.
   a. Magnetic particle inspection: Yes: _____ No: _____
   b. Penetrating dyes: Yes: _____ No: _____
   c. Pressure testing: Yes: _____ No: _____
   d. Vacuum testing: Yes: _____ No: _____
   e. Ultrasonic testing: Yes: _____ No: _____
   f. None of the above: Yes: _______
      i. If none of the above, name the method your workshop uses: ________________
   g. Outsource testing and repairs: Yes: _____ No: _____

2. Reference the appropriate service information; list the procedure and all safety precautions that must be observed when carrying out an inspection of a cylinder head for cracks/damage.
   a. List, or print off and attach to this sheet, the steps involved in inspecting a cylinder head for cracks/damage:
   b. Determine what safety precautions must be observed when inspecting a cylinder head for cracks/damage:

3. Discuss these procedures and safety precautions with your instructor. Determine what method of testing will be carried out:

4. If directed by your instructor, begin crack testing the cylinder head. Follow the procedures listed above and reference the appropriate service information.
   a. List your observations:
   b. Meets the manufacturer's specifications: Yes: _____ No: _____
   c. Determine any necessary action(s):

5. Reference the appropriate service information; list the procedure for checking for warpage of the cylinder head mating surfaces:
   a. List, or print off and attach to this sheet, the steps involved in checking the cylinder head for warpage:

      ____
      ____
      ____

   b. Determine what safety precautions must be observed when checking the cylinder head for warpage:

      ____
      ____
      ____

6. Following the procedures listed above, and while referencing the appropriate service information, check for any warpage of the cylinder head mating surfaces.
   a. List your findings for maximum warpage:

      ____
      ____

   b. Meets the manufacturer's specifications: Yes: _____ No: _____

   c. Determine any necessary action(s):

      ____
      ____
      ____

7. Referring to the appropriate service information, check the condition of passages and inspect the core/expansion and gallery plugs.
   a. List your findings of the condition of passages and core/expansion and gallery plugs:

      ____
      ____

   b. Meets the manufacturer's specifications: Yes: _____ No: _____

   c. Determine any necessary action(s):

      ____
      ____
      ____
      ____

8. Discuss the findings with your instructor.

Performance Rating

CDX Tasksheet Number: H034

☐	☐	☐	☐	☐
0	1	2	3	4

Supervisor/instructor signature ______________________________ Date__________

Student/intern information:

Name_______________ Date_______________ Class_______________

Vehicle used for this activity:

Year_______________ Make_______________ Model_______________

Odometer_______________ VIN _______________

TASK Disassemble head and inspect valves, guides, seats, springs, retainers, rotators, locks, and seals; determine needed action. NATEF 1B2

Time off_______________

Time on_______________

Total time_______________

CDX Tasksheet Number: H035

1. Research the following specifications in the appropriate service information:
   a. Valve stem diameter: Intake: _______________ in/mm Exhaust: _______________ in/mm
   b. Valve margin thickness: Intake: _______________ in/mm Exhaust: _______________ in/mm

2. While referencing the appropriate service information, dismantle the cylinder head using the recommended special tools. When removing the components, store all the nuts and bolts in order in storage trays.
   a. As you dismantle each valve assembly, keep them in order so that they can be evaluated as a unit. Lay out the components so as to identify their original position.
   b. Remove and inspect the retainers.
      i. Meets the manufacturer's specifications: Yes: _____ No: _____
   c. Remove and inspect the rotators.
      i. Meets the manufacturer's specifications: Yes: _____ No: _____
   d. Remove and inspect the springs for twists, distortions, and nicks.
      i. Meets the manufacturer's specifications: Yes: _____ No: _____
   e. Remove and inspect the seals.
      i. Meets the manufacturer's specifications: Yes: _____ No: _____
   f. Remove and inspect the valves. Measure valve stem diameter and valve margin thickness using the recommended special tools. Record your findings in the tables below.

	Valve stem diameter in/mm				
Cylinder	Valve 1	Valve 2	Valve 3	Valve 4	Valve 5
1					
2					
3					
4					
5					
6					
7					
8					

Cylinder	Valve margin thickness in/mm				
	Valve 1	Valve 2	Valve 3	Valve 4	Valve 5
1					
2					
3					
4					
5					
6					
7					
8					

3. Determine any necessary action(s):

____

____

____

____

____

4. Discuss the findings with your instructor.

Performance Rating

CDX Tasksheet Number: H035

☐ 0 ☐ 1 ☐ 2 ☐ 3 ☐ 4

Supervisor/instructor signature ______________________ Date__________

Student/intern information:

Name__________ Date__________ Class__________

Vehicle used for this activity:

Year__________ Make__________ Model__________

Odometer__________ VIN __________

TASK Measure valve head height relative to deck and valve face-to-seat contact; determine needed action. NATEF 1B3

Time off__________

Time on__________

Total time__________

CDX Tasksheet Number: H036

1. Research the following specifications in the appropriate service information:
   a. Valve head height relative to deck: __________ in/mm
   b. Valve face-to-seat contact:

   ____

2. While referencing the appropriate service information, measure valve head height relative to the deck and valve face-to-seat contact using the recommended special tools. Record your findings in the tables below.

	Valve head height relative to deck				
Cylinder	Valve 1	Valve 2	Valve 3	Valve 4	Valve 5
1					
2					
3					
4					
5					
6					
7					
8					

	Valve face-to-seat contact (Use coding below)				
Cylinder	Valve 1	Valve 2	Valve 3	Valve 4	Valve 5
1					
2					
3					
4					
5					
6					
7					
8					

Valve face-to-seat contact coding: Unserviceable = US; Requires Servicing = RS; Serviceable = S; Requires Replacement = RR

3. Determine any necessary action(s):

____
____
____
____
____

4. Discuss your findings with your instructor.

Performance Rating

CDX Tasksheet Number: H036

☐ 0 ☐ 1 ☐ 2 ☐ 3 ☐ 4

Supervisor/instructor signature _______________________ Date_________

Student/intern information:

Name_______________ Date_______ Class_______________

Vehicle used for this activity:

Year_______ Make_______________ Model_______________

Odometer_______________ VIN _______________

TASK Inspect injector sleeves and seals; measure injector tip or nozzle protrusion; determine needed action. NATEF 1B4

Time off_______

Time on_______

Total time_______

CDX Tasksheet Number: H037

1. Research the following specifications in the appropriate service information:
   a. Injector tip or nozzle protrusion: _______________
2. While referencing the appropriate service information, inspect injector sleeves and seals.
   a. List your observations: _______________
   b. Meets the manufacturer's specifications: Yes: _____ No: _____
   c. Determine any necessary action(s): _______________
3. While referencing the appropriate service information, and using the recommended special tools, measure the injector tip or nozzle protrusion and record your findings in the table below.

Cylinder	Injector tip or nozzle protrusion
1	
2	
3	
4	
5	
6	
7	
8	

   a. Determine any necessary action(s): _______________
4. Discuss your findings with your instructor.

Performance Rating

CDX Tasksheet Number: H037

☐ 0 ☐ 1 ☐ 2 ☐ 3 ☐ 4

Supervisor/instructor signature _______________ Date_______

Student/intern information:

Name____________________ Date__________ Class________________

Vehicle used for this activity:

Year__________ Make____________________ Model________________

Odometer____________________ VIN ________________________

TASK Inspect valve train components; determine needed action. NATEF 1B5

Time off__________

Time on__________

Total time__________

CDX Tasksheet Number: H038

1. Research the following specifications in the appropriate service information:
   a. Valve spring height: ________________ in/mm
   b. Valve spring tension: ________ ft-lbs (Nm)

2. While referencing the appropriate service information, inspect all the components that are applicable to your task in the table below.

Component	Serviceable	Repairable	Unserviceable
Camshaft/lobes			
Cam Followers			
Bucket tappets			
Adjusting shims			
Rockers			
Cam rollers			
Cam gear(s)			
Cam retaining caps			
Timing belt/chain			
Rocker shaft(s)			

3. Valve spring inspection and assessment:

Valve spring height (inches or mm) and tension (ft/lbs or Nm)									
Cylinder		1	2	3	4	5	6	7	8
Valve 1	Height								
	Tension								
Valve 2	Height								
	Tension								
Valve 3	Height								
	Tension								

Valve 4	Height								
	Tension								
Valve 5	Height								
	Tension								
Valve 6	Height								
	Tension								
Valve 7	Height								
	Tension								
Valve 8	Height								
	Tension								

a. Meets the manufacturer's specifications: Yes: _____ No: _____

b. Determine any necessary action(s):

____

____

____

____

____

4. Discuss the findings with your instructor.

Performance Rating

CDX Tasksheet Number: H038

☐ 0 ☐ 1 ☐ 2 ☐ 3 ☐ 4

Supervisor/instructor signature _______________________________ Date_____________

Diesel Engines: Cylinder Head and Valve Train 2

Student/intern information:

Name__________ Date__________ Class__________

Vehicle used for this activity:

Year__________ Make__________ Model__________

Odometer__________ VIN __________

Learning Objective / Task	CDX Tasksheet Number	2014 NATEF Priority Level	2014 NATEF Reference Number
• Reassemble cylinder head.	H039	P-3	1B6
• Inspect, measure, and replace/reinstall overhead camshaft; measure/adjust end play and backlash.	H040	P-3	1B7
• Inspect electronic wiring harness and brackets for wear, bending, cracks, and looseness; determine needed action.	H041	P-1	1B8
• Adjust valve bridges (crossheads); adjust valve clearances and injector settings.	H042	P-2	1B9

Materials Required

- Vehicle with possible engine concern
- Vehicle manufacturer's service information
- Manufacturer-specific tools depending on the concern
- Vehicle lifting equipment if applicable

Some Safety Issues to Consider

- Diagnosis of this fault may require test driving the vehicle on the school grounds or on a hoist, both of which carry severe risks. Attempt this task only with full permission from your supervisor/instructor and follow all the guidelines exactly.
- Caution: If you are working in an area where there could be "brake dust" present (may contain asbestos, which has been determined to cause cancer when inhaled or ingested), ensure you wear and use all OSHA-approved asbestos protective/removal equipment.
- Lifting equipment such as vehicle jacks and stands, vehicle hoists, and engine hoists are important tools that increase productivity and make the job easier. However, they can also cause severe injury or death if used improperly. Make sure you follow the manufacturer's operation procedures. Also make sure you have your supervisor/instructor's permission to use any particular type of lifting equipment.
- Comply with personal and environmental safety practices associated with clothing; eye protection; hand tools; power equipment; proper ventilation; and the handling, storage, and disposal of chemicals/materials in accordance with federal, state, and local regulations.
- Always wear the correct protective eyewear and clothing and use the appropriate safety equipment, as well as fender covers, seat protectors, and floor mat protectors.
- Make sure you understand and observe all legislative and personal safety procedures when carrying out practical assignments. If you are unsure of what these are, ask your supervisor/instructor.

Performance Standard

0–No exposure: No information or practice provided during the program; complete training required

1–Exposure only: General information provided with no practice time; close supervision needed; additional training required

2–Limited practice: Has practiced job during training program; additional training required to develop skill

3–Moderately skilled: Has performed job independently during training program; limited additional training may be required

4–Skilled: Can perform job independently with no additional training

Student/intern information:

Name____________________ Date__________ Class________________

Vehicle used for this activity:

Year__________ Make____________________ Model________________

Odometer____________________ VIN ____________________

TASK Reassemble cylinder head. NATEF 1B6

Time off________

Time on________

Total time________

CDX Tasksheet Number: H039

1. Research the following specifications in the appropriate service information:
   a. Valve head height relative to the deck: ________________ in/mm
   b. injector tip or nozzle protrusion:
   ____
2. Ensure all cylinder head and associated parts have been cleaned and dried.
3. Secure the cylinder head to the bench to ensure it does not fall and is safe to work on.
4. Have the valves been ground in accordance with the manufacturer's specifications?
   a. Meets the manufacturer's specifications: Yes: _____ No: _____
   b. If no, discuss with your instructor if he or she requires this action to be undertaken.
   c. If yes, list the steps involved in servicing the valves:
   ____
   ____
   ____
5. Have the valve seats been ground in accordance with the manufacturer's specifications?
   a. Meets the manufacturer's specifications: Yes: _____ No: _____
   b. If no, discuss with your instructor if he or she requires this action to be undertaken.
   c. If yes, list the steps involved in servicing the valve seats:
   ____
   ____
   ____
6. Have the valves been lapped into the valve seats in accordance with the manufacturer's specifications?
   a. Meets the manufacturer's specifications: Yes: _____ No: _____
   b. If no, discuss with your instructor if he or she requires this action to be undertaken.
   c. If yes, list the steps involved in lapping the valves faces onto the valve seats:
   ____
   ____
   ____

7. Reference the appropriate service information; list the procedure and all safety precautions that must be observed when reassembling the cylinder head.
   a. List, or print and attach to this sheet, the steps involved in reassembling the cylinder head:

      ____

      ____

      ____

   b. Determine what safety precautions must be observed when reassembling the cylinder head:

      ____

      ____

      ____

8. Discuss these procedures and safety precautions with your instructor.

9. If directed by your instructor, begin reassembling the cylinder head.
   a. Source all the special tooling required as recommended by the manufacturer and your instructor.
   b. Source all necessary spare parts and repair kit(s) from your stores area or spare parts department.

10. Following the procedures listed above, and while referencing the appropriate service information, reassemble the cylinder head.
    a. Insert the valves into their relative seats as per their reconditioning results (or original position, depending on the level of servicing).
    b. Fit the valve oil seal(s) if applicable.
    c. Fit the new valve springs and shims (or original valve springs and to they original position, depending on the level of servicing).
    d. Fit the rotators and valve keepers as required.

11. Following the procedures listed above, and while referencing the appropriate service information, measure the assembled height of all the valves assembled in the cylinder head.
    a. Measure valve head height relative to the deck using the recommended special tools and compare the heights before and after in the table below.

	Valve head height relative to the deck				
Cylinder	Valve 1	Valve 2	Valve 3	Valve 4	Valve 5
1					
2					
3					
4					
5					
6					
7					
8					

       i. Meets the manufacturer's specifications: Yes: _____ No: _____

       ii. Determine any necessary action(s):

       ____

       ____

       ____

12. Following the procedures listed above, and while referencing the appropriate service information, reassemble the injector sleeves and injectors into the cylinder head.
    a. Insert the injector sleeves and new seals into their position relative as per their reconditioning results (or original position, depending on the level of servicing).
    b. Fit the injectors into their original position.
    c. Assemble the injector clamps or securing devices and tighten to the recommended manufacturer's tension specifications.

13. While referencing the appropriate service information and using the recommended special tools, measure the injector tip or nozzle protrusion.
    a. Measure the injector tip or nozzle protrusion using the recommended special tools, and compare the heights before and after in the table below.

Cylinder	Injector tip or nozzle protrusion
1	
2	
3	
4	
5	
6	
7	
8	

       i. Meets the manufacturer's specifications: Yes: _____ No: _____

       ii. Determine any necessary action(s):

___

___

___

___

___

14. If your workshop has pressure testing capabilities, pressure test the newly install valves for correct sealing under operating pressures. Refer to your instructor for directions and assistance to carry this operation out, if applicable. List your observations:

___

___

___

___

___

15. Have your instructor inspect your assembled cylinder head to this point and discuss the findings with him or her.

Performance Rating

CDX Tasksheet Number: H039

☐	☐	☐	☐	☐
0	1	2	3	4

Supervisor/instructor signature ______________________ Date______

Student/intern information:

Name____________________ Date__________ Class____________________

Vehicle used for this activity:

Year__________ Make____________________ Model____________________

Odometer____________________ VIN ____________________

TASK Inspect, measure, and replace/reinstall overhead camshaft; measure/adjust end play and backlash. NATEF 1B7

Time off__________

Time on__________

Total time__________

CDX Tasksheet Number: H040

1. Follow the procedures listed in the appropriate service information. Reassemble the camshaft into the cylinder head (applicable only to overhead mounted camshaft(s). Continue if this is an OHC assembly.
   a. Check the camshaft bearings; replace if necessary.
   b. Locate the camshaft into the cylinder head.
   c. Fit cam mounting brackets and torque to the manufacturer's specifications.
      i. Manufacturer's specified torque: __________ ft/lbs (Nm)
      ii. Actual torque: __________ ft/lbs (Nm)

2. Following the procedures listed in the appropriate service information, use the recommended special tools to measure/adjust end play and backlash (applicable only to overhead mounted camshaft(s)). Continue if this is an OHC assembly.
   a. Manufacturer's specification–end play: __________ in/mm
   b. Actual end play measurement: __________ in/mm
   c. Manufacturer's specification–backlash: __________ in/mm
   d. Actual backlash measurement: __________ in/mm

3. Discuss the findings with your instructor.

Performance Rating

CDX Tasksheet Number: H040

☐ 0 ☐ 1 ☐ 2 ☐ 3 ☐ 4

Supervisor/instructor signature ____________________ Date__________

Student/intern information:

Name________________ Date________ Class________________

Vehicle used for this activity:

Year________ Make________________ Model________________

Odometer________________ VIN________________

TASK Inspect electronic wiring harness and brackets for wear, bending, cracks, and looseness; determine needed action. NATEF 1B8

Time off________

Time on________

Total time________

CDX Tasksheet Number: H041

1. Follow the procedures listed in the appropriate service information. Inspect the electronic wiring harness and brackets for wear, bending, cracks, and looseness.
   a. List your observations:
   ____
   ____
   ____
   b. Meets the manufacturer's specifications: Yes: _____ No: _____
   c. Determine any necessary action(s):
   ____
   ____
   ____
2. Discuss your findings with your instructor.

Performance Rating

CDX Tasksheet Number: H041

☐	☐	☐	☐	☐
0	1	2	3	4

Supervisor/instructor signature ________________ Date________

Student/intern information:

Name______________________________ Date__________ Class______________________

Vehicle used for this activity:

Year__________ Make______________________________ Model____________________

Odometer________________________ VIN ____________________________________

◂◂ TASK Adjust valve bridges (crossheads); adjust valve clearances and injector settings.

NATEF 1B9

Time off__________

Time on__________

Total time__________

CDX Tasksheet Number: H042

1. Reference the appropriate service information; list the procedure to adjust valve bridges (crossheads).
   a. List, or print and attach to this sheet, the steps involved to adjust valve bridges (crossheads):

   b. Determine what safety precautions must be observed when adjusting the valve bridges (crossheads):

2. Following the procedures listed above, and while referencing the appropriate service information, adjust the valve bridges (crossheads).
   a. List your observations:

   b. Meets the manufacturer's specifications: Yes: _____ No: _____

   c. Determine any necessary action(s):

3. Reference the appropriate service information; list the procedure to adjust the valve and injector settings.
   a. List, or print and attach to this sheet, the steps involved to adjust the valve and injector settings:
      ____
      ____
      ____
   b. Determine what safety precautions must be observed when adjusting the settings:
      ____
      ____
      ____
4. Following the procedures listed above, and while referencing the appropriate service information, adjust the valve and injector settings.
   a. List your observations:
      ____
      ____
      ____
      ____
      ____
   b. Meets the manufacturer's specifications: Yes: _____ No: _____
   c. Determine any necessary action(s):
      ____
      ____
      ____
      ____
      ____
5. Discuss your findings with your instructor.

Performance Rating

CDX Tasksheet Number: H042

☐ 0 ☐ 1 ☐ 2 ☐ 3 ☐ 4

Supervisor/instructor signature ______________________________ Date______________

Diesel Engines: Engine Block 1

Student/intern information:

Name__________ Date__________ Class__________

Vehicle used for this activity:

Year__________ Make__________ Model__________

Odometer__________ VIN __________

Time off__________

Time on__________

Total time__________

Learning Objective / Task	CDX Tasksheet Number	2014 NATEF Priority Level	2014 NATEF Reference Number
• Perform crankcase pressure test; determine needed action.	H043	P-1	1C1
• Remove, inspect, service, and install pans, covers, gaskets, seals, wear rings, and crankcase ventilation components.	H044	P-2	1C2
• Disassemble, clean, and inspect engine block for cracks/damage; measure mating surfaces for warpage; check condition of passages, core/expansion, and gallery plugs; inspect threaded holes, studs, dowel pins, and bolts for serviceability; determine needed action.	H045	P-2	1C3
• Inspect cylinder sleeve counter bore and lower bore; check bore distortion; determine needed action.	H046	P-2	1C4
• Clean, inspect, and measure cylinder walls or liners for wear and damage; determine needed action.	H047	P-2	1C5

Materials Required

- Vehicle with possible engine concern
- Vehicle manufacturer's service information
- Manufacturer-specific tools depending on the concern
- Vehicle lifting equipment if applicable

Some Safety Issues to Consider

- Diagnosis of this fault may require test driving the vehicle on the school grounds or on a hoist, both of which carry severe risks. Attempt this task only with full permission from your supervisor/instructor and follow all the guidelines exactly.
- Caution: If you are working in an area where there could be "brake dust" present (may contain asbestos, which has been determined to cause cancer when inhaled or ingested), ensure you wear and use all OSHA-approved asbestos protective/removal equipment.
- Lifting equipment such as vehicle jacks and stands, vehicle hoists, and engine hoists are important tools that increase productivity and make the job easier. However, they can also cause severe injury or death if used improperly. Make sure you follow the manufacturer's operation procedures. Also make sure you have your supervisor/instructor's permission to use any particular type of lifting equipment.
- Comply with personal and environmental safety practices associated with clothing; eye protection; hand tools; power equipment; proper ventilation; and the handling, storage, and disposal of chemicals/materials in accordance with federal, state, and local regulations.
- Always wear the correct protective eyewear and clothing and use the appropriate safety equipment, as well as fender covers, seat protectors, and floor mat protectors.

- Make sure you understand and observe all legislative and personal safety procedures when carrying out practical assignments. If you are unsure of what these are, ask your supervisor/instructor.

Performance Standard

0—No exposure: No information or practice provided during the program; complete training required
1—Exposure only: General information provided with no practice time; close supervision needed; additional training required
2—Limited practice: Has practiced job during training program; additional training required to develop skill
3—Moderately skilled: Has performed job independently during training program; limited additional training may be required
4—Skilled: Can perform job independently with no additional training

Student/intern information:

Name__________ Date__________ Class__________

Vehicle used for this activity:

Year__________ Make__________ Model__________

Odometer__________ VIN __________

TASK Perform crankcase pressure test; determine needed action. NATEF 1C1

Time off__________

Time on__________

Total time__________

CDX Tasksheet Number: H043

1. Reference the appropriate service information; list the procedure and all safety precautions that must be observed when performing a crankcase pressure test.
   a. List, or print and attach to this sheet, the steps involved when performing a crankcase pressure test:

   b. Determine what safety precautions must be observed when performing a crankcase pressure test:

2. Discuss these procedures and safety precautions with your instructor.

3. If directed by your instructor, perform a crankcase pressure test following the procedures listed above and while referencing the appropriate service information.
   Note: The manufacturer's specifications will be in inches of water or Liters per minute (L/min).
   a. List your observations:

   b. Meets the manufacturer's specifications: Yes: _____ No: _____

   c. Determine any necessary action(s):

4. Discuss the findings with your instructor.

Performance Rating

CDX Tasksheet Number: H043

☐	☐	☐	☐	☐
0	1	2	3	4

Supervisor/instructor signature __________ Date__________

Student/intern information:

Name________________________ Date____________ Class________________________

Vehicle used for this activity:

Year____________ Make________________________ Model____________________

Odometer____________________ VIN ____________________________

Time off________

Time on________

Total time________

TASK Remove, inspect, service, and install pans, covers, gaskets, seals, wear rings, and crankcase ventilation components. NATEF 1C2

CDX Tasksheet Number: H044

1. Reference the appropriate service information; remove, inspect, and service pans, covers, gaskets, seals, and wear rings.
   Note: In most cases, the manufacturer will list torque specifications that should be followed when installing pans and covers. In many cases, the manufacturer will also list any gasket sealers that should be used.
   a. List your observations:
      ____
      ____
      ____
   b. Meets the manufacturer's specifications: Yes: _____ No: _____
   c. Determine any necessary action(s):
      ____
      ____
      ____
   d. Have your supervisor or instructor verify that the cover is ready to be reinstalled
      Supervisor's/instructor's initials: ____________
2. Reference the appropriate service information; remove, inspect, service, and install the crankcase ventilation components.
   a. List your observations:
      ____
      ____
      ____
   b. Meets the manufacturer's specifications: Yes: _____ No: _____
   c. Determine any necessary action(s):
      ____
      ____
      ____
3. Discuss the findings with your instructor.

Performance Rating

CDX Tasksheet Number: H044

☐	☐	☐	☐	☐
0	1	2	3	4

Supervisor/instructor signature ______________________________ Date____________

Student/intern information:

Name____________________ Date__________ Class________________

Vehicle used for this activity:

Year__________ Make____________________ Model________________

Odometer__________________ VIN ________________________

TASK Disassemble, clean, and inspect engine block for cracks/damage; measure mating surfaces for warpage; check condition of passages, core/expansion and gallery plugs; inspect threaded holes, studs, dowel pins, and bolts for serviceability; determine needed action. NATEF 1C3

Time off__________

Time on__________

Total time__________

CDX Tasksheet Number: H045

1. Research the procedure and specifications for disassembling and inspecting the engine block in the appropriate service information.
    a. Print the procedure for disassembling the block and attach it to this sheet.
    b. List the specifications for crankshaft end play: ________________ in/mm

2. Discuss these procedures and safety precautions with your instructor.

3. If directed by your instructor, mount the engine block into an engine rollover stand.
   Note: Make sure the engine stand is rated for the weight of the engine you are mounting on it. Also, use bolts with the proper strength and length. Severe injury could occur if the engine were to fall due to failure of the engine stand or bolts.

4. Following the removal procedures listed above, and while referencing the manufacturer's workshop manual, disassemble the engine block.
    a. If the removed engine block is dirty and possibly has an oily coating; in the designated cleaning bay, clean the engine.
    b. Using a suitable sized container, drain the oil from the engine and dispose of it in accordance with your shop's procedure and in compliance with all government and environmental protect legislation.
    c. If there is any coolant in the engine, use a suitable sized container, drain the remaining coolant from the engine, and dispose of it in accordance with your shop's procedure and in compliance with all government and environmental protect legislation.

5. Begin the dismantling procedure.
    a. When removing the components, store all the nuts and bolts in order in storage trays.
    b. Store all removed components on oil collection trays to prevent oil spillage on the workshop floor (safety requirement).
    c. Remove all the necessary components as indicated by the manufacturer in their appropriate service information.
        i. Before removing the connecting rod caps, mark their location and position.
        ii. Check to see if there is a wear lip at the top of the cylinder that could catch the piston rings: Yes: _____ No: _____
        iii. Determine any necessary action(s):

____

____

____

____

____

6. Discuss these recommendations with your instructor.

7. If directed by your instructor, remove the wear lip as described in the appropriate service information. Follow all procedures and safety requirements.
   a. Remove the piston assemblies and store in a safe location.
   b. Remove the flywheel assembly and store in a safe location.
   c. Remove oil pump and store in an oil collection container.

8. Before removing the crankshaft main bearing caps, mark their location and position. Measure the crankshaft end play: ____________________ in/mm.
   a. Loosen and remove the main bearing caps.
   b. Carefully lift the crankshaft out and store in a safe location.
   c. Collect the thrust bearings and store.
   d. Replace the main bearing caps into their original position and screw the cap bolts back finger tight.

9. With reference to the appropriate service information, complete the dismantling of the engine block including wet sleeve cylinder liners (if applicable). Ensure that you number their location and store components in a safe location.

10. While observing all lifting safety precautions, transport the disassembled block and disassembled components to the designated cleaning bay.
    a. Clean the block and components.
    b. Dry the engine block and components.
    c. After cleaning and drying the engine block, remount onto an engine rollover stand and secure.
    d. Lay out the components in an orderly manner to assist in reassembly.

11. Reference the appropriate service information; list the procedure for measure mating surfaces for warpage.
    a. List, or print and attach to this sheet, the steps involved to measure mating surfaces for warpage:
    ____
    ____
    ____
    ____

    b. Determine what safety precautions must be observed when measuring mating surfaces for warpage:
    ____
    ____
    ____
    ____

12. Following the procedures listed above, and while referencing the appropriate service information, measure mating surfaces for warpage.
    a. Manufacturer's specifications: ____________________ in/mm
    b. List your measurements:
    ____
    ____
    ____
    ____

c. Meets the manufacturer's specifications: Yes: _____ No: _____
d. Determine any necessary action(s):

____

____

____

____

13. Referring to the appropriate service information, check the condition of passages, core/expansion, and gallery plugs; inspect threaded holes, studs, dowel pins, and bolts for serviceability.
    a. List your observations:

____

____

____

____

    b. Meets the manufacturer's specifications: Yes: _____ No: _____
    c. Determine any necessary action(s):

____

____

____

____

14. Discuss the findings with your instructor.

Performance Rating

CDX Tasksheet Number: H045

☐ 0 ☐ 1 ☐ 2 ☐ 3 ☐ 4

Supervisor/instructor signature _______________ Date_______________

Student/intern information:

Name____________________ Date__________ Class________________

Vehicle used for this activity:

Year__________ Make____________________ Model________________

Odometer____________________ VIN ____________________

TASK Inspect cylinder sleeve counter bore and lower bore; check bore distortion; determine needed action. NATEF 1C4

Time off________

Time on________

Total time________

CDX Tasksheet Number: H046

1. Referring to the appropriate service information, inspect the cylinder sleeve counterbore and lower bore; check bore distortion.
   a. Manufacturer's specifications: ________________ in/mm
   b. Measure the counterbore in multiple spots for concentricity and depth according to manufacturer's specification.
      i. Record the measurements: ____________________
   c. Inspect counter bore for cracking and gaulling from loose liner condition.
      i. List your observations:
      ____
      ____
      ii. Meets manufacturer's specifications? Yes: _____ No: _____
   d. Inspect lower counter bore for pitting or water damage due to improper pH or alkalinity levels.
      i. Meets manufacturer's specifications? Yes: _____ No: _____
   e. Determine any necessary action(s):
   ____
   ____
   ____
   ____

2. Discuss the findings with your instructor.

Performance Rating

CDX Tasksheet Number: H046

☐ 0 ☐ 1 ☐ 2 ☐ 3 ☐ 4

Supervisor/instructor signature ____________________ Date________

Student/intern information:

Name____________________ Date__________ Class____________________

Vehicle used for this activity:

Year__________ Make____________________ Model____________________

Odometer____________________ VIN ____________________

TASK Clean, inspect, and measure cylinder walls or liners for wear and damage; determine needed action. NATEF 1C5

Time off__________

Time on__________

Total time__________

CDX Tasksheet Number: H047

1. Research the following specifications in the appropriate service information:
   a. Cylinder diameter: ____________________ in/mm
   b. Cylinder taper: ____________________ in/mm
   c. Cylinder out-of-round: ____________________ in/mm
   d. Minimum wall thickness: ____________________ in/mm
   e. Cylinder wall construction: ____________________
   f. Carry out a visual inspection of the cylinders.
      i. Meets the manufacturer's specifications: Yes: _____ No: _____
      ii. If no, list the areas of concern and your recommendations for any rectifications:

____

____

____

   g. Referring to the appropriate service information and using the correct recommended tools, measure and record the reading for each engine's cylinders. Record your findings in the table below. Calculate Cylinder Taper and Out-of-Round.

Cylinder	Diameter (Top)	Diameter @ 90° (top)	Diameter (Bottom)	Diameter @ 90° (Bottom)	Cylinder Taper	Cylinder Out-of-Round
1						
2						
3						
4						
5						
6						
7						
8						

      i. Meets the manufacturer's specifications: Yes: _____ No: _____

ii. Determine any necessary action(s): ______________________________

2. Discuss your findings with your instructor.

Performance Rating

CDX Tasksheet Number: H047

☐ 0 ☐ 1 ☐ 2 ☐ 3 ☐ 4

Supervisor/instructor signature ____________________ Date__________

Diesel Engines: Engine Block 2

Student/intern information:

Name____________________ Date__________ Class____________________

Vehicle used for this activity:

Year__________ Make____________________ Model____________________

Odometer____________________ VIN ______________________________

Time off__________

Time on__________

Total time__________

Learning Objective / Task	CDX Tasksheet Number	2014 NATEF Priority Level	2014 NATEF Reference Number
• Replace/reinstall cylinder liners and seals; check and adjust liner height (protrusion).	H048	P-2	1C6
• Inspect in-block camshaft bearings for wear and damage; determine needed action.	H049	P-3	1C7
• Inspect, measure, and replace/reinstall in-block camshaft; measure/adjust end play.	H050	P-3	1C8
• Clean and inspect crankshaft for surface cracks and journal damage; check condition of oil passages; check passage plugs; measure journal diameter; determine needed action.	H051	P-2	1C9
• Inspect main bearings for wear patterns and damage; replace as needed; check bearing clearances; check and correct crankshaft end play.	H052	P-2	1C10
• Inspect, install, and time gear train; measure gear backlash; determine needed action.	H053	P-2	1C11

Materials Required

- Vehicle with possible engine concern
- Vehicle manufacturer's service information
- Manufacturer-specific tools depending on the concern
- Vehicle lifting equipment if applicable

Some Safety Issues to Consider

- Diagnosis of this fault may require test driving the vehicle on the school grounds or on a hoist, both of which carry severe risks. Attempt this task only with full permission from your supervisor/instructor and follow all the guidelines exactly.
- Caution: If you are working in an area where there could be "brake dust" present (may contain asbestos, which has been determined to cause cancer when inhaled or ingested), ensure you wear and use all OSHA-approved asbestos protective/removal equipment.
- Lifting equipment such as vehicle jacks and stands, vehicle hoists, and engine hoists are important tools that increase productivity and make the job easier. However, they can also cause severe injury or death if used improperly. Make sure you follow the manufacturer's operation procedures. Also make sure you have your supervisor/instructor's permission to use any particular type of lifting equipment.
- Comply with personal and environmental safety practices associated with clothing; eye protection; hand tools; power equipment; proper ventilation; and the handling, storage, and disposal of chemicals/materials in accordance with federal, state, and local regulations.

- Always wear the correct protective eyewear and clothing and use the appropriate safety equipment, as well as fender covers, seat protectors, and floor mat protectors.
- Make sure you understand and observe all legislative and personal safety procedures when carrying out practical assignments. If you are unsure of what these are, ask your supervisor/instructor.

Performance Standard

0–No exposure: No information or practice provided during the program; complete training required
1–Exposure only: General information provided with no practice time; close supervision needed; additional training required
2–Limited practice: Has practiced job during training program; additional training required to develop skill
3–Moderately skilled: Has performed job independently during training program; limited additional training may be required
4–Skilled: Can perform job independently with no additional training

Student/intern information:

Name____________________ Date__________ Class________________

Vehicle used for this activity:

Year__________ Make____________________ Model________________

Odometer__________________ VIN ________________________

TASK Replace/reinstall cylinder liners and seals; check and adjust liner height (protrusion).

NATEF 1C6

Time off________

Time on________

Total time________

CDX Tasksheet Number: H048

1. Reference the appropriate service information. List the specifications, procedure, and all safety precautions that must be observed when you replace/reinstall the cylinder liners and seals and check and adjust the liner height (protrusion).
   a. Specified liner height (protrusion): ____________________
   b. List, or print and attach to this sheet, the steps involved when you replace/reinstall the cylinder liners and seals:
   c. Determine what safety precautions must be observed when you replace/reinstall the cylinder liners and seals and check and adjust the liner height (protrusion):
2. Discuss these procedures and safety precautions with your instructor. At this time you are ready to remove the liners.
3. Have your supervisor or instructor verify that the liners are ready to be reinstalled. Supervisor's/instructor's initials: __________
4. If directed by your instructor, replace/reinstall the cylinder liners and seals.
   a. List your observations:

5. Record your measurements in the table below.

Cylinder	Protrusion measurement (in/mm)
1	
2	
3	
4	
5	
6	
7	
8	

6. Determine any necessary action(s):

____

____

____

____

____

7. Discuss the findings with your instructor.

Performance Rating

CDX Tasksheet Number: H048

☐ 0 ☐ 1 ☐ 2 ☐ 3 ☐ 4

Supervisor/instructor signature ______________________________ Date ____________

Student/intern information:

Name____________________ Date__________ Class______________

Vehicle used for this activity:

Year__________ Make____________________ Model______________

Odometer__________________ VIN ____________________

TASK Inspect in-block camshaft bearings for wear and damage; determine needed action.

NATEF 1C7

Time off__________

Time on__________

Total time__________

CDX Tasksheet Number: H049

1. Research the following specifications in the appropriate service information:
   a. Bearing diameter: ________________ in/mm
   b. Bearing taper: ________________ in/mm
   c. Bearing out-of-round: ________________ in/mm

2. Reference the appropriate service information and inspect the in-block camshaft bearings for wear and damage.

   Note: This is a visual check of the bearings.
   a List your observations:

   b. Meets the manufacturer's specifications: Yes: _____ No: _____

   c. Determine any necessary action(s):

3. While using the appropriate measuring instrument(s), measure the bearings and record your findings in the table below. Calculate Bearing Taper and Out-of-Round.

Journal	Diameter Front	Diameter @ 90° Front	Diameter Back	Diameter @ 90° Back	Bearing Taper	Bearing Out-of-Round
1						
2						
3						
4						
5						
6						
7						
8						

a. Meets the manufacturer's specifications: Yes: _____ No: _____

b. Determine any necessary action(s):

____

____

____

____

____

4. Discuss the findings with your instructor.

Performance Rating

CDX Tasksheet Number: H049

☐ 0 ☐ 1 ☐ 2 ☐ 3 ☐ 4

Supervisor/instructor signature ______________________________ Date______________

Student/intern information:

Name____________________ Date__________ Class____________________

Vehicle used for this activity:

Year__________ Make____________________ Model____________________

Odometer____________________ VIN ____________________

TASK Inspect, measure, and replace/reinstall in-block camshaft; measure/adjust end play.

NATEF 1C8

Time off__________

Time on__________

Total time__________

CDX Tasksheet Number: H050

1. Reference the appropriate service information. List the specifications, procedure, and all safety precautions that must be observed when you inspect, measure, and replace/reinstall the in-block camshaft and measure/adjust the end play.
   a. Camshaft journal diameter: ____________________ in/mm
   b. Camshaft journal out-of-round: ____________________ in/mm
   c. Camshaft end play: ____________________ in/mm
   d. List, or print and attach to this sheet, the steps involved to inspect, measure, and replace/reinstall the in-block camshaft and to measure/adjust the end play:

   e. Determine what safety precautions must be observed as you inspect, measure, and replace/reinstall the in-block camshaft and measure/adjust the end play:

2. Discuss these procedures and safety precautions with your instructor. At this time, remove the camshaft.

3. Measure the camshaft journals and list your measurements:

Cam Journal Number	Journal Diameter	Journal Out-of-Round

4. Determine any necessary action(s):
____
____
____
____
____

5. Have your supervisor or instructor verify that the camshaft is ready to be reinstalled. Supervisor's/instructor's initials: _______________

6. If directed by your instructor, replace/reinstall the in-block camshaft and measure/adjust the end play.

7. Referring to the appropriate service information, measure the camshaft end play.
   a. Actual:
      i. Camshaft end play: ____________________ in/mm
   b. Meets the manufacturer's specifications: Yes: _____ No: _____
   c. Determine any necessary action(s):
   ____
   ____
   ____
   ____
   ____

8. Discuss the findings with your instructor.

Performance Rating

CDX Tasksheet Number: H050

☐ 0 ☐ 1 ☐ 2 ☐ 3 ☐ 4

Supervisor/instructor signature _______________________________ Date_______________

Student/intern information:

Name________________ Date________ Class____________

Vehicle used for this activity:

Year________ Make________________ Model____________

Odometer______________ VIN ________________

◂◂ TASK Clean and inspect crankshaft for surface cracks and journal damage; check condition of oil passages; check passage plugs; measure journal diameter; determine needed action.

NATEF 1C9

Time off________

Time on________

Total time________

CDX Tasksheet Number: H051

1. Research the procedure and specifications for inspecting the crankshaft in the appropriate service information. List the following crankshaft specifications:
   a. Main journal diameter: ____________ in/mm
   b. Main journal out-of-round (max): ____________ in/mm
   c. Main journal taper (max): ____________ in/mm
   d. Rod journal diameter: ____________ in/mm
   e. Rod journal out-of-round (max): ____________ in/mm
   f. Rod journal taper (max): ____________ in/mm
   g. List any precautions you need to take when inspecting the crankshaft:

2. Following the specified procedures, clean and visually inspect the crankshaft for surface cracks and journal damage. List your observations:

3. Following the specified procedures, check the condition of the oil passages and passage plugs. List your observations:

4. While using the appropriate measuring instrument(s), measure the crankshaft main and rod journals and record your findings in the table below. Bearing taper and out-of-round will need to be calculated.

Journal	Diameter Front	Diameter @ 90º Front	Diameter Back	Diameter @ 90º Back	Bearing Taper	Bearing Out-of-Round
1						
2						
3						
4						
5						
6						
7						
8						
9						
10						

a. Meets the manufacturer's specifications: Yes: _____ No: _____

b. Determine any necessary action(s):

____

____

____

____

____

5. Discuss the findings with your instructor.

Performance Rating

CDX Tasksheet Number: H051

☐ 0 ☐ 1 ☐ 2 ☐ 3 ☐ 4

Supervisor/instructor signature _______________________________ Date_____________

Student/intern information:

Name______________________________ Date__________ Class____________________

Vehicle used for this activity:

Year__________ Make______________________________ Model__________________

Odometer_________________________ VIN ______________________________________

◀◀ TASK Inspect main bearings for wear patterns and damage; replace as needed; check bearing clearances; check and correct crankshaft end play. NATEF 1C10

Time off__________

Time on__________

Total time__________

CDX Tasksheet Number: H052

1. Reference the appropriate service information. List the specifications, procedure, and all safety precautions that must be observed when you inspect the main bearings for wear patterns and damage and replace as needed, check the bearing clearances, and check and correct the crankshaft end play.
   a. Main bearing journal clearance: __________________ in/mm
   b. Crankshaft end play: __________________ in/mm
   c. List, or print and attach to this sheet, the steps involved to inspect the main bearings for wear patterns and damage and replace as needed, to check the bearing clearances, and to check and correct the crankshaft end play:

   d. Determine what safety precautions must be observed as you inspect the main bearings for wear patterns and damage and replace as needed, check the bearing clearances, and check and correct the crankshaft end play:

2. Following the procedures listed above, and while referencing the appropriate service information, inspect the main bearings for wear patterns and damage.
   a. List your observations:

   b. Meets the manufacturer's specifications: Yes: _____ No: _____
   c. Determine any necessary action(s):

3. Following the procedures listed above, and while referencing the appropriate service information, check the bearing clearances and record your findings in the table below.

Main bearing number	Bearing clearances (in/mm)
1	
2	
3	
4	
5	
6	

   a. Meets the manufacturer's specifications: Yes: _____ No: _____
   b. Determine any necessary action(s):

____

____

____

____

4. While referring to the appropriate service information, install the crankshaft and torque main bearing caps.
   a. Specifications:
      i. Crankshaft main bearing cap torque: ___________ ft/lbs (Nm)
   b. Actual:
      i. Crankshaft main bearing cap torque: ___________ ft/lbs (Nm)

5. While referring to the appropriate service information, measure the crankshaft end play.
   a. Actual:
      i. Crankshaft end play: ___________________ in/mm
   b. Meets the manufacturer's specifications: Yes: _____ No: _____
   c. Determine any necessary action(s):

____

____

____

____

6. Discuss the findings with your instructor.

Performance Rating

CDX Tasksheet Number: H052

☐ 0 ☐ 1 ☐ 2 ☐ 3 ☐ 4

Supervisor/instructor signature ______________________________ Date______________

Student/intern information:

Name____________________ Date__________ Class________________

Vehicle used for this activity:

Year__________ Make____________________ Model________________

Odometer____________________ VIN ____________________________

TASK Inspect, install, and time gear train; measure gear backlash; determine needed action.

NATEF 1C11

Time off__________

Time on__________

Total time__________

CDX Tasksheet Number: H053

1. Research the following specifications in the appropriate service information:
   a. Cam drive gear backlash: __________________ in/mm
2. While referring to the appropriate service information, inspect, install, and time the gear train.
3. While referring to the appropriate service information, measure the gear backlash.
   a. Actual:
      i. Gear backlash: __________________ in/mm
   b. Meets the manufacturer's specifications: Yes: _____ No: _____
   c. Determine any necessary action(s):

____

____

____

____

4. Discuss the findings with your instructor.

Performance Rating

CDX Tasksheet Number: H053

☐ 0 ☐ 1 ☐ 2 ☐ 3 ☐ 4

Supervisor/instructor signature ____________________________ Date__________

Diesel Engines: Engine Block 3

Student/intern information:

Name________________ Date________ Class________________

Vehicle used for this activity:

Year________ Make________________ Model________________

Odometer________________ VIN ________________

Time off________

Time on________

Total time________

Learning Objective / Task	CDX Tasksheet Number	2014 NATEF Priority Level	2014 NATEF Reference Number
• Inspect connecting rod and bearings for wear patterns; measure pistons, pins, retainers, and bushings; perform needed action.	H054	P-3	1C12
• Determine piston-to-cylinder wall clearance; check ring-to-groove fit and end gap; install rings on pistons.	H055	P-3	1C13
• Assemble pistons and connecting rods; install in block; install rod bearings and check clearances.	H056	P-2	1C14

Materials Required

- Vehicle with possible engine concern
- Vehicle manufacturer's service information
- Manufacturer-specific tools depending on the concern
- Vehicle lifting equipment if applicable

Some Safety Issues to Consider

- Diagnosis of this fault may require test driving the vehicle on the school grounds or on a hoist, both of which carry severe risks. Attempt this task only with full permission from your supervisor/instructor and follow all the guidelines exactly.
- Caution: If you are working in an area where there could be 'brake dust' present (may contain asbestos, which has been determined to cause cancer when inhaled or ingested), ensure you wear and use all OSHA-approved asbestos protective / removal equipment.
- Lifting equipment such as vehicle jacks and stands, vehicle hoists, and engine hoists are important tools that increase productivity and make the job easier. However, they can also cause severe injury or death if used improperly. Make sure you follow the manufacturer's operation procedures. Also make sure you have your supervisor/instructor's permission to use any particular type of lifting equipment.
- Comply with personal and environmental safety practices associated with clothing; eye protection; hand tools; power equipment; proper ventilation; and the handling, storage, and disposal of chemicals/materials in accordance with federal, state, and local regulations.
- Always wear the correct protective eyewear and clothing and use the appropriate safety equipment, as well as fender covers, seat protectors, and floor mat protectors.
- Make sure you understand and observe all legislative and personal safety procedures when carrying out practical assignments. If you are unsure of what these are, ask your supervisor/instructor.

Performance Standard

0–No exposure: No information or practice provided during the program; complete training required

1–Exposure only: General information provided with no practice time; close supervision needed; additional training required

2–Limited practice: Has practiced job during training program; additional training required to develop skill

3–Moderately skilled: Has performed job independently during training program; limited additional training may be required

4–Skilled: Can perform job independently with no additional training

Student/intern information:

Name____________________ Date__________ Class________________

Vehicle used for this activity:

Year__________ Make____________________ Model________________

Odometer__________________ VIN ________________________

TASK Inspect connecting rod and bearings for wear patterns; measure pistons, pins, retainers, and bushings; perform needed action. NATEF 1C12

Time off__________

Time on__________

Total time__________

CDX Tasksheet Number: H054

1. Research the following specifications in the appropriate service information:
   a. Piston diameter: ______________ in/mm
   b. Piston taper: ______________ in/mm
   c. Piston out-of-round: ______________ in/mm
   d. Piston pin diameter: ______________ in/mm
   e. Piston pin bushing inside diameter: ______________ in/mm
   f. Other (describe): ____________________ Spec: ______________ in/mm

2. Reference the appropriate service information; visually inspect connecting rod and bearings for wear patterns:
   a. List your observations:

      ____

   b. Meets the manufacturer's specifications: Yes: _____ No: _____

   c. Determine any necessary action(s):

      ____

3. Reference the appropriate service information; measure pistons, pins and retainers, using the appropriate measuring instrument(s).

Piston	Measurement-in/mm					
	Diameter Top	Diameter @ 90° Top	Diameter Bottom	Diameter @ 90° Bottom	Piston Out-of-Round/ Taper	Piston Pin (outside diameter)

a. Meets the manufacturer's specifications: Yes: _____ No: _____

b. Determine any necessary action(s):

____

____

____

____

____

4. Discuss the findings with your instructor.

Performance Rating

CDX Tasksheet Number: H054

☐ 0 ☐ 1 ☐ 2 ☐ 3 ☐ 4

Supervisor/instructor signature _______________________________ Date_____________

Student/intern information:

Name________________________ Date__________ Class________________

Vehicle used for this activity:

Year__________ Make____________________ Model__________

Odometer________________ VIN ________________________

TASK Determine piston-to-cylinder wall clearance; check ring-to-groove fit and end gap; install rings on pistons. NATEF 1C13

Time off__________

Time on__________

Total time__________

CDX Tasksheet Number: H055

1. Research the following specifications in the appropriate service information:
   a. Piston-to-cylinder wall clearance: ________________ in/mm
   b. Compression ring grooves clearance: ________________ in/mm
   c. Oil ring groove clearance: ________________ in/mm
   d. Compression ring end gap clearance: ________________ in/mm
   e. Oil ring end gap clearance: ________________ in/mm

2. Reference the appropriate service information; determine the piston-to-cylinder wall clearance for all pistons and cylinders.
   a. Piston #1: ________________ in/mm
   b. Piston #2: ________________ in/mm
   c. Meets the manufacturer's specifications: Yes: _____ No: _____
   d. Determine any necessary action(s):

____

____

____

3. Reference the appropriate service information; check ring-to-groove fit and end gap:

Piston	Measurement-in/mm		
	Compression Ring 1 (groove clearance/ end gap)	**Compression Ring 2 (groove clearance/ end gap)**	**Oil Control Ring (groove clearance/ end gap)**
1			
2			
3			
4			
5			
6			
7			
8			

a. Meets the manufacturer's specifications: Yes: _____ No: _____

b. Determine any necessary action(s):

____

____

____

____

____

4. Discuss the findings with your instructor.

Performance Rating

CDX Tasksheet Number: H055

☐	☐	☐	☐	☐
0	1	2	3	4

Supervisor/instructor signature ____ Date_______________

Student/intern information:

Name____________________ Date__________ Class________________

Vehicle used for this activity:

Year__________ Make____________________ Model________________

Odometer____________________ VIN ____________________________

TASK Assemble pistons and connecting rods; install in block; install rod bearings and check clearances. NATEF 1C14

Time off__________

Time on__________

Total time__________

CDX Tasksheet Number: H056

1. Research the following specifications in the appropriate service information:
   a. Connecting rod bearing clearance: ______________ in/mm

2. Reference the appropriate service information; assemble pistons and connecting rods:
   a. List, or print and attach to this sheet, the procedure for assembling pistons and connecting rods.

3. Following the specified procedure, assemble the pistons and connecting rods. List your observations:

   a. Meets the manufacturer's specifications: Yes: _____ No: _____

   b. Determine any necessary action(s):

4. Reference the appropriate service information; install pistons and connecting rods:
   a. Reference the appropriate service information and install the rings on the pistons.
   b. Oil the piston assembly.
   c. Oil the cylinder.
   d. As each piston assembly is being installed, remove the big end cap as the piston assembly is about to be installed.
   e. Using an appropriate piston ring installation tool:
      i. Install each piston assembly.
      ii. Install connecting rod bearing and refit connecting rod cap and bolts.

5. Reference appropriate service information; list the procedure when you check clearances for connecting rod bearing:

____
____
____

6. Reference the appropriate service information; check clearances for connecting rod bearing:

Connecting Rod Bearing Number	Bearing Clearance

   a. Determine any necessary action(s):

   ____
   ____
   ____
   ____
   ____

7. Discuss the findings with your instructor.

Performance Rating

CDX Tasksheet Number: H056

☐ 0 ☐ 1 ☐ 2 ☐ 3 ☐ 4

Supervisor/instructor signature ______________________________ Date______________

Diesel Engines: Engine Block 4

Student/intern information:

Name__________ Date__________ Class__________

Vehicle used for this activity:

Year__________ Make__________ Model__________

Odometer__________ VIN __________

Time off__________

Time on__________

Total time__________

Learning Objective / Task	CDX Tasksheet Number	2014 NATEF Priority Level	2014 NATEF Reference Number
• Check condition of piston cooling jets (nozzles); determine needed action.	H057	P-2	1C15
• Inspect crankshaft vibration damper; determine needed action.	H058	P-3	1C16
• Install and align flywheel housing; inspect flywheel housing(s) to transmission housing/engine mating surface(s) and measure flywheel housing face and bore runout; determine needed action.	H059	P-3	1C17
• Inspect flywheel/flexplate (including ring gear) and mounting surfaces for cracks and wear; measure runout; determine needed action.	H060	P-2	1C18

Materials Required

- Vehicle with possible engine concern
- Vehicle manufacturer's service information
- Manufacturer-specific tools depending on the concern
- Vehicle lifting equipment if applicable

Some Safety Issues to Consider

- Diagnosis of this fault may require test driving the vehicle on the school grounds or on a hoist, both of which carry severe risks. Attempt this task only with full permission from your supervisor/instructor and follow all the guidelines exactly.
- Caution: If you are working in an area where there could be "brake dust" present (may contain asbestos, which has been determined to cause cancer when inhaled or ingested), ensure you wear and use all OSHA-approved asbestos protective/removal equipment.
- Lifting equipment such as vehicle jacks and stands, vehicle hoists, and engine hoists are important tools that increase productivity and make the job easier. However, they can also cause severe injury or death if used improperly. Make sure you follow the manufacturer's operation procedures. Also make sure you have your supervisor/instructor's permission to use any particular type of lifting equipment.
- Comply with personal and environmental safety practices associated with clothing; eye protection; hand tools; power equipment; proper ventilation; and the handling, storage, and disposal of chemicals/materials in accordance with federal, state, and local regulations.
- Always wear the correct protective eyewear and clothing and use the appropriate safety equipment, as well as fender covers, seat protectors, and floor mat protectors.
- Make sure you understand and observe all legislative and personal safety procedures when carrying out practical assignments. If you are unsure of what these are, ask your supervisor/instructor.

Performance Standard

0–No exposure: No information or practice provided during the program; complete training required

1–Exposure only: General information provided with no practice time; close supervision needed; additional training required

2–Limited practice: Has practiced job during training program; additional training required to develop skill

3–Moderately skilled: Has performed job independently during training program; limited additional training may be required

4–Skilled: Can perform job independently with no additional training

Student/intern information:

Name____________________ Date__________ Class________________

Vehicle used for this activity:

Year__________ Make____________________ Model________________

Odometer____________________ VIN ____________________

TASK Check condition of piston cooling jets (nozzles); determine needed action.

NATEF 1C15

Time off__________

Time on__________

Total time__________

CDX Tasksheet Number: H057

1. Reference the appropriate service information and check the condition of the piston cooling jets (nozzles).
   a. List, or print and attach to this sheet, the procedures to evaluate the condition of the piston cooling jets (nozzles).

   b. Inspect the piston cooling jets and list your observations:

   c. Meets the manufacturer's specifications: Yes: _____ No: _____

   d. Determine any necessary action(s):

2. Discuss the findings with your instructor.

Performance Rating

CDX Tasksheet Number: H057

☐	☐	☐	☐	☐
0	1	2	3	4

Supervisor/instructor signature ____________________ Date__________

Student/intern information:

Name________________________ Date____________ Class________________________

Vehicle used for this activity:

Year____________ Make________________________ Model________________________

Odometer________________________ VIN ________________________

TASK Inspect crankshaft vibration damper; determine needed action. NATEF 1C16

Time off________

Time on________

Total time________

CDX Tasksheet Number: H058

1. Reference the appropriate service information and inspect the crankshaft vibration damper.
   a. Inspect the viscous dampers for dents or other damage. List your observations:
   b. Check for run out using a dial indicator.
      i. Record the reading: ____________
      ii. Compare the reading to manufacturer's specifications.
   c. Determine any necessary action(s):
2. Discuss the findings with your instructor.

Performance Rating

CDX Tasksheet Number: H058

☐ 0 ☐ 1 ☐ 2 ☐ 3 ☐ 4

Supervisor/instructor signature ________________________ Date____________

Student/intern information:

Name__________________ Date__________ Class__________________

Vehicle used for this activity:

Year__________ Make__________________ Model__________________

Odometer__________________ VIN__________________

TASK Install and align flywheel housing; inspect flywheel housing(s) to transmission housing/engine mating surface(s) and measure flywheel housing face and bore runout; determine needed action. NATEF 1C17

Time off__________

Time on__________

Total time__________

CDX Tasksheet Number: H059

1. Research the following specifications in the appropriate service information:
   a. Flywheel housing face runout: __________ in/mm
   b. Flywheel housing bore runout: __________ in/mm

2. Reference the appropriate service information to install and align the flywheel housing.
   a. List, or print and attach to this sheet, the procedure to install and align the flywheel housing.

   ____
   ____
   ____

   b. Visually inspect the transmission housing and engine mating surfaces. List your observations:

   ____
   ____
   ____

   c. Meets the manufacturer's specifications: Yes: _____ No: _____

   d. Determine any necessary action(s):

   ____
   ____
   ____

3. Reference the appropriate service information and install and align the flywheel housing.
   a. List your observations:

   ____
   ____
   ____

   b. Meets the manufacturer's specifications: Yes: _____ No: _____

   c. Determine any necessary action(s):

   ____
   ____
   ____

4. While referring to the appropriate service information, measure the flywheel housing face and bore runout.
   a. Actual:
      i. Flywheel housing face runout: _______________ in/mm
      ii. Flywheel housing bore runout: _______________ in/mm
   b. Meets the manufacturer's specifications: Yes: _____ No: _____
   c. Determine any necessary action(s):
      ____
      ____
      ____
5. Discuss the findings with your instructor.

Performance Rating

CDX Tasksheet Number: H059

☐	☐	☐	☐	☐
0	1	2	3	4

Supervisor/instructor signature ____ Date____________

Student/intern information:

Name____________________ Date__________ Class____________________

Vehicle used for this activity:

Year__________ Make____________________ Model____________________

Odometer____________________ VIN ____________________

TASK Inspect flywheel/flexplate (including ring gear) and mounting surfaces for cracks and wear; measure runout; determine needed action. NATEF 1C18

Time off__________

Time on__________

Total time__________

CDX Tasksheet Number: H060

1. Research the following specifications in the appropriate service information:
   a. Flywheel/flexplate runout: ____________________ in/mm
2. Reference the appropriate service information to inspect the flywheel/flexplate (including the ring gear) and mounting surfaces for cracks and wear.
   a. List, or print and attach to this sheet, the procedure for inspecting the flywheel/flexplate (including the ring gear) and mounting surfaces for cracks and wear.
   b. Visually inspect the flywheel/flexplate (including the ring gear) and mounting surfaces for cracks, wear, and damage. List your observations:
   c. Meets the manufacturer's specifications: Yes: _____ No: _____
   d. Determine any necessary action(s):
3. While referring to the appropriate service information, measure the flywheel/flexplate runout using a dial indicator.
   a. Actual:
      i. Runout: ____________________ in/mm
   b. Meets the manufacturer's specifications: Yes: _____ No: _____

c. Determine any necessary action(s): ______________________________

4. Discuss the findings with your instructor.

Performance Rating

CDX Tasksheet Number: H060

☐ 0 ☐ 1 ☐ 2 ☐ 3 ☐ 4

Supervisor/instructor signature ______________________________ Date ______________

Diesel Engines: Lubrication Systems

Student/intern information:

Name__________ Date__________ Class__________

Vehicle used for this activity:

Year__________ Make__________ Model__________

Odometer__________ VIN __________

Time off__________

Time on__________

Total time__________

Learning Objective / Task	CDX Tasksheet Number	2014 NATEF Priority Level	2014 NATEF Reference Number
• Test engine oil pressure and check operation of pressure sensor, gauge, and/or sending unit; test engine oil temperature and check operation of temperature sensor; determine needed action.	H061	P-1	1D1
• Check engine oil level, condition, and consumption; determine needed action.	H062	P-1	1D2
• Inspect and measure oil pump, drives, inlet pipes, and pick-up screens; check drive gear clearances; determine needed action.	H063	P-3	1D3
• Inspect oil pressure regulator valve(s), by-pass and pressure relief valve(s), oil thermostat, and filters; determine needed action.	H064	P-3	1D4
• Inspect, clean, and test oil cooler and components; determine needed action.	H065	P-3	1D5
• Inspect turbocharger lubrication systems; determine needed action.	H066	P-2	1D6
• Determine proper lubricant and perform oil and filter change.	H067	P-1	1D7

Materials Required

- Vehicle with possible engine concern
- Vehicle manufacturer's service information
- Manufacturer-specific tools depending on the concern
- Vehicle lifting equipment if applicable

Some Safety Issues to Consider

- Diagnosis of this fault may require test driving the vehicle on the school grounds or on a hoist, both of which carry severe risks. Attempt this task only with full permission from your supervisor/instructor and follow all the guidelines exactly.
- Caution: If you are working in an area where there could be "brake dust" present (may contain asbestos, which has been determined to cause cancer when inhaled or ingested), ensure you wear and use all OSHA-approved asbestos protective/removal equipment.
- Lifting equipment such as vehicle jacks and stands, vehicle hoists, and engine hoists are important tools that increase productivity and make the job easier. However, they can also cause severe injury or death if used improperly. Make sure you follow the manufacturer's operation procedures. Also make sure you have your supervisor/instructor's permission to use any particular type of lifting equipment.

- Comply with personal and environmental safety practices associated with clothing; eye protection; hand tools; power equipment; proper ventilation; and the handling, storage, and disposal of chemicals/materials in accordance with federal, state, and local regulations.
- Always wear the correct protective eyewear and clothing and use the appropriate safety equipment, as well as fender covers, seat protectors, and floor mat protectors.
- Make sure you understand and observe all legislative and personal safety procedures when carrying out practical assignments. If you are unsure of what these are, ask your supervisor/instructor.

Performance Standard

0–No exposure: No information or practice provided during the program; complete training required

1–Exposure only: General information provided with no practice time; close supervision needed; additional training required

2–Limited practice: Has practiced job during training program; additional training required to develop skill

3–Moderately skilled: Has performed job independently during training program; limited additional training may be required

4–Skilled: Can perform job independently with no additional training

Student/intern information:

Name____________________ Date__________ Class______________

Vehicle used for this activity:

Year__________ Make____________________ Model______________

Odometer__________________ VIN ________________________

◂◂ TASK Test engine oil pressure and check operation of pressure sensor, gauge, and/or sending unit; test engine oil temperature and check operation of temperature sensor; determine needed action. NATEF 1D1

Time off________

Time on________

Total time________

CDX Tasksheet Number: H061

1. While referencing the appropriate service information, test the engine oil pressure and check operation of the pressure sensor, gauge, and/or sending unit.
   a. List, or print and attach to this sheet, the procedure for testing engine oil pressure and checking the operation of the pressure sensor, gauge, and/or sending unit.

   b. Test the engine oil pressure and the operation of the pressure sensor, gauge, and/or sending unit. List your observations:

   c. Meets the manufacturer's specifications: Yes: _____ No: _____

   d. Determine any necessary action(s):

2. While referencing the appropriate service information, test the engine oil temperature and check operation of the temperature sensor.
   a. List, or print and attach to this sheet, the procedure for testing engine oil temperature and checking the operation of the temperature sensor.

   b. Test the engine oil temperature and the operation of the temperature sensor. List your observations:

c. Meets the manufacturer's specifications: Yes: _____ No: _____
d. Determine any necessary action(s):

____
____
____
____

3. Discuss the findings with your instructor.

Performance Rating

CDX Tasksheet Number: H061

☐	☐	☐	☐	☐
0	1	2	3	4

Supervisor/instructor signature ______________________________ Date__________

Student/intern information:

Name____________________ Date________ Class____________

Vehicle used for this activity:

Year________ Make__________________ Model____________

Odometer__________________ VIN ____________________

TASK Check engine oil level, condition, and consumption; determine needed action.

NATEF 1D2

Time off________

Time on________

Total time________

CDX Tasksheet Number: H062

1. Reference the appropriate service information and check the engine oil level, condition, and consumption.
   a. List, or print and attach to this sheet, the procedure for checking the engine oil level, condition, and consumption.
   b. Check the engine oil level, condition, and consumption. List your observations:
   c. Meets the manufacturer's specifications: Yes: _____ No: _____
   d. Determine any necessary action(s):
2. Discuss the findings with your instructor.

Performance Rating

CDX Tasksheet Number: H062

☐ 0 ☐ 1 ☐ 2 ☐ 3 ☐ 4

Supervisor/instructor signature ____________________ Date________

Student/intern information:

Name_______________ Date_______ Class_______________

Vehicle used for this activity:

Year_______ Make_______________ Model_______________

Odometer_______________ VIN _______________

TASK Inspect and measure oil pump, drives, inlet pipes, and pick-up screens; check drive gear clearances; determine needed action. NATEF 1D3

Time off_______

Time on_______

Total time_______

CDX Tasksheet Number: H063

1. Reference the appropriate service information and inspect and measure the oil pump, drives, inlet pipes, and pick-up screens.
   a. List, or print and attach to this sheet, the procedure to inspect and measure the oil pump, drives, inlet pipes and pick-up screens.

   b. Inspect and measure the oil pump, drives, inlet pipes, and screens. List your observations:

   c. Meets the manufacturer's specifications: Yes: _____ No: _____

   d. Determine any necessary action(s):

2. Reference the appropriate service information and check the drive gear clearances.
   a. List, or print and attach to this sheet, the procedure for checking the drive gear clearances.

   b. Inspect the gear drive clearances. List your observations:

   c. Meets the manufacturer's specifications: Yes: _____ No: _____

d. Determine any necessary action(s): ______________________________

3. Discuss the findings with your instructor.

Performance Rating

CDX Tasksheet Number: H063

☐ 0 ☐ 1 ☐ 2 ☐ 3 ☐ 4

Supervisor/instructor signature ______________________________ Date__________

Student/intern information:

Name_______________ Date_______ Class_______________

Vehicle used for this activity:

Year_______ Make_______________ Model_______________

Odometer_______________ VIN _______________

TASK Inspect oil pressure regulator valve(s), by-pass and pressure relief valve(s), oil thermostat, and filters; determine needed action. NATEF 1D4

Time off_______

Time on_______

Total time_______

CDX Tasksheet Number: H064

1. Reference the appropriate service information and inspect the oil pressure regulator valve(s), by-pass and pressure relief valve(s), oil thermostat, and filters.
   a. List, or print and attach to this sheet, the procedure for inspecting the oil pressure regulator valve(s), by-pass and pressure relief valve(s), oil thermostat, and filters.

   b. Inspect the oil pressure regulator valve(s), by-pass valve(s), pressure relief valve(s), oil thermostat, and filters. List your observations:

   c. Meets the manufacturer's specifications: Yes: _____ No: _____

   d. Determine any necessary action(s):

2. Discuss the findings with your instructor.

Performance Rating

CDX Tasksheet Number: H064

☐ 0 ☐ 1 ☐ 2 ☐ 3 ☐ 4

Supervisor/instructor signature _______________ Date_______

Student/intern information:

Name________________ Date________ Class________

Vehicle used for this activity:

Year________ Make________________ Model________

Odometer________________ VIN ________________

TASK Inspect, clean, and test oil cooler and components; determine needed action.

NATEF 1D5

Time off________

Time on________

Total time________

CDX Tasksheet Number: H065

1. Reference the appropriate service information and inspect, clean, and test the oil cooler and components.
   Note: Oil cooler should be replaced at time of overhaul.
   a. List, or print and attach to this sheet, the procedure to inspect, clean, and test the oil cooler and components.
   b. Inspect, clean, and test the oil cooler and its components. List your observations:
   c. Meets the manufacturer's specifications: Yes: _____ No: _____
   d. Determine any necessary action(s):
2. Discuss the findings with your instructor.

Performance Rating

CDX Tasksheet Number: H065

☐ 0 ☐ 1 ☐ 2 ☐ 3 ☐ 4

Supervisor/instructor signature ________________ Date________

Student/intern information:

Name____________________ Date__________ Class____________________

Vehicle used for this activity:

Year__________ Make____________________ Model____________________

Odometer____________________ VIN ____________________

TASK Inspect turbocharger lubrication systems; determine needed action.

NATEF 1D6

Time off__________

Time on__________

Total time__________

CDX Tasksheet Number: H066

1. Reference the appropriate service information and inspect the turbocharger lubrication systems.
   a. List, or print and attach to this sheet, the procedure to inspect the turbocharger lubrication systems.

   b. Inspect the turbocharger lubrication system. List your observations:

   c. Meets the manufacturer's specifications: Yes: _____ No: _____

   d. Determine any necessary action(s):

2. Discuss the findings with your instructor.

Performance Rating

CDX Tasksheet Number: H066

☐ 0 ☐ 1 ☐ 2 ☐ 3 ☐ 4

Supervisor/instructor signature ____________________ Date__________

Student/intern information:

Name____________________ Date__________ Class________________

Vehicle used for this activity:

Year__________ Make____________________ Model________________

Odometer____________________ VIN ____________________

TASK Determine proper lubricant and perform oil and filter change. NATEF 1D7

Time off__________

Time on__________

Total time__________

CDX Tasksheet Number: H067

1 Research the following specifications in the appropriate service information:
   a. Specified oil type: ____________________
   b. Specified oil viscosity: ____________________
   c. Specified oil quantity: ____________________
   d. Specified oil filter number: ____________________

2. While referencing the appropriate service information, determine the proper lubricant and perform an oil and filter change.
   a. List, or print and attach to this sheet, the procedure required to perform an oil and filter change.

   b. Drain the oil and remove the oil filter. Did you remove all O-rings and seals?
      Yes: _____ No: _____
   c. Have your instructor verify removal of oil and filter.
      Supervisor's/instructor's Initials: __________
   d. Install the oil drain plug and oil filter. Add the proper amount of oil.
   e. Start the engine and check for leaks. List your observations:

   f. Shut off the engine and check the oil level. List the level: ____________________

   g. Meets the manufacturer's specifications: Yes: _____ No: _____

h. Determine any necessary action(s):

____

____

____

____

3. Discuss the findings with your instructor.

Performance Rating

CDX Tasksheet Number: H067

☐	☐	☐	☐	☐
0	1	2	3	4

Supervisor/instructor signature ______________________________ Date______________

Diesel Engines: Cooling System 1

Student/intern information:

Name__________ Date__________ Class__________

Vehicle used for this activity:

Year__________ Make__________ Model__________

Odometer__________ VIN __________

Learning Objective / Task	CDX Tasksheet Number	2014 NATEF Priority Level	2014 NATEF Reference Number
• Check engine coolant type, level, condition, and consumption; test coolant for freeze protection and additive package concentration; determine needed action.	H068	P-1	1E1
• Test coolant temperature and check operation of temperature and level sensors, gauge, and/or sending unit; determine needed action.	H069	P-1	1E2
• Inspect and reinstall/replace pulleys, tensioners, and drive belts; adjust drive belts and check alignment.	H070	P-1	1E3
• Inspect thermostat(s), by-passes, housing(s), and seals; replace as needed.	H071	P-2	1E4
• Recover coolant, flush, and refill with recommended coolant/additive package; bleed cooling system.	H072	P-1	1E5

Time off__________

Time on__________

Total time__________

Materials Required

- Vehicle with possible engine concern
- Vehicle manufacturer's service information
- Manufacturer-specific tools depending on the concern
- Vehicle lifting equipment if applicable

Some Safety Issues to Consider

- Diagnosis of this fault may require test driving the vehicle on the school grounds or on a hoist, both of which carry severe risks. Attempt this task only with full permission from your supervisor/instructor and follow all the guidelines exactly.
- Caution: If you are working in an area where there could be "brake dust" present (may contain asbestos, which has been determined to cause cancer when inhaled or ingested), ensure you wear and use all OSHA-approved asbestos protective/removal equipment.
- Lifting equipment such as vehicle jacks and stands, vehicle hoists, and engine hoists are important tools that increase productivity and make the job easier. However, they can also cause severe injury or death if used improperly. Make sure you follow the manufacturer's operation procedures. Also make sure you have your supervisor/instructor's permission to use any particular type of lifting equipment.
- Comply with personal and environmental safety practices associated with clothing; eye protection; hand tools; power equipment; proper ventilation; and the handling, storage, and disposal of chemicals/materials in accordance with federal, state, and local regulations.
- Always wear the correct protective eyewear and clothing and use the appropriate safety equipment, as well as fender covers, seat protectors, and floor mat protectors.
- Make sure you understand and observe all legislative and personal safety procedures when carrying out practical assignments. If you are unsure of what these are, ask your supervisor/instructor.

Performance Standard

0–No exposure: No information or practice provided during the program; complete training required
1–Exposure only: General information provided with no practice time; close supervision needed; additional training required
2–Limited practice: Has practiced job during training program; additional training required to develop skill
3–Moderately skilled: Has performed job independently during training program; limited additional training may be required
4–Skilled: Can perform job independently with no additional training

Student/intern information:

Name____________________ Date__________ Class________________

Vehicle used for this activity:

Year__________ Make____________________ Model________________

Odometer__________________ VIN __________________________

TASK Check engine coolant type, level, condition, and consumption; test coolant for freeze protection and additive package concentration; determine needed action.

NATEF 1E1

Time off__________

Time on__________

Total time__________

CDX Tasksheet Number: H068

1. Reference the appropriate service information and check engine coolant type, level, condition, and consumption.
   a. Manufacturer's specifications:
      i. Coolant type: __________________
      ii. Coolant quantity: ________________ pts/liters
      iii. Cooling system pressure cap: __________ psi/kPa
2. Check the coolant level. List your observations:

____

____

3. Pressure test the cooling system pressure cap: Actual _______ psi/kPa
4. Pressure test the cooling system for leaks. List your observations:

____

____

5. Draw off a sample of the coolant; have it tested for its condition.

   Note: If bad coolant caused catastrophic failure, send a sample out to an independent lab for analysis.
   a. Meets the manufacturer's specifications: Yes: _____ No: _____
   b. Determine any necessary action(s):

____

____

6. Reference the appropriate service information and test the coolant for freeze protection and additive package concentration.
   a. List, or print and attach to this sheet, the procedure for testing the coolant for freeze protection and additive package concentration.

____

____

   b. Test the antifreeze protection and additive package concentration. List your observations:

____

____

   c. Meets the manufacturer's specifications: Yes: _____ No: _____

d. Determine any necessary action(s):

____

____

____

____

7. Discuss the findings with your instructor.

Performance Rating

CDX Tasksheet Number: H068

☐ 0 ☐ 1 ☐ 2 ☐ 3 ☐ 4

Supervisor/instructor signature ______________________________ Date ____________

Student/intern information:

Name____________________ Date________ Class________________

Vehicle used for this activity:

Year________ Make____________________ Model________________

Odometer__________________ VIN __________________________

TASK Test coolant temperature and check operation of temperature and level sensors, gauge, and/or sending unit; determine needed action. NATEF 1E2

Time off________

Time on________

Total time________

CDX Tasksheet Number: H069

1. Reference the appropriate service information and test the coolant temperature.
   a. Manufacturer's specifications:
      i. Engine coolant operating temperature: ________________
2. Check the coolant temperature cold: ________
3. Bring the engine to operating temperature; check and record the coolant temperature: ________
   a. Meets the manufacturer's specifications: Yes: _____ No: _____
   b. Determine any necessary action(s):
4. Reference the appropriate service information and check the operation of temperature and level sensors, gauge, and/or sending unit.
   a. List, or print and attach to this sheet, the procedure for checking the operation of temperature and level sensors, gauge, and/or sending unit.
   b. Inspect the operation of the temperature and level sensors, gauge, and/or sending unit. List your observations:
   c. Meets the manufacturer's specifications: Yes: _____ No: _____
   d. Determine any necessary action(s):
5. Discuss the findings with your instructor.

Performance Rating

CDX Tasksheet Number: H069

☐ 0 ☐ 1 ☐ 2 ☐ 3 ☐ 4

Supervisor/instructor signature ________________________ Date________

Student/intern information:

Name________________ Date________ Class____________

Vehicle used for this activity:

Year________ Make________________ Model____________

Odometer________________ VIN ________________

TASK Inspect and reinstall/replace pulleys, tensioners, and drive belts; adjust drive belts and check alignment. NATEF 1E3

Time off________

Time on________

Total time________

CDX Tasksheet Number: H070

1. Reference the appropriate service information and inspect and reinstall/replace the pulleys, tensioners, and drive belts; adjust the drive belts and check alignment.
    a. Manufacturer's specifications:
        i. Number of grooves in the pulley: ________
        ii. Type of tensioner: ________
        iii. Engine coolant drive belt tension: ________ ft-lbs (Nm)

2. Inspect the pulleys.
    a. Require replacement: Yes: ____ No: ____
    b. Re-install, if necessary.

3. Inspect the belt tensioner(s).
    a. Require replacement: Yes: ____ No: ____

4. Inspect the drive belt(s).
    a. Require replacement: Yes: ____ No: ____
    b. Adjust to the manufacturer's specifications.

5. Check pulley alignment.
    a. Require re-alignment: Yes: ____ No: ____
    b. If directed by your instructor, follow the appropriate service information's instructions and re-align the pulleys.

6. Overall assessment
    a. Meets the manufacturer's specifications: Yes: ____ No: ____
    b. Determine any necessary action(s):

____

____

____

____

7. Discuss the findings with your instructor.

Performance Rating

CDX Tasksheet Number: H070

☐ 0 ☐ 1 ☐ 2 ☐ 3 ☐ 4

Supervisor/instructor signature ________________ Date________

Student/intern information:

Name____________________ Date__________ Class____________________

Vehicle used for this activity:

Year__________ Make____________________ Model____________________

Odometer____________________ VIN ____________________

TASK Inspect thermostat(s), by-passes, housing(s), and seals; replace as needed.

NATEF 1E4

Time off__________

Time on__________

Total time__________

CDX Tasksheet Number: H071

1. Reference the appropriate service information and inspect the thermostat(s), by-passes, housing(s), and seals; replace as needed.
    a. Manufacturer's specifications:
        i. Engine thermostat opening temperature: __________

2. Inspect the thermostat(s). In some cases this may require the removal of the thermostat. It is a recommended replacement upon engine overhaul.
    a. Require replacement: Yes: _____ No: _____
    b. Re-install with a new gasket, if necessary.

3. Inspect the by-passes.
    a. Require replacement: Yes: _____ No: _____

4. Inspect the housing(s).
    a. Require replacement: Yes: _____ No: _____

5. Check the seals.
    a. Require replacement: Yes: _____ No: _____
    b. Replace the seals, if necessary.

6. Overall assessment
    a. Meets the manufacturer's specifications: Yes: _____ No: _____
    b. Determine any necessary action(s):

____

____

____

____

____

7. Discuss the findings with your instructor.

Performance Rating

CDX Tasksheet Number: H071

☐ 0 ☐ 1 ☐ 2 ☐ 3 ☐ 4

Supervisor/instructor signature ____________________ Date__________

Student/intern information:

Name____________________ Date__________ Class____________________

Vehicle used for this activity:

Year__________ Make____________________ Model____________________

Odometer____________________ VIN ____________________

TASK Recover coolant, flush, and refill with recommended coolant/additive package; bleed cooling system. NATEF 1E5

Time off__________

Time on__________

Total time__________

CDX Tasksheet Number: H072

1. Reference the appropriate service information and recover, flush, and refill with the recommended coolant/additive package.
   a. Manufacturer's specifications:
      i. Coolant type: ____________________
      ii. Coolant quantity: ____________________ pts/liters
      iii. Cooling system pressure cap: ____________________ psi/kPa
2. Using a collection container adequate for the amount of coolant to be drained, drain the coolant.
3. Ensure that the discarded coolant is disposed of in accordance with all environmental legislative and government regulations.
4. With reference to the appropriate service information, flush the cooling system. Use a coolant flush machine to make sure adequate flush of entire system.
5. Refill the cooling system with the manufacturer's recommended coolant and with the recommended quantity.
6. Run the engine.
7. Shut down the engine and recheck the coolant level.
8. While referencing the appropriate service information, bleed the cooling system.
9. Cooling system checks and inspections/flushing/refilling meets the manufacturer's specifications: Yes: _____ No: _____
   a. Determine any necessary action(s):

____

____

____

____

10. Discuss the findings with your instructor.

Performance Rating

CDX Tasksheet Number: H072

☐ 0 ☐ 1 ☐ 2 ☐ 3 ☐ 4

Supervisor/instructor signature ____________________ Date__________

Diesel Engines: Cooling System 2

Student/intern information:

Name__________ Date__________ Class__________

Vehicle used for this activity:

Year__________ Make__________ Model__________

Odometer__________ VIN __________

Time off__________

Time on__________

Total time__________

Learning Objective / Task	CDX Tasksheet Number	2014 NATEF Priority Level	2014 NATEF Reference Number
• Inspect coolant conditioner/filter assembly for leaks; inspect valves, lines, and fittings; replace as needed.	H073	P-1	1E6
• Inspect water pump and hoses; replace as needed.	H074	P-1	1E7
• Inspect, clean, and pressure test radiator, pressure cap, tank(s), and recovery systems; determine needed action.	H075	P-1	1E8
• Inspect thermostatic cooling fan system (hydraulic, pneumatic, and electronic) and fan shroud; replace as needed.	H076	P-1	1E9
• Inspect turbocharger cooling systems; determine needed action.	H077	P-2	1E10

Materials Required

- Vehicle with possible engine concern
- Vehicle manufacturer's service information
- Manufacturer-specific tools depending on the concern
- Vehicle lifting equipment if applicable

Some Safety Issues to Consider

- Diagnosis of this fault may require test driving the vehicle on the school grounds or on a hoist, both of which carry severe risks. Attempt this task only with full permission from your supervisor/instructor and follow all the guidelines exactly.
- Caution: If you are working in an area where there could be "brake dust" present (may contain asbestos, which has been determined to cause cancer when inhaled or ingested), ensure you wear and use all OSHA-approved asbestos protective/removal equipment.
- Lifting equipment such as vehicle jacks and stands, vehicle hoists, and engine hoists are important tools that increase productivity and make the job easier. However, they can also cause severe injury or death if used improperly. Make sure you follow the manufacturer's operation procedures. Also make sure you have your supervisor/instructor's permission to use any particular type of lifting equipment.
- Comply with personal and environmental safety practices associated with clothing; eye protection; hand tools; power equipment; proper ventilation; and the handling, storage, and disposal of chemicals/materials in accordance with federal, state, and local regulations.
- Always wear the correct protective eyewear and clothing and use the appropriate safety equipment, as well as fender covers, seat protectors, and floor mat protectors.
- Make sure you understand and observe all legislative and personal safety procedures when carrying out practical assignments. If you are unsure of what these are, ask your supervisor/instructor.

Performance Standard

0–No exposure: No information or practice provided during the program; complete training required

1–Exposure only: General information provided with no practice time; close supervision needed; additional training required

2–Limited practice: Has practiced job during training program; additional training required to develop skill

3–Moderately skilled: Has performed job independently during training program; limited additional training may be required

4–Skilled: Can perform job independently with no additional training

Student/intern information:

Name________________________ Date____________ Class________________________

Vehicle used for this activity:

Year____________ Make________________________ Model________________________

Odometer________________________ VIN ________________________

TASK Inspect coolant conditioner/filter assembly for leaks; inspect valves, lines, and fittings; replace as needed. NATEF 1E6

Time off________

Time on________

Total time________

CDX Tasksheet Number: H073

1. Reference the appropriate service information and inspect the coolant conditioner/filter assembly for leaks; inspect the valves, lines, and fittings.
   a. Manufacturer's specifications:
      i. Coolant conditioner/filter type: ________________
2. Check and inspect the coolant conditioner/filter assembly for leaks. List your observations:

____
____
____

3. Pressurize the cooling system and re-check and inspect the coolant conditioner/filter assembly for leaks.
4. Inspect the valves.
5. Inspect the lines and fittings.
6. Draw off a sample of the coolant; have it tested for its condition, with your instructor's approval.
   a. Meets the manufacturer's specifications: Yes: _____ No: _____
   b. Determine any necessary action(s):

____
____
____

7. Reference the appropriate service information; after inspecting the coolant conditioner/filter assembly for leaks etc., replace as needed.
   a. List, or print and attach to this sheet, the procedure for inspecting the coolant conditioner/filter assembly for leaks etc.; replace as needed.

____
____
____

   b. Replace the coolant conditioner/filter assembly, valves, lines, and fittings as needed. List your observations:

____
____
____

c. Meets the manufacturer's specifications: Yes: _____ No: _____

d. Determine any necessary action(s):

____

____

____

8. Discuss the findings with your instructor.

Performance Rating

CDX Tasksheet Number: H073

☐	☐	☐	☐	☐
0	1	2	3	4

Supervisor/instructor signature ______________________________ Date__________

Student/intern information:

Name____________________ Date__________ Class____________________

Vehicle used for this activity:

Year__________ Make____________________ Model____________________

Odometer____________________ VIN ____________________

TASK Inspect water pump and hoses; replace as needed.

NATEF 1E7

Time off__________

Time on__________

Total time__________

CDX Tasksheet Number: H074

1. Reference the appropriate service information and check and inspect the water pump and hoses. Look closely at the weep hole in the bottom of the pump for dried coolant residue. If present, replace the pump. Always replace upon engine overhaul.
   a. Inspect the water pump and hoses for leaks or damage. List your observations:
   b. Meets the manufacturer's specifications: Yes: _____ No: _____
   c. Determine any necessary action(s):
2. Reference the appropriate service information; after inspection of the water pump and hoses, replace as needed.
   a. If directed by your instructor, remove the water pump following the specified procedure. List your observations:
   b. Meets the manufacturer's specifications: Yes: _____ No: _____
   c. Determine any necessary action(s):
   d. Have your instructor verify removal and your answers. Supervisor's/instructor's Initials: ________________
   e. Reinstall the water pump. List your observations:
3. Discuss the findings with your instructor.

Performance Rating

CDX Tasksheet Number: H074

☐	☐	☐	☐	☐
0	1	2	3	4

Supervisor/instructor signature ____________________ Date__________

Student/intern information:

Name________________ Date________ Class____________

Vehicle used for this activity:

Year________ Make________________ Model____________

Odometer______________ VIN ____________________

TASK Inspect, clean, and pressure test radiator, pressure cap, tank(s), and recovery systems; determine needed action. NATEF 1E8

Time off________

Time on________

Total time________

CDX Tasksheet Number: H075

1. List, or print and attach to this sheet, the procedure to inspect, clean, and pressure test the radiator, pressure cap, tank(s), and recovery systems.

2. Inspect the radiator cap and pressure test cap. List your observations:

3. Inspect the radiator and pressure test system. List your observations:

4. Inspect the recovery tanks for leaks, corrosion, or splits.
   a. List your observations:

   b. Meets the manufacturer's specifications: Yes: _____ No: _____

   c. Determine any necessary action(s):

5. Discuss the findings with your instructor.

Performance Rating

CDX Tasksheet Number: H075

☐ 0 ☐ 1 ☐ 2 ☐ 3 ☐ 4

Supervisor/instructor signature ____________________ Date________

Student/intern information:

Name____________________ Date__________ Class________________

Vehicle used for this activity:

Year__________ Make____________________ Model________________

Odometer____________________ VIN ________________________

TASK Inspect thermostatic cooling fan system (hydraulic, pneumatic, and electronic) and fan shroud; replace as needed. NATEF 1E9

Time off__________

Time on__________

Total time__________

CDX Tasksheet Number: H076

1. Reference the appropriate service information and inspect the thermostatic cooling fan system (hydraulic, pneumatic, and electronic) and fan shroud.
   a. List the manufacturer's preferred thermostatic cooling fan system: ________________
2. Check and inspect the thermostatic cooling fan system for damage. List your observations:
3. Check and inspect the thermostatic cooling fans for correct operation. Inspect fan fins for malformation or missing or broken condition. List your observations:
4. Check and inspect the thermostatic cooling fans' electrical harness for correct operation and damage. List your observations:
5. Check and inspect the cooling fan shroud for damage.
   a. List your observations:
   b. Meets the manufacturer's specifications: Yes: _____ No: _____
   c. Determine any necessary action(s):

6. Reference the appropriate service information to replace the the thermostatic cooling fan system and fan shroud.
    a. List, or print and attach to this sheet, the procedure for the replacement of the thermostatic cooling fan system and fan shroud.

    ____
    ____
    ____
    ____

    b. Remove the thermostatic cooling fan and fan shroud. List your observations:

    ____
    ____
    ____
    ____

    c. Meets the manufacturer's specifications: Yes: _____ No: _____

    d. Determine any necessary action(s):

    ____
    ____
    ____

    e. Have your instructor verify removal and your answers.
    Supervisor's/instructor's Initials: ______________

7. Discuss the findings with your instructor.

Performance Rating

CDX Tasksheet Number: H075

☐	☐	☐	☐	☐
0	1	2	3	4

Supervisor/instructor signature ______________________________ Date______________

Student/intern information:

Name_______________ Date_______________ Class_______________

Vehicle used for this activity:

Year_______________ Make_______________ Model_______________

Odometer_______________ VIN _______________

TASK Inspect turbocharger cooling systems; determine needed action. NATEF 1E10

Time off_______________

Time on_______________

Total time_______________

CDX Tasksheet Number: H077

1. Inspect supply line from the primary oil gallery on side of the block for leakage due to a possible loose connection and or faulty fittings.
   a. Condition of supply line:

2. Inspect return line at the bottom of the turbocharger for leakage at the connections.
   a. Condition of return line:

3. If necessary, remove and inspect both lines for blockage in case of a catastrophic turbocharger failure.

4. Take a supply line oil pressure reading to ensure the turbocharger is receiving the correct pressure to maintain proper operation at all times.
   a. Reading of supply line oil pressure:

5. Inspect hood openings and clearance between the hood, turbocharger and the engine to make sure of proper airflow over turbocharger housing.
   a. Condition of hood openings and clearance:

____
____
____
____
____

6. Discuss the findings with your instructor.

Performance Rating

CDX Tasksheet Number: H077

☐	☐	☐	☐	☐
0	1	2	3	4

Supervisor/instructor signature ______________________________ Date______________

Diesel Engines: Air Induction and Exhaust Systems 1

Student/intern information:

Name__________ Date__________ Class__________

Vehicle used for this activity:

Year__________ Make__________ Model__________

Odometer__________ VIN __________

Learning Objective / Task	CDX Tasksheet Number	2014 NATEF Priority Level	2014 NATEF Reference Number
• Perform air intake system restriction and leakage tests; determine needed action.	H078	P-1	1F1
• Perform intake manifold pressure (boost) test; determine needed action.	H079	P-3	1F2
• Check exhaust back pressure; determine needed action.	H080	P-3	1F3
• Inspect turbocharger(s), wastegate, and piping systems; determine needed action.	H081	P-2	1F4
• Check air induction system: piping, hoses, clamps, and mounting; service or replace air filter as needed.	H083	P-1	1F6
• Remove and reinstall turbocharger/wastegate assembly.	H084	P-3	1F7

Time off__________

Time on__________

Total time__________

Materials Required

- Vehicle with possible engine concern
- Vehicle manufacturer's service information
- Manufacturer-specific tools depending on the concern
- Vehicle lifting equipment if applicable

Some Safety Issues to Consider

- Diagnosis of this fault may require test driving the vehicle on the school grounds or on a hoist, both of which carry severe risks. Attempt this task only with full permission from your supervisor/instructor and follow all the guidelines exactly.
- Caution: If you are working in an area where there could be "brake dust" present (may contain asbestos, which has been determined to cause cancer when inhaled or ingested), ensure you wear and use all OSHA-approved asbestos protective/removal equipment.
- Lifting equipment such as vehicle jacks and stands, vehicle hoists, and engine hoists are important tools that increase productivity and make the job easier. However, they can also cause severe injury or death if used improperly. Make sure you follow the manufacturer's operation procedures. Also make sure you have your supervisor/instructor's permission to use any particular type of lifting equipment.
- Comply with personal and environmental safety practices associated with clothing; eye protection; hand tools; power equipment; proper ventilation; and the handling, storage, and disposal of chemicals/materials in accordance with federal, state, and local regulations.
- Always wear the correct protective eyewear and clothing and use the appropriate safety equipment, as well as fender covers, seat protectors, and floor mat protectors.
- Make sure you understand and observe all legislative and personal safety procedures when carrying out practical assignments. If you are unsure of what these are, ask your supervisor/instructor.

Performance Standard

0–No exposure: No information or practice provided during the program; complete training required

1–Exposure only: General information provided with no practice time; close supervision needed; additional training required

2–Limited practice: Has practiced job during training program; additional training required to develop skill

3–Moderately skilled: Has performed job independently during training program; limited additional training may be required

4–Skilled: Can perform job independently with no additional training

Student/intern information:

Name________________________ Date__________ Class________________

Vehicle used for this activity:

Year__________ Make______________________ Model______________

Odometer____________________ VIN ______________________________

TASK Perform air intake system restriction and leakage tests; determine needed action.

NATEF 1F1

Time off________

Time on________

Total time________

CDX Tasksheet Number: H078

1. Reference the appropriate service information and perform air intake system restriction tests using the manufacturer's recommended tooling.
    a. Manufacturer's specifications:
        i. Maximum restriction/leakage permissible: ____________________

2. Perform an air intake system restriction test. Check filter minder for operation. Or, if necessary, use a manometer for flow restriction. Check all plumbing for kinking or obstruction.
    a. List your observations:

    ____
    ____
    ____
    ____
    ____

    b. Meets the manufacturer's specifications: Yes: _____ No: _____

    c. Determine any necessary action(s):

    ____
    ____
    ____
    ____
    ____

3. Reference the appropriate service information; perform air intake system leakage tests using the manufacturer's recommended tooling.

4. Perform an air intake system leakage test.
    a. List, or print and attach to this sheet, the procedure to perform air intake system leakage tests using the manufacturer's recommended tooling.

    ____
    ____
    ____
    ____
    ____

    b. Perform an air intake system leakage test. List your observations:

    ____
    ____
    ____
    ____

c. Meets the manufacturer's specifications: Yes: _____ No: _____

d. Determine any necessary action(s):

____

____

____

____

____

5. Discuss the findings with your instructor.

Performance Rating

CDX Tasksheet Number: H078

☐	☐	☐	☐	☐
0	1	2	3	4

Supervisor/instructor signature _______________________________ Date__________

Student/intern information:

Name________________ Date________ Class__________

Vehicle used for this activity:

Year________ Make________________ Model__________

Odometer________________ VIN ____________________

TASK Perform intake manifold pressure (boost) test; determine needed action. NATEF 1F2

Time off________

Time on________

Total time________

CDX Tasksheet Number: H079

1. Reference the appropriate service information and perform the intake manifold pressure (boost) test.
    a. List, or print and attach to this sheet, the procedure to perform the intake manifold pressure (boost) test.
    b. Perform the intake manifold pressure (boost) test. List your observations:
    c. Meets the manufacturer's specifications: Yes: _____ No: _____
    d. Determine any necessary action(s):
2. Discuss the findings with your instructor.

Performance Rating

CDX Tasksheet Number: H079

☐	☐	☐	☐	☐
0	1	2	3	4

Supervisor/instructor signature ____________________ Date________

Student/intern information:

Name____________________ Date__________ Class____________________

Vehicle used for this activity:

Year__________ Make____________________ Model____________________

Odometer____________________ VIN ____________________

TASK Check exhaust back pressure; determine needed action. NATEF 1F3

Time off__________

Time on__________

Total time__________

CDX Tasksheet Number: H080

1. Reference the appropriate service information and perform the exhaust back pressure test; determine needed action.
   a. List, or print and attach to this sheet, the procedure to perform the exhaust back pressure test; determine needed action.

   b. Perform the exhaust back pressure test. List your observations:

   c. Meets the manufacturer's specifications: Yes: _____ No: _____

   d. Determine any necessary action(s):

2. Discuss the findings with your instructor.

Performance Rating

CDX Tasksheet Number: H080

☐ 0 ☐ 1 ☐ 2 ☐ 3 ☐ 4

Supervisor/instructor signature ____________________ Date__________

Student/intern information:

Name____________________ Date__________ Class____________________

Vehicle used for this activity:

Year__________ Make____________________ Model____________________

Odometer____________________ VIN ____________________

TASK Inspect turbocharger(s), wastegate, and piping systems; determine needed action.

NATEF 1F4

Time off__________

Time on__________

Total time__________

CDX Tasksheet Number: H081

1. List, or print and attach to this sheet, the procedure to inspect the turbocharger(s), wastegate, and piping systems.

2. Check and inspect the turbocharger and wastegate for damage or faults. List your observations:

3. Check and inspect the turbocharger and wastegate for correct operation.

4. Check and inspect the turbocharger piping for damage or faults.
   a. List your observations:

   b. Meets the manufacturer's specifications: Yes: _____ No: _____

   c. Determine any necessary action(s):

5. Discuss the findings with your instructor.

Performance Rating

CDX Tasksheet Number: H081

☐	☐	☐	☐	☐
0	1	2	3	4

Supervisor/instructor signature ____________________ Date__________

Student/intern information:

Name_______________ Date_______ Class_______________

Vehicle used for this activity:

Year_______ Make_______________ Model_______________

Odometer_______________ VIN _______________

◀◀ TASK Check air induction system: piping, hoses, clamps, and mounting; service or replace air filter as needed. NATEF 1F6

Time off_______

Time on_______

Total time_______

CDX Tasksheet Number: H083

1. List, or print and attach to this sheet, the procedure to check the air induction system: piping, hoses, clamps, and mounting.
____
____
____

2. Check and inspect the air induction piping hoses and clamps for damage, faults, and mounting security.
   a. List your observations:
   ____
   ____
   ____
   b. Meets the manufacturer's specifications: Yes: _____ No: _____
   c. Determine any necessary action(s):
   ____
   ____
   ____

3. Reference the appropriate service information and service or replace the air filter as needed.
4. Clean and inspect the air filter in accordance with the manufacturer's specifications.
5. Inspect the air filter for serviceability.
   a. List your observations:
   ____
   ____
   ____
   b. Meets the manufacturer's specifications: Yes: _____ No: _____
   c. Determine any necessary action(s):
   ____
   ____
   ____
   d. Have your instructor verify removal and your answers.
   Supervisor's/instructor's Initials: _____________

6. If directed by your instructor, replace the air filter if required.
7. Discuss the findings with your instructor.

Performance Rating

CDX Tasksheet Number: H083

☐ 0 ☐ 1 ☐ 2 ☐ 3 ☐ 4

Supervisor/instructor signature ______________________ Date______________

Student/intern information:

Name________________ Date________ Class________________

Vehicle used for this activity:

Year________ Make________________ Model________________

Odometer________________ VIN ________________

Time off________

Time on________

Total time________

TASK Remove and reinstall turbocharger/wastegate assembly. NATEF 1F7

CDX Tasksheet Number: H084

1. Reference the appropriate service information and list the procedure and all safety precautions that must be observed when you remove and reinstall the turbocharger/wastegate assembly.
   a. List, or print and attach to this sheet, the steps involved when you remove and reinstall the turbocharger/wastegate assembly:
   b. Determine what safety precautions must be observed when you remove and reinstall the turbocharger/wastegate assembly:
2. Following the procedures listed above, and while referencing the appropriate service information, remove the turbocharger/wastegate assembly.
   a. List your observations:
   b. Meets the manufacturer's specifications: Yes: _____ No: _____
   c. Determine any necessary action(s):
   d. Have your instructor verify removal and your answers.
   Supervisor's/instructor's Initials: ____________

e. Following the specified procedure, reinstall the turbocharger/wastegate assembly. List your observations:

___

___

___

3. Discuss the findings with your instructor.

Performance Rating

CDX Tasksheet Number: H084

☐ 0 ☐ 1 ☐ 2 ☐ 3 ☐ 4

Supervisor/instructor signature ___ Date___

Diesel Engines: Air Induction and Exhaust Systems 2

Student/intern information:

Name________________ Date________ Class________________

Vehicle used for this activity:

Year________ Make________________ Model________________

Odometer________________ VIN ________________

Learning Objective / Task	CDX Tasksheet Number	2014 NATEF Priority Level	2014 NATEF Reference Number
• Inspect intake manifold, gaskets, and connections; replace as needed.	H085	P-3	1F8
• Inspect, clean, and test charge air cooler assemblies; replace as needed.	H086	P-2	1F9
• Inspect exhaust manifold, piping, mufflers, and mounting hardware; repair or replace as needed.	H087	P-2	1F10
• Inspect exhaust after treatment devices; determine necessary action.	H088	P-2	1F11

Time off________

Time on________

Total time________

Materials Required

- Vehicle with possible engine concern
- Vehicle manufacturer's service information
- Manufacturer-specific tools depending on the concern
- Vehicle lifting equipment if applicable

Some Safety Issues to Consider

- Diagnosis of this fault may require test driving the vehicle on the school grounds or on a hoist, both of which carry severe risks. Attempt this task only with full permission from your supervisor/instructor and follow all the guidelines exactly.
- Caution: If you are working in an area where there could be "brake dust" present (may contain asbestos, which has been determined to cause cancer when inhaled or ingested), ensure you wear and use all OSHA-approved asbestos protective/removal equipment.
- Lifting equipment such as vehicle jacks and stands, vehicle hoists, and engine hoists are important tools that increase productivity and make the job easier. However, they can also cause severe injury or death if used improperly. Make sure you follow the manufacturer's operation procedures. Also make sure you have your supervisor/instructor's permission to use any particular type of lifting equipment.
- Comply with personal and environmental safety practices associated with clothing; eye protection; hand tools; power equipment; proper ventilation; and the handling, storage, and disposal of chemicals/materials in accordance with federal, state, and local regulations.
- Always wear the correct protective eyewear and clothing and use the appropriate safety equipment, as well as fender covers, seat protectors, and floor mat protectors.
- Make sure you understand and observe all legislative and personal safety procedures when carrying out practical assignments. If you are unsure of what these are, ask your supervisor/instructor.

Performance Standard

0–No exposure: No information or practice provided during the program; complete training required

1–Exposure only: General information provided with no practice time; close supervision needed; additional training required

2–Limited practice: Has practiced job during training program; additional training required to develop skill

3–Moderately skilled: Has performed job independently during training program; limited additional training may be required

4–Skilled: Can perform job independently with no additional training

Student/intern information:

Name________________________ Date__________ Class________________

Vehicle used for this activity:

Year__________ Make________________________ Model________________

Odometer____________________ VIN ____________________________

TASK Inspect intake manifold, gaskets, and connections; replace as needed. NATEF 1F8

Time off__________

Time on__________

Total time__________

CDX Tasksheet Number: H085

1. Reference the appropriate service information and inspect the intake manifold, gaskets, and connections.
    a. List, or print and attach to this sheet, the procedure to inspect the intake manifold, gaskets, and connections.

    ____

    ____

    ____

    b. Inspect the intake manifold, gaskets, and connections. List your observations:

    ____

    ____

    ____

    c. Meets the manufacturer's specifications: Yes: _____ No: _____

    d. Determine any necessary action(s):

    ____

    ____

    ____

    ____

2. Discuss the findings with your instructor.

Performance Rating

CDX Tasksheet Number: H085

☐ 0 ☐ 1 ☐ 2 ☐ 3 ☐ 4

Supervisor/instructor signature ________________________ Date__________

Student/intern information:

Name____________________ Date__________ Class________________

Vehicle used for this activity:

Year__________ Make____________________ Model________________

Odometer____________________ VIN ____________________

TASK Inspect, clean, and test charge air cooler assemblies; replace as needed. NATEF 1F9

Time off__________

Time on__________

Total time__________

CDX Tasksheet Number: H086

1. Reference the appropriate service information and inspect, clean, and test the charge air cooler assemblies.
2. List, or print and attach to this sheet, the procedure to inspect, clean, and test the charge air cooler assemblies.
3. Inspect the air cooler assemblies. List your observations:
4. Clean the air cooler assemblies. List your observations:
5. Test the charge air cooler assemblies.
   a. List your observations:
   b. Meets the manufacturer's specifications: Yes: _____ No: _____
   c. Determine any necessary action(s):
6. If directed by your instructor, replace the components as necessary.
7. Discuss the findings with your instructor.

Performance Rating

CDX Tasksheet Number: H086

☐ 0 ☐ 1 ☐ 2 ☐ 3 ☐ 4

Supervisor/instructor signature ____________________ Date__________

Student/intern information:

Name____________ Date________ Class__________

Vehicle used for this activity:

Year________ Make____________ Model________

Odometer____________ VIN ____________

TASK Inspect exhaust manifold, piping, mufflers, and mounting hardware; repair or replace as needed. NATEF 1F10

Time off________

Time on________

Total time________

CDX Tasksheet Number: H087

1. Reference the appropriate service information and inspect the exhaust manifold, piping, mufflers, and mounting hardware.
   a. List, or print and attach to this sheet, the procedure to inspect the exhaust manifold, piping, mufflers, and mounting hardware.

   ____

   ____

   b. Inspect the exhaust manifold.
      i. Require replacement: Yes: _____ No: _____
   c. Inspect the exhaust piping.
      i. Require replacement: Yes: _____ No: _____
   d. Inspect the muffler.
      i. Require replacement: Yes: _____ No: _____
   e. Inspect the exhaust pipe mounting hardware.
      i. Require replacement: Yes: _____ No: _____
2. Overall assessment
   a. List your observations:

   ____

   ____

   b. Meets the manufacturer's specifications: Yes: _____ No: _____
   c. Determine any necessary action(s):

   ____

   ____
3. If directed by your instructor, follow the appropriate service information's instructions and repair or replace the components as needed.
4. Discuss the findings with your instructor.

Performance Rating

CDX Tasksheet Number: H087

☐	☐	☐	☐	☐
0	1	2	3	4

Supervisor/instructor signature ________________ Date________

Student/intern information:

Name____________________ Date________ Class______________

Vehicle used for this activity:

Year________ Make____________________ Model______________

Odometer__________________ VIN ________________________

TASK Inspect exhaust after treatment devices; determine necessary action. NATEF 1F11

Time off________

Time on________

Total time________

CDX Tasksheet Number: H088

1. Identify the type of treatment device fitted to your vehicle:____________________
2. Reference the appropriate service information and inspect the exhaust after treatment devices.
   a. Carry out a visual inspection of the treatment device.
      i. Require replacement: Yes: _____ No: _____

   b. If the treatment device is a "diesel particulate filter," attach the diagnostic code reader to the vehicle.

   c. Are there any codes present or stored in the reader? Yes: _____ No: _____
      i. If yes, list the codes:

   d. Carry out a forced re-generation of the particulate filter. **Caution!** Obtain the permission of your instructor before performing this task. Due to very high exhaust temperatures there is an extreme fire hazard. Refer to appropriate service information for the exact procedure.
3. If your vehicle is fitted with another type of exhaust treatment device, name the device:

4. Briefly describe the testing procedure for this unit as outlined in the appropriate service information:

5. As outlined above, carry out a visual inspection of the treatment device.
   a. List your observations: ______________________________

   b. Determine any necessary action(s): ______________________________

6. Discuss the findings with your instructor.

Performance Rating

CDX Tasksheet Number: H088

☐	☐	☐	☐	☐
0	1	2	3	4

Supervisor/instructor signature ______________________________ Date ______________

Diesel Fuel System, DT102

CONTENTS

Diesel Fuel System: General

Student/intern information:

Name________________ Date________ Class________________

Vehicle used for this activity:

Year__________ Make____________________ Model____________

Odometer________________ VIN ____________________

Time off________

Time on________

Total time________

Learning Objective / Task	CDX Tasksheet Number	2014 NATEF Priority Level	2014 NATEF Reference Number
• Check engine no cranking, cranks but fails to start, hard starting, and starts but does not continue to run problems; determine needed action.	H030	P-1	1A5
• Identify causes of surging, rough operation, misfiring, low power, slow deceleration, slow acceleration, and shutdown problems; determine needed action.	H031	P-1	1A6
• Check and record electronic diagnostic codes.	H033	P-1	1A8

Materials Required

- Vehicle with possible engine concern
- Vehicle manufacturer's service information
- Manufacturer-specific tools depending on the concern
- Vehicle lifting equipment if applicable

Some Safety Issues to Consider

- Modern diesel fuel injection systems can develop pressures as high as 30,000 psi (2068 bar); fuel can stream out at this high pressure, which will easily cut and penetrate the skin and cause serious bodily harm, and may even lead to blood poisoning. Appropriate safety equipment should be worn to prevent injury.
- Diagnosis of this fault may require test driving the vehicle on the school grounds or on a hoist, both of which carry severe risks. Attempt this task only with full permission from your supervisor/instructor and follow all the guidelines exactly.
- Caution: If you are working in an area where there could be "brake dust" present (may contain asbestos, which has been determined to cause cancer when inhaled or ingested), ensure you wear and use all OSHA-approved asbestos protective/removal equipment.
- Lifting equipment such as vehicle jacks and stands, vehicle hoists, and engine hoists are important tools that increase productivity and make the job easier. However, they can also cause severe injury or death if used improperly. Make sure you follow the manufacturer's operation procedures. Also make sure you have your supervisor/instructor's permission to use any particular type of lifting equipment.
- Comply with personal and environmental safety practices associated with clothing; eye protection; hand tools; power equipment; proper ventilation; and the handling, storage, and disposal of chemicals/materials in accordance with federal, state, and local regulations.
- Always wear the correct protective eyewear and clothing and use the appropriate safety equipment, as well as fender covers, seat protectors, and floor mat protectors.

- Make sure you understand and observe all legislative and personal safety procedures when carrying out practical assignments. If you are unsure of what these are, ask your supervisor/instructor.

Performance Standard

0–No exposure: No information or practice provided during the program; complete training required

1–Exposure only: General information provided with no practice time; close supervision needed; additional training required

2–Limited practice: Has practiced job during training program; additional training required to develop skill

3–Moderately skilled: Has performed job independently during training program; limited additional training may be required

4–Skilled: Can perform job independently with no additional training

Student/intern information:

Name__________ Date__________ Class__________

Vehicle used for this activity:

Year__________ Make__________ Model__________

Odometer__________ VIN __________

TASK Check engine no cranking, cranks but fails to start, hard starting, and starts but does not continue to run problems; determine needed action. NATEF 1A5

Time off__________

Time on__________

Total time__________

CDX Tasksheet Number: H030

1. Reference the appropriate service information for the common causes for a "no crank" situation.
   a. List, or print off and attach to this sheet, all possible causes for "no crank" (the engine will not turn over using the starter motor):
   b. Determine what action will be required for "no crank":
2. Reference the appropriate service information for the common causes for a "cranks but fails to start" situation.
   a. List, or print off and attach to this sheet, all possible causes for "cranks but fails to start" (the engine turns over by the starter motor but fails to run):
   b. Determine what action will be required for "cranks but fails to start":
   c. Ask your instructor to assign a suitable vehicle that has been set up to serve as an example of "cranks but fails to start." List your observations:
   d. Determine any necessary action(s):

3. Reference the appropriate service information for the common causes for a "hard starting" situation (the engine will run but takes longer than usual to start).
    a. List, or print off and attach to this sheet, all possible causes for "hard starting":
    ____
    ____
    ____
    ____
    b. Determine what action will be required for "hard starting":
    ____
    ____
    ____
    ____
4. Reference the appropriate service information for the common causes for a "starts but does not continue to run problem" situation.
    a. List, or print off and attach to this sheet, all possible causes for "starts but does not continue to run problem":
    ____
    ____
    ____
    ____
    b. Determine what action will be required for "starts but does not continue to run problem":
    ____
    ____
    ____
    ____
5. Discuss the findings with your instructor.

Performance Rating

CDX Tasksheet Number: H030

☐	☐	☐	☐	☐
0	1	2	3	4

Supervisor/instructor signature ______________________________ Date______________

Student/intern information:

Name________________ Date________ Class________

Vehicle used for this activity:

Year________ Make________________ Model________

Odometer________________ VIN ________________

TASK Identify causes of surging, rough operation, misfiring, low power, slow deceleration, slow acceleration, and shutdown problems; determine needed action. NATEF 1A6

Time off________

Time on________

Total time________

CDX Tasksheet Number: H031

1. Reference the appropriate service information for the common causes for a "surging" situation.
   a. List all possible causes of "surging" (uneven or rolling idle):

   b. Determine what action will be required of "surging":

2. Reference the appropriate service information for the common causes for an engine's "rough operation" situation.
   a. List all possible causes for an engine's "rough operation":

   b. Determine what action will be required for an engine's "rough operation":

3. Reference the appropriate service information for the common causes for an engine's "misfiring" situation.
   a. List all possible causes for an engine's "misfiring":

      ____
      ____
      ____
      ____
      ____

   b. Determine what action will be required for an engine's "misfiring":

      ____
      ____
      ____
      ____
      ____

4. Reference the appropriate service information for the common causes for an engine's "low power" situation.
   a. List, or print off and attach to this sheet, all possible causes for an engine's "low power" condition.

      ____
      ____
      ____
      ____
      ____

   b. Determine what action will be required for an engine's "low power" condition:

      ____
      ____
      ____
      ____
      ____

5. Reference the appropriate service information for the common causes for an engine's "slow deceleration and/or slow acceleration" situation.
   a. List, or print off and attach to this sheet, all possible causes for an engine's "slow deceleration and/or slow acceleration" situation:

      ____
      ____
      ____
      ____
      ____

   b. Determine what action will be required for an engine's "slow deceleration and/or slow acceleration" situation:

      ____
      ____
      ____
      ____
      ____

6. Reference the appropriate service information for the common causes for an engine's "shutdown" problems.
   a. List, or print off and attach to this sheet, all possible causes for an engine's "shutdown" problems:

      ____
      ____
      ____
      ____
      ____

   b. Determine what action will be required for an engine's "shutdown" problems:

      ____
      ____
      ____
      ____
      ____

7. Discuss the findings with your instructor.

Performance Rating

CDX Tasksheet Number: H031

☐	☐	☐	☐	☐
0	1	2	3	4

Supervisor/instructor signature _______________________________ Date_____________

Student/intern information:

Name________________ Date________ Class____________

Vehicle used for this activity:

Year________ Make________________ Model____________

Odometer________________ VIN ________________________

◀◀ TASK Check and record electronic diagnostic codes. **NATEF 1A8**

Time off________

Time on________

Total time________

CDX Tasksheet Number: H033

1. Research the procedure and specifications for checking and recording electronic diagnostic codes in the appropriate service information.

   a. Connect the scan tool to the vehicle in accordance with the manufacturer's instructions.

   b. Retrieve and record any diagnostic trouble codes and their descriptions:

   c. List any other observations:

   d. Determine any necessary action(s):

2. Discuss your findings with your instructor.

Performance Rating

CDX Tasksheet Number: H033

☐ 0 ☐ 1 ☐ 2 ☐ 3 ☐ 4

Supervisor/instructor signature ________________________ Date________

Diesel Fuel System: Air Induction and Exhaust Systems

Student/intern information:

Name__________ Date__________ Class__________

Vehicle used for this activity:

Year__________ Make__________ Model__________

Odometer__________ VIN __________

Learning Objective / Task	CDX Tasksheet Number	2014 NATEF Priority Level	2014 NATEF Reference Number
• Inspect and test turbocharger(s) (variable ratio/geometry VGT), pneumatic, hydraulic, electronic controls, and actuators.	H082	P-2	1F5
• Inspect exhaust after treatment devices; determine necessary action.	H088	P-2	1F11
• Inspect and test preheater/inlet air heater, or glow plug system and controls; perform needed action.	H089	P-2	1F12
• Inspect exhaust gas recirculation (EGR) system including EGR valve, cooler, piping, filter, electronic sensors, controls, and wiring; determine needed action.	H090	P-2	1F13

Time off__________

Time on__________

Total time__________

Materials Required

- Vehicle with possible engine concern
- Vehicle manufacturer's service information
- Manufacturer-specific tools depending on the concern
- Vehicle lifting equipment if applicable

Some Safety Issues to Consider

- Modern diesel fuel injection systems can develop pressures as high as 30,000 psi (2068 bar); fuel can stream out at this high pressure, which will easily cut and penetrate the skin and cause serious bodily harm, and may even lead to blood poisoning. Appropriate safety equipment should be worn to prevent injury.
- Diagnosis of this fault may require test driving the vehicle on the school grounds or on a hoist, both of which carry severe risks. Attempt this task only with full permission from your supervisor/instructor and follow all the guidelines exactly.
- Caution: If you are working in an area where there could be "brake dust" present (may contain asbestos, which has been determined to cause cancer when inhaled or ingested), ensure you wear and use all OSHA-approved asbestos protective/removal equipment.
- Lifting equipment such as vehicle jacks and stands, vehicle hoists, and engine hoists are important tools that increase productivity and make the job easier. However, they can also cause severe injury or death if used improperly. Make sure you follow the manufacturer's operation procedures. Also make sure you have your supervisor/instructor's permission to use any particular type of lifting equipment.
- Comply with personal and environmental safety practices associated with clothing; eye protection; hand tools; power equipment; proper ventilation; and the handling, storage, and disposal of chemicals/materials in accordance with federal, state, and local regulations.
- Always wear the correct protective eyewear and clothing and use the appropriate safety equipment, as well as fender covers, seat protectors, and floor mat protectors.
- Make sure you understand and observe all legislative and personal safety procedures when carrying out practical assignments. If you are unsure of what these are, ask your supervisor/instructor.

Performance Standard

0–No exposure: No information or practice provided during the program; complete training required

1–Exposure only: General information provided with no practice time; close supervision needed; additional training required

2–Limited practice: Has practiced job during training program; additional training required to develop skill

3–Moderately skilled: Has performed job independently during training program; limited additional training may be required

4–Skilled: Can perform job independently with no additional training

Student/intern information:

Name_______________ Date_______ Class_______________

Vehicle used for this activity:

Year_______ Make_______________ Model_______________

Odometer_______________ VIN _______________

TASK Inspect and test turbocharger(s) (variable ratio/geometry VGT), pneumatic, hydraulic, electronic controls, and actuators. **NATEF 1F5**

Time off_______

Time on_______

Total time_______

CDX Tasksheet Number: H082

1. Reference the vehicle's specifications and identify the type of turbocharger fitted as standard equipment.
   a. Type of turbocharger: _______________

2. Identify and name the type of turbocharger fitted to this vehicle:
   a. Type of turbocharger: _______________
   b. Type of controls: _______________

Note: The most common cause of turbocharger failure can be caused by hot shut down. Hot shut down is when the vehicle is driven hard, exhaust temperature is too hot, and the engine is shut down before the turbocharger has had idle time to cool off.

3. Reference the appropriate service information and inspect the turbocharger(s) (variable ratio/geometry VGT); pneumatic, hydraulic, and electronic controls; and actuators.
   a. List, or print off and attach to this sheet, the procedure for the inspection of the turbocharger.
   ____
   ____
   ____
   b. Inspect the turbocharger system. List your observations:
   ____
   ____
   ____
   c. Meets the manufacturer's specifications: Yes: _____ No: _____
   d. Determine any necessary action(s):
   ____
   ____
   ____

4. Discuss the findings with your instructor.

Performance Rating

CDX Tasksheet Number: H082

☐ 0 ☐ 1 ☐ 2 ☐ 3 ☐ 4

Supervisor/instructor signature _______________ Date_______

Student/intern information:

Name________________ Date__________ Class__________

Vehicle used for this activity:

Year________ Make________________ Model__________

Odometer________________ VIN ________________

TASK Inspect exhaust after treatment devices; determine necessary action. NATEF 1F11

Time off________

Time on________

Total time________

CDX Tasksheet Number: H088

1. Identify the type of treatment device fitted to your vehicle:________________

2. Reference the appropriate service information and inspect the exhaust after treatment devices.
    a. Carry out a visual inspection of the treatment device.
        i. Require replacement: Yes: _____ No: _____

    b. If the treatment device is a "diesel particulate filter," attach the diagnostic code reader to the vehicle.

    c. Are there any codes present or stored in the vehicle's PCM?
        i. If yes, list the codes and their descriptions:

    d. Carry out a forced re-generation of the particulate filter.

    Note: Check with your instructor before starting this operation. The vehicle must be parked in a safe location away from people and any object that could catch fire from being exposed to the extremely high temperature of the exhaust system.

3. If your vehicle is fitted with another type of exhaust treatment device, name the device:

4. Briefly describe the testing procedure for this unit as outlined in the appropriate appropriate service information:

5. As outlined above, carry out a visual inspection of the treatment device.
   a. Require replacement: Yes: _____ No: _____
   b. Determine any necessary action(s):
   ____
   ____
   ____
   ____
   ____
6. Discuss the findings with your instructor.

Performance Rating

CDX Tasksheet Number: H088

☐ 0 ☐ 1 ☐ 2 ☐ 3 ☐ 4

Supervisor/instructor signature ______________________________ Date__________

Student/intern information:

Name________________ Date________ Class____________

Vehicle used for this activity:

Year________ Make________________ Model____________

Odometer________________ VIN ________________

TASK Inspect and test preheater/inlet air heater, or glow plug system and controls; perform needed action. NATEF 1F12

Time off________

Time on________

Total time________

CDX Tasksheet Number: H089

1. Identify the type of air induction system heating device fitted to your vehicle:____________

2. Reference the appropriate service information and inspect and test the preheater/inlet air heater.
   a. Carry out a visual inspection of the heating device.
      i. List your observations:

   b. Carry out a visual inspection of the glow plug system. List your observations:

   c. Following the specified procedure, test the glow plug system. List your tests and results:

      i. Require replacement: Yes: _____ No: _____

      ii. Determine any necessary action(s):

3. Discuss the findings with your instructor.

Performance Rating

CDX Tasksheet Number: H089

☐	☐	☐	☐	☐
0	1	2	3	4

Supervisor/instructor signature ________________ Date________

Student/intern information:

Name_______________ Date_______ Class_______________

Vehicle used for this activity:

Year_______ Make_______________ Model_______________

Odometer_______________ VIN _______________

TASK Inspect exhaust gas recirculation (EGR) system including EGR valve, cooler, piping, filter, electronic sensors, controls, and wiring; determine needed action. NATEF 1F13

Time off_______

Time on_______

Total time_______

CDX Tasksheet Number: H090

1. Reference the appropriate service information and inspect the exhaust gas recirculation (EGR) system including the EGR valve, cooler, piping, filter, electronic sensors, controls, and wiring. This may require use of OBDII scan tool.
   a. Inspect the exhaust gas recirculation (EGR) system including the EGR valve.
      i. Require replacement: Yes: _____ No: _____
   b. Inspect the cooler and piping.
      i. Require replacement: Yes: _____ No: _____
   c. Inspect the filter.
      i. Require replacement: Yes: _____ No: _____
   d. Inspect the electronic sensors.
      i. Require replacement: Yes: _____ No: _____
   e. Inspect the controls and wiring.
      i. Require replacement: Yes: _____ No: _____
2. Overall assessment
   a. Meets the manufacturer's specifications: Yes: _____ No: _____
   b. Determine any necessary action(s):
      ____
      ____
      ____
      ____
      ____
3. Discuss the findings with your instructor.

Performance Rating

CDX Tasksheet Number: H090

☐ 0 ☐ 1 ☐ 2 ☐ 3 ☐ 4

Supervisor/instructor signature _______________ Date_______

Diesel Fuel System: Fuel Supply System

Student/intern information:

Name________________ Date________ Class____________

Vehicle used for this activity:

Year________ Make________________ Model____________

Odometer______________ VIN ____________________

Time off________

Time on________

Total time________

Learning Objective / Task	CDX Tasksheet Number	2014 NATEF Priority Level	2014 NATEF Reference Number
• Check fuel level and condition; determine needed action.	H091	P-1	1G1.1
• Perform fuel supply and return system tests; determine needed action.	H092	P-1	1G1.2
• Inspect fuel tanks, vents, caps, mounts, valves, screens, crossover system, supply and return lines, and fittings; determine needed action.	H093	P-1	1G1.3
• Inspect, clean, and test fuel transfer (lift) pump, pump drives, screens, fuel/water separators/ indicators, filters, heaters, coolers, ECM cooling plates, and mounting hardware; determine needed action.	H094	P-1	1G1.4
• Inspect and test pressure regulator systems (check valves, pressure regulator valves, and restrictive fittings); determine needed action.	H095	P-1	1G1.5
• Check fuel system for air; determine needed action; prime and bleed fuel system; check primer pump.	H096	P-1	1G1.6

Materials Required

- Vehicle with possible engine concern
- Vehicle manufacturer's service information
- Manufacturer-specific tools depending on the concern
- Vehicle lifting equipment if applicable

Some Safety Issues to Consider

- Modern diesel fuel injection systems can develop pressures as high as 30,000 psi (2068 bar); fuel can stream out at this high pressure, which will easily cut and penetrate the skin and cause serious bodily harm, and may even lead to blood poisoning. Appropriate safety equipment should be worn to prevent injury.
- Diagnosis of this fault may require test driving the vehicle on the school grounds or on a hoist, both of which carry severe risks. Attempt this task only with full permission from your supervisor/instructor and follow all the guidelines exactly.
- Caution: If you are working in an area where there could be "brake dust" present (may contain asbestos, which has been determined to cause cancer when inhaled or ingested), ensure you wear and use all OSHA-approved asbestos protective/removal equipment.
- Lifting equipment such as vehicle jacks and stands, vehicle hoists, and engine hoists are important tools that increase productivity and make the job easier. However, they can also cause severe injury or death if used improperly. Make sure you follow the manufacturer's operation procedures. Also make sure you have your supervisor/instructor's permission to use any particular type of lifting equipment.

- Comply with personal and environmental safety practices associated with clothing; eye protection; hand tools; power equipment; proper ventilation; and the handling, storage, and disposal of chemicals/materials in accordance with federal, state, and local regulations.
- Always wear the correct protective eyewear and clothing and use the appropriate safety equipment, as well as fender covers, seat protectors, and floor mat protectors.
- Make sure you understand and observe all legislative and personal safety procedures when carrying out practical assignments. If you are unsure of what these are, ask your supervisor/instructor.

Performance Standard

0—No exposure: No information or practice provided during the program; complete training required

1—Exposure only: General information provided with no practice time; close supervision needed; additional training required

2—Limited practice: Has practiced job during training program; additional training required to develop skill

3—Moderately skilled: Has performed job independently during training program; limited additional training may be required

4—Skilled: Can perform job independently with no additional training

Student/intern information:

Name____________________ Date__________ Class________________

Vehicle used for this activity:

Year__________ Make____________________ Model________________

Odometer____________________ VIN ____________________

TASK Check fuel level and condition; determine needed action. **NATEF 1G1.1**

Time off__________

Time on__________

Total time__________

CDX Tasksheet Number: H091

1. Check the fuel level(s).
   a. Meets the manufacturer's specifications: Yes: _____ No: _____
2. Draw off a sample of the fuel and have it tested for its condition.
   a. Meets the manufacturer's specifications: Yes: _____ No: _____
   b. Determine any necessary action(s):
   ____
   ____
   ____
   ____
   ____
3. Discuss the findings with your instructor.

Performance Rating

CDX Tasksheet Number: H091

☐ 0 ☐ 1 ☐ 2 ☐ 3 ☐ 4

Supervisor/instructor signature ______________________________ Date__________

Student/intern information:

Name_____________________________ Date___________ Class______________________

Vehicle used for this activity:

Year_____________ Make______________________________ Model____________________

Odometer___________________________ VIN ______________________________________

TASK Perform fuel supply and return system tests; determine needed action. NATEF 1G1.2

Time off_____________

Time on_____________

Total time_____________

CDX Tasksheet Number: H092

1. Research the procedure and specifications for performing tests on the fuel supply and return systems in the appropriate service information.

   Note: Modern diesel fuel injection systems can develop pressures as high as 30,000 psi (2068 bar); fuel can stream out at this high pressure, which will easily cut and penetrate the skin and cause serious bodily harm, and may even lead to blood poisoning. Appropriate safety equipment should be worn to prevent injury.

2. Using the manufacturer's recommended tools and gauges, perform fuel supply and return system tests.
   a. List your tests and results:

   ____
   ____
   ____
   ____
   ____
   ____

   b. Meets the manufacturer's specifications: Yes: _____ No: _____

   c. Determine any necessary action(s):

   ____
   ____
   ____

3. Discuss your findings with your instructor.

Performance Rating

CDX Tasksheet Number: H092

☐	☐	☐	☐	☐
0	1	2	3	4

Supervisor/instructor signature ____ Date____________

Student/intern information:

Name_________________________ Date____________ Class____________________

Vehicle used for this activity:

Year____________ Make____________________________ Model____________________

Odometer______________________ VIN ______________________________

Time off______

Time on______

Total time______

TASK Inspect fuel tanks, vents, caps, mounts, valves, screens, crossover system, supply and return lines, and fittings; determine needed action. **NATEF 1G1.3**

CDX Tasksheet Number: H093

1. Inspect the surface of the fuel tank for any signs of structural damage or leakage.
    a. Any signs of structural damage: Yes: _____ No: _____
    b. Determine any necessary action(s):

2. Inspect the fuel tank cap/vents for any signs of damage or blockage.
    a. Any signs of damage/blockage: Yes: _____ No: _____
    b. Determine any necessary action(s):

3. Inspect the fuel tank mounts for any signs of structural damage or loose bolts.
    a. Any signs of structural damage: Yes: _____ No: _____
    b. Determine any necessary action(s):

4. Are fuel tank mounting bolts correctly torqued to the manufacturer's specifications or leaking from any of the structurally damaged areas?
    a. Manufacturer's recommended torque setting: ____________ ft-lbs (Nm)
    b. Have the mounting bolts been torqued to specifications? Yes: ____ No: ____
    c. If no, detail why these mounts have not been torqued to specifications:

5. Inspect the fuel tank valves for any signs of malfunction.
   a. Any signs of malfunction: Yes: _____ No: _____
   b. Determine any necessary action(s):

____
____
____
____
____

6. Inspect the fuel tank screens for any signs of damage.
   a. Any signs of damage: Yes: _____ No: _____
   b. Determine any necessary action(s):

____
____
____
____
____

7. Inspect the fuel tank cross-over pipe system for any signs of damage.
   a. Any signs of damage: Yes: _____ No: _____
   b. Determine any necessary action(s):

____
____
____
____
____

8. Inspect the fuel supply and return lines and fittings for any signs of damage or deterioration.
   a. Any signs of damage/deterioration: Yes: _____ No: _____
   b. Determine any necessary action(s):

____
____
____
____
____

9. Discuss the findings with your instructor.

Performance Rating

CDX Tasksheet Number: H093

☐ 0 ☐ 1 ☐ 2 ☐ 3 ☐ 4

Supervisor/instructor signature ______________________________ Date__________

Student/intern information:

Name________________ Date________ Class__________

Vehicle used for this activity:

Year________ Make________________ Model__________

Odometer______________ VIN ____________________

◀◀ TASK Inspect, clean, and test fuel transfer (lift) pump, pump drives, screens, fuel/water separators/indicators, filters, heaters, coolers, ECM cooling plates, and mounting hardware; determine needed action. NATEF 1G1.4

Time off________

Time on________

Total time________

CDX Tasksheet Number: H094

1. Research the specifications and procedures to inspect, clean, and test the fuel transfer (lift) pump, pump drives, screens, fuel/water separators/indicators, filters, heaters, coolers, ECM cooling plates, and mounting hardware, in the appropriate service information.
   a. Specified fuel transfer pump pressure: __________ psi (kPa)
   b. List any other specifications relevant to this task:

2. Following the specified procedure, inspect, clean, and test the fuel transfer (lift) pump.
   a. Visually inspect the fuel transfer (lift) pump. List your observations:

   b. Clean the fuel transfer (lift) pump. List your observations:

   c. Test the fuel transfer (lift) pump pressure. List your reading: ________ psi (kPa)

   d. Determine any necessary action(s):

3. Following the specified procedure, inspect the pump drive.
   a. Visually inspect the pump drive. List your observations:

   b. Determine any necessary action(s):

4. Following the specified procedure, inspect, clean, and test screens, fuel/water separators/indicators, and filters.
   a. Visually inspect the screens, fuel/water separators/indicators, and filters. List your observations:

      ____
      ____
      ____

   b. Determine any necessary action(s):

      ____
      ____
      ____

5. Following the specified procedure, inspect, clean, and test the heaters, coolers, ECM cooling plates, and mounting hardware.
   a. List your observations:

      ____
      ____
      ____

   b. Determine any necessary action(s):

      ____
      ____
      ____

6. Discuss the findings with your instructor.

Performance Rating

CDX Tasksheet Number: H094

☐	☐	☐	☐	☐
0	1	2	3	4

Supervisor/instructor signature ______________________________ Date__________

Student/intern information:

Name________________ Date________ Class________________

Vehicle used for this activity:

Year________ Make________________ Model________________

Odometer________________ VIN ________________

Time off________

Time on________

Total time________

TASK Inspect and test pressure regulator systems (check valves, pressure regulator valves, and restrictive fittings); determine needed action. NATEF 1G1.5

CDX Tasksheet Number: H095

1. Research the procedure and specifications for inspecting and testing pressure regulator systems (check valves, pressure regulator valves, and restrictive fillings) in the appropriate service information.

   Note: Modern diesel fuel injection systems can develop pressures as high as 30,000 psi (2068 bar); fuel can stream out at this high pressure, which will easily cut and penetrate the skin and cause serious bodily harm, and may even lead to blood poisoning. Appropriate safety equipment should be worn to prevent injury.

   a. Use the manufacturer's specified tooling and gauges.

   b. Carry out the inspection and testing.

      i. List your tests and observations:

      ____

      ____

      ____

      ____

      ____

      ____

      ii. Meets the manufacturer's specifications: Yes: _____ No: _____

      iii. Determine any necessary action(s):

      ____

      ____

      ____

2. Discuss your findings with your instructor.

Performance Rating

CDX Tasksheet Number: H095

☐	☐	☐	☐	☐
0	1	2	3	4

Supervisor/instructor signature ________________ Date________

Student/intern information:

Name________________ Date________ Class________________

Vehicle used for this activity:

Year________ Make________________ Model________________

Odometer________________ VIN ________________

TASK Check fuel system for air; determine needed action; prime and bleed fuel system; check primer pump. **NATEF 1G1.6**

Time off________

Time on________

Total time________

CDX Tasksheet Number: H096

Note: Modern diesel fuel injection systems can develop pressures as high as 30,000 psi (2068 bar); fuel can stream out at this high pressure, which will easily cut and penetrate the skin and cause serious bodily harm, and may even lead to blood poisoning. Appropriate safety equipment should be worn to prevent injury.

1. Research the procedure and specifications for checking the system for air in the appropriate service information. In some cases, a sight glass may be needed to determine if air is present.
   a. Inspect the fuel system for air and list your observations:

   ____

   b. Meets the manufacturer's specifications: Yes: _____ No: _____

   c. Determine any necessary action(s):

   ____

2. Reference the appropriate service information and prime and bleed the fuel system; check the primer pump.
   a. List your observations:

   ____

   b. Meets the manufacturer's specifications: Yes: _____ No: _____

   c. Determine any necessary action(s):

   ____

3. Discuss your findings with your instructor.

Performance Rating

CDX Tasksheet Number: H096

☐	☐	☐	☐	☐
0	1	2	3	4

Supervisor/instructor signature ________________ Date________

Diesel Fuel System: Electronic Fuel Management System 1

Student/intern information:

Name________________________ Date____________ Class________________________

Vehicle used for this activity:

Year____________ Make________________________ Model________________________

Odometer________________________ VIN ________________________

Time off________________

Time on________________

Total time________________

Learning Objective / Task	CDX Tasksheet Number	2014 NATEF Priority Level	2014 NATEF Reference Number
• Inspect and test power and ground circuits and connections; measure and interpret voltage, voltage drop, amperage, and resistance readings using a digital multimeter (DMM); determine needed action.	H097	P-1	1G2.1
• Interface with vehicle's on-board computer; perform diagnostic procedures using electronic service tools (to include PC-based software and/or data scan tools); determine needed action.	H098	P-1	1G2.2
• Check and record electronic diagnostic codes and trip/operational data; monitor electronic data; clear codes; determine further diagnosis.	H099	P-1	1G2.3
• Locate and use relevant service information (to include diagnostic procedures, flow charts, and wiring diagrams).	H100	P-1	1G2.4
• Inspect and replace electrical connector terminals, seals, and locks.	H101	P-1	1G2.5
• Inspect and test switches, sensors, controls, actuator components, and circuits; adjust or replace as needed.	H102	P-1	1G2.6
• Using electronic service tool(s) access and interpret customer programmable parameters.	H103	P-1	1G2.7

Materials Required

- Vehicle with possible engine concern
- Vehicle manufacturer's service information
- Manufacturer-specific tools depending on the concern
- Vehicle lifting equipment if applicable

Some Safety Issues to Consider

- Modern diesel fuel injection systems can develop pressures as high as 30,000 psi (2068 bar); fuel can stream out at this high pressure, which will easily cut and penetrate the skin and cause serious bodily harm, and may even lead to blood poisoning. Appropriate safety equipment should be worn to prevent injury.
- Diagnosis of this fault may require test driving the vehicle on the school grounds or on a hoist, both of which carry severe risks. Attempt this task only with full permission from your supervisor/instructor and follow all the guidelines exactly.
- Caution: If you are working in an area where there could be "brake dust" present (may contain asbestos, which has been determined to cause cancer when inhaled or ingested), ensure you wear and use all OSHA-approved asbestos protective/removal equipment.
- Lifting equipment such as vehicle jacks and stands, vehicle hoists, and engine hoists are important tools

that increase productivity and make the job easier. However, they can also cause severe injury or death if used improperly. Make sure you follow the manufacturer's operation procedures. Also make sure you have your supervisor/instructor's permission to use any particular type of lifting equipment.

- Comply with personal and environmental safety practices associated with clothing; eye protection; hand tools; power equipment; proper ventilation; and the handling, storage, and disposal of chemicals/materials in accordance with federal, state, and local regulations.
- Always wear the correct protective eyewear and clothing and use the appropriate safety equipment, as well as fender covers, seat protectors, and floor mat protectors.
- Make sure you understand and observe all legislative and personal safety procedures when carrying out practical assignments. If you are unsure of what these are, ask your supervisor/instructor.

Performance Standard

0–No exposure: No information or practice provided during the program; complete training required
1–Exposure only: General information provided with no practice time; close supervision needed; additional training required
2–Limited practice: Has practiced job during training program; additional training required to develop skill
3–Moderately skilled: Has performed job independently during training program; limited additional training may be required
4–Skilled: Can perform job independently with no additional training

Student/intern information:

Name____________________ Date__________ Class______________

Vehicle used for this activity:

Year__________ Make____________________ Model______________

Odometer__________________ VIN ____________________

TASK Inspect and test power and ground circuits and connections; measure and interpret voltage, voltage drop, amperage, and resistance readings using a digital multimeter (DMM); determine needed action. **NATEF 1G2.1**

Time off________

Time on________

Total time________

CDX Tasksheet Number: H097

1. Inspect and test power and ground circuits and connections.
    a. List your tests and observations:
    b. Meets the manufacturer's specifications: Yes: _____ No: _____
    c. Determine any necessary action(s):
2. Reference the appropriate service information for the appropriate specifications and measure and interpret voltage, voltage drop, amperage, and resistance readings using a digital multimeter (DMM).
    a. List your tests and observations:
    b. Meets the manufacturer's specifications: Yes: _____ No: _____
    c. Determine any necessary action(s):
3. Discuss the findings with your instructor.

Performance Rating

CDX Tasksheet Number: H097

☐ 0 ☐ 1 ☐ 2 ☐ 3 ☐ 4

Supervisor/instructor signature ____________________ Date________

Student/intern information:

Name____________________ Date__________ Class________________

Vehicle used for this activity:

Year__________ Make____________________ Model________________

Odometer____________________ VIN ____________________

TASK Interface with vehicle's on-board computer; perform diagnostic procedures using electronic service tools (to include PC-based software and/or data scan tools); determine needed action. **NATEF 1G2.2**

Time off__________

Time on__________

Total time__________

CDX Tasksheet Number: H098

1. Identify the type of electronic service tool available in your workshop.
    a. PC-based unit: Yes: _____ No: _____
    b. If yes, list the make and model:
    c. Hand-held data scanner: Yes: _____ No: _____
    d. If yes, list the make and model:
2. Reference the appropriate service information and the service tool service information and connect the unit to the vehicle's interface.
    a. Perform diagnostic procedures as outlined by the manufacturer.
        i. List your tests and observations:
        ii. Meets the manufacturer's specifications: Yes: _____ No: _____
        iii. Determine any necessary action(s):
3. Discuss the findings with your instructor.

Performance Rating

CDX Tasksheet Number: H098

☐ 0 ☐ 1 ☐ 2 ☐ 3 ☐ 4

Supervisor/instructor signature ____________________ Date__________

Student/intern information:

Name__________ Date__________ Class__________

Vehicle used for this activity:

Year__________ Make__________ Model__________

Odometer__________ VIN __________

TASK Check and record electronic diagnostic codes and trip/operational data; monitor electronic data; clear codes; determine further diagnosis. **NATEF 1G2.3**

Time off__________

Time on__________

Total time__________

CDX Tasksheet Number: H099

1. Record all diagnostic codes and trip/operational data stored in the system:
2. Refer to the appropriate service information and identify each stored code below.
   a. Code: __________ Description: __________
   b. Code: __________ Description: __________
   c. Code: __________ Description: __________
   d. Code: __________ Description: __________
      i. Are any of these codes detrimental to the vehicle's operation? Yes: _____ No: _____
3. List scan tool data for at least four main sensors. List the sensor and data:
4. Determine any necessary action(s):
5. Clear all stored codes.
6. Discuss the findings with your instructor.

Performance Rating

CDX Tasksheet Number: H099

☐ 0 ☐ 1 ☐ 2 ☐ 3 ☐ 4

Supervisor/instructor signature __________ Date__________

Student/intern information:

Name____________________ Date__________ Class______________

Vehicle used for this activity:

Year__________ Make____________________ Model______________

Odometer____________________ VIN ____________________

TASK Locate and use relevant service information (to include diagnostic procedures, flow charts, and wiring diagrams). **NATEF 1G2.4**

Time off__________

Time on__________

Total time__________

CDX Tasksheet Number: H100

1. Reference the appropriate service information and locate and use relevant service information (to include diagnostic procedures, flow charts, and wiring diagrams) as required throughout the servicing procedures.
   a. List the service information you obtained while performing a service, diagnosis, or repair:
   b. Meets the manufacturer's specifications: Yes: _____ No: _____
   c. Determine any necessary action(s):
2. Discuss the findings with your instructor.

Performance Rating

CDX Tasksheet Number: H100

☐ 0 ☐ 1 ☐ 2 ☐ 3 ☐ 4

Supervisor/instructor signature ____________________ Date__________

Student/intern information:

Name______________________ Date__________ Class__________________

Vehicle used for this activity:

Year__________ Make______________________ Model__________________

Odometer__________________ VIN ______________________________

TASK Inspect and replace electrical connector terminals, seals, and locks. **NATEF 1G2.5**

Time off__________

Time on__________

Total time__________

CDX Tasksheet Number: H101

1. Research the procedure and specifications for inspecting and replacing electrical connector terminals, seals, and locks.
   a. List any specifications or requirements:
   ____
   ____
   ____
   b. Inspect the electrical connector terminals, seals, and locks. List the connectors you inspected and your observations:
   ____
   ____
   ____
   ____
   ____
   ____
   c. Meets the manufacturer's specifications: Yes: _____ No: _____
   d. Determine any necessary action(s):
   ____
   ____
   ____
2. Discuss the findings with your instructor.

Performance Rating

CDX Tasksheet Number: H101

☐ 0 ☐ 1 ☐ 2 ☐ 3 ☐ 4

Supervisor/instructor signature ______________________ Date__________

Student/intern information:

Name________________ Date________ Class____________

Vehicle used for this activity:

Year________ Make________________ Model____________

Odometer________________ VIN ____________________

TASK Inspect and test switches, sensors, controls, actuator components, and circuits; adjust or replace as needed. **NATEF 1G2.6**

Time off________

Time on________

Total time________

CDX Tasksheet Number: H102

1. Research the procedure and specifications to inspect and test switches, sensors, controls actuator components, and circuits in the appropriate service information.
   a. Inspect and test the switches.
      i. List the switches you tested and your observations:
      ____
      ____
      ____
      ____
      ii. Meets the manufacturer's specifications: Yes: _____ No: _____
   b. Inspect and test the sensors.
      i. List the sensors you tested and your observations:
      ____
      ____
      ____
      ____
      ii. Meets the manufacturer's specifications: Yes: _____ No: _____
   c. Inspect and test the controls.
      i. List the controls you tested and your observations:
      ____
      ____
      ____
      ____
      ii. Meets the manufacturer's specifications: Yes: _____ No: _____
   d. Inspect and test the actuator components.
      i. List the actuator components you tested and your observations:
      ____
      ____
      ____
      ____
      ii. Meets the manufacturer's specifications: Yes: _____ No: _____

e. Inspect and test the circuits.
    i. List the circuit wiring you tested and your observations:
    ____
    ____
    ____
    ____
    ii. Meets the manufacturer's specifications: Yes: _____ No: _____
f. Determine any necessary action(s):
    ____
    ____
    ____
    ____

2. Discuss the findings with your instructor.

Performance Rating

CDX Tasksheet Number: H102

☐ 0 ☐ 1 ☐ 2 ☐ 3 ☐ 4

Supervisor/instructor signature ______________________ Date______

Student/intern information:

Name________________ Date________ Class________________

Vehicle used for this activity:

Year________ Make________________ Model________________

Odometer________________ VIN ________________________

TASK Using electronic service tool(s) access and interpret customer programmable parameters. NATEF 1G2.7

Time off________

Time on________

Total time________

CDX Tasksheet Number: H103

1. With the diagnostic tool connected in accordance with the manufacturer's specifications, fill out the table below.

Programmable parameter	Default (D) / Programmed (P)	Programmed Parameter Setting
Example: Engine rpm	P	2200 rpm

a. List your observations: ________________________________

b. Meets the manufacturer's specifications: Yes: _____ No: _____

c. Determine any necessary action(s): ________________________________

2. Discuss the findings with your instructor.

Performance Rating

CDX Tasksheet Number: H103

☐ 0 ☐ 1 ☐ 2 ☐ 3 ☐ 4

Supervisor/instructor signature ________________________ Date________

Diesel Fuel System: Electronic Fuel Management System 2

Student/intern information:

Name__________ Date__________ Class__________

Vehicle used for this activity:

Year__________ Make__________ Model__________

Odometer__________ VIN __________

Time off__________

Time on__________

Total time__________

Learning Objective / Task	CDX Tasksheet Number	2014 NATEF Priority Level	2014 NATEF Reference Number
• Perform on-engine inspections, tests and adjustments on electronic unit injectors (EUI); determine needed action.	H104	P-2	1G2.8
• Remove and install electronic unit injectors (EUI) and related components; recalibrate ECM (if applicable).	H105	P-2	1G2.9
• Perform cylinder contribution test utilizing recommended electronic service tools.	H106	P-1	1G2.10
• Perform on-engine inspections and tests on hydraulic electronic unit injectors (HEUI) and system electronic controls; determine needed action.	H107	P-2	1G2.11
• Perform on-engine inspections and tests on hydraulic electronic unit injector (HEUI) high pressure oil supply and control systems; determine needed action.	H108	P-2	1G2.12
• Perform on-engine inspections and tests on high pressure common rail (HPCR) type systems; determine needed action.	H109	P-2	1G2.13
• Inspect high pressure injection lines, hold downs, fittings and seals; determine needed action.	H110	P-2	1G2.14

Materials Required

- Vehicle with possible engine concern
- Vehicle manufacturer's service information
- Manufacturer-specific tools depending on the concern
- Vehicle lifting equipment if applicable

Some Safety Issues to Consider

- Modern diesel fuel injection systems can develop pressures as high as 30,000 psi (2068 bar); fuel can stream out at this high pressure, which will easily cut and penetrate the skin and cause serious bodily harm, and may even lead to blood poisoning. Appropriate safety equipment should be worn to prevent injury.
- Diagnosis of this fault may require test driving the vehicle on the school grounds or on a hoist, both of which carry severe risks. Attempt this task only with full permission from your supervisor/instructor and follow all the guidelines exactly.
- Caution: If you are working in an area where there could be "brake dust" present (may contain asbestos, which has been determined to cause cancer when inhaled or ingested), ensure you wear and use all OSHA-approved asbestos protective/removal equipment.

- Lifting equipment such as vehicle jacks and stands, vehicle hoists, and engine hoists are important tools that increase productivity and make the job easier. However, they can also cause severe injury or death if used improperly. Make sure you follow the manufacturer's operation procedures. Also make sure you have your supervisor/instructor's permission to use any particular type of lifting equipment.
- Comply with personal and environmental safety practices associated with clothing; eye protection; hand tools; power equipment; proper ventilation; and the handling, storage, and disposal of chemicals/materials in accordance with federal, state, and local regulations.
- Always wear the correct protective eyewear and clothing and use the appropriate safety equipment, as well as fender covers, seat protectors, and floor mat protectors.
- Make sure you understand and observe all legislative and personal safety procedures when carrying out practical assignments. If you are unsure of what these are, ask your supervisor/instructor.

Performance Standard

0–No exposure: No information or practice provided during the program; complete training required
1–Exposure only: General information provided with no practice time; close supervision needed; additional training required
2–Limited practice: Has practiced job during training program; additional training required to develop skill
3–Moderately skilled: Has performed job independently during training program; limited additional training may be required
4–Skilled: Can perform job independently with no additional training

Student/intern information:

Name__________ Date__________ Class__________

Vehicle used for this activity:

Year__________ Make__________ Model__________

Odometer__________ VIN __________

TASK Perform on-engine inspections, tests and adjustments on electronic unit injectors (EUIs); determine needed action. **NATEF 1G2.8**

Time off__________

Time on__________

Total time__________

CDX Tasksheet Number: H104

1. Research the procedure and specifications to inspect, test, and adjust the electronic unit injectors (EUI) in the appropriate service information.

   Note: Modern diesel fuel injection systems can develop pressures as high as 30,000 psi (2068 bar); fuel can stream out at this high pressure, which will easily cut and penetrate the skin and cause serious bodily harm, and may even lead to blood poisoning. Appropriate safety equipment should be worn to prevent injury.

   a. Following the specified procedure, inspect and test the electronic unit injectors (EUIs).

   b. List each test and your observations:

   c. Meets the manufacturer's specifications: Yes: _____ No: _____

   d. Determine any necessary action(s):

2. Discuss the findings with your instructor.

Performance Rating

CDX Tasksheet Number: H104

☐ 0 ☐ 1 ☐ 2 ☐ 3 ☐ 4

Supervisor/instructor signature __________ Date__________

Student/intern information:

Name____________________ Date________ Class____________

Vehicle used for this activity:

Year________ Make____________________ Model____________

Odometer________________ VIN ____________________

TASK Remove and install electronic unit injectors (EUI) and related components; recalibrate ECM (if applicable). **NATEF 1G2.9**

Time off________

Time on________

Total time________

CDX Tasksheet Number: H105

1. Research the procedure, tools and specifications for removing the electronic unit injectors (EUI) and related components in the appropriate service information.

   Note: Modern diesel fuel injection systems can develop pressures as high as 30,000 psi (2068 bar); fuel can stream out at this high pressure, which will easily cut and penetrate the skin and cause serious bodily harm, and may even lead to blood poisoning. Appropriate safety equipment should be worn to prevent injury.

   a. Remove and number the electronic unit injectors (EUI) and related components.
      i. Keep all components together for each cylinder in an appropriate parts tray.
      ii. Inspect each injector unit and component (including any wiring harness if applicable).

   b. List your observations:

   c. Meets the manufacturer's specifications: Yes: _____ No: _____

   d. Determine any necessary action(s):

2. Discuss the findings with your instructor.
   a. Perform diagnostic procedures as outlined by the manufacturer.
      i. List each test and your observations:

      ii. Meets the manufacturer's specifications: Yes: _____ No: _____

      iii. Determine any necessary action(s):

3. Reference the appropriate service information and appropriate tool(s) service information and re-install the electronic unit injectors (EUI) and related components.
    a. Torque all the components to their specified torque and record the manufacturer's torque specifications below.
        i. Unit injector holding clamp: _______________ ft-lbs (Nm)
        ii. Fuel connecting pipes (if applicable): _________ ft-lbs (Nm)
    b. Record the actual torque readings below.
        i. Unit injector holding clamp: _______________ ft-lbs (Nm)
        ii. Fuel connecting pipes (if applicable): _________ ft-lbs (Nm)
    c. Start and run the engine.
    d. Check the injectors and components for any leakage.
    e. Shut down the engine.
        i. List your observations:
        ____
        ____
        ____
        ii. Meets the manufacturer's specifications: Yes: _____ No: _____
        iii. Determine any necessary action(s):
        ____
        ____
        ____

4. Discuss the findings with your instructor.

Performance Rating

CDX Tasksheet Number: H105

☐ 0 ☐ 1 ☐ 2 ☐ 3 ☐ 4

Supervisor/instructor signature ______________________________ Date__________

Student/intern information:

Name____________________ Date__________ Class________________

Vehicle used for this activity:

Year__________ Make____________________ Model________________

Odometer____________________ VIN ________________________

TASK Perform cylinder contribution test utilizing recommended electronic service tools.

NATEF 1G2.10

Time off________

Time on________

Total time________

CDX Tasksheet Number: H106

1. Research the procedure and specifications to perform cylinder contribution tests utilizing the electronic service tools recommended in the appropriate service information.
    a. While referencing the appropriate service information, list the procedures involved in carrying out the cylinder contribution test:

2. Discuss these procedures with your instructor. When your instructor is satisfied with your proposed testing procedures, start the test.

3. While following the specified procedure, perform the cylinder contribution test.
    a. List your observations:

    b. Meets the manufacturer's specifications: Yes: _____ No: _____

    c. Determine any necessary action(s):

4. Discuss the findings with your instructor.

Performance Rating

CDX Tasksheet Number: H106

☐	☐	☐	☐	☐
0	1	2	3	4

Supervisor/instructor signature ________________________ Date________

Student/intern information:

Name_______________ Date_______ Class_______________

Vehicle used for this activity:

Year_______ Make_______________ Model_______________

Odometer_______________ VIN _______________

Time off_______

Time on_______

Total time_______

TASK Perform on-engine inspections and tests on hydraulic electronic unit injectors (HEUI) and system electronic controls; determine needed action. **NATEF 1G2.11**

CDX Tasksheet Number: H107

1. Research the procedure and specifications to perform on-engine inspections and tests on hydraulic electronic unit injectors and system electronic controls in the appropriate service information.
   a. While referencing the appropriate service information, list the procedures involved in carrying out the inspections and test:

   ____
   ____
   ____

2. Discuss these procedures with your instructor. When your instructor is satisfied with your proposed testing procedures, start the test.

3. Perform on-engine inspections and tests on hydraulic electronic unit injectors and system electronic controls.
   a. List each test and your observations:

   ____
   ____
   ____
   ____
   ____
   ____

   b. Meets the manufacturer's specifications: Yes: _____ No: _____

   c. Determine any necessary action(s):

   ____
   ____
   ____

4. Discuss the findings with your instructor.

Performance Rating

CDX Tasksheet Number: H107

☐	☐	☐	☐	☐
0	1	2	3	4

Supervisor/instructor signature _______________ Date_______

Student/intern information:

Name____________________ Date________ Class____________

Vehicle used for this activity:

Year________ Make____________________ Model____________

Odometer________________ VIN ____________________

TASK Perform on-engine inspections and tests on hydraulic electronic unit injector (HEUI) high pressure oil supply and control systems; determine needed action. **NATEF 1G2.12**

Time off________

Time on________

Total time________

CDX Tasksheet Number: H108

1. Research the procedure and specifications to perform on-engine inspections and tests on hydraulic electronic unit injector (HEUI) in the appropriate service information.
   a. While referencing the appropriate service information, list the procedures involved in carrying out the inspections and test.

2. Discuss these procedures with your instructor. When your instructor is satisfied with your proposed testing procedures, start the test.

3. Perform on-engine inspections and tests on hydraulic electronic unit injector high pressure oil supply and control systems.
   a. List each test and your observations:

   b. Meets the manufacturer's specifications: Yes: _____ No: _____

   c. Determine any necessary action(s):

4. Discuss the findings with your instructor.

Performance Rating

CDX Tasksheet Number: H108

☐	☐	☐	☐	☐
0	1	2	3	4

Supervisor/instructor signature ____________________ Date________

Student/intern information:

Name____________________________ Date__________ Class____________________

Vehicle used for this activity:

Year__________ Make____________________________ Model____________________

Odometer________________________ VIN ______________________________

TASK Perform on-engine inspections and tests on high pressure common rail (HPCR) type systems; determine needed action. **NATEF 1G2.13**

Time off__________

Time on__________

Total time__________

CDX Tasksheet Number: H109

1. Research the procedure and specifications to perform on-engine inspections and tests on high-pressure common rail (HPCR) systems in the appropriate service information.
   Note: Modern diesel fuel injection systems can develop pressures as high as 30,000 psi (2068 bar); fuel can stream out at this high pressure, which will easily cut and penetrate the skin and cause serious bodily harm, and may even lead to blood poisoning. Appropriate safety equipment should be worn to prevent injury.
   a. While referencing the appropriate service information, list the procedures involved in carrying out the inspections and test.

2. Discuss these procedures with your instructor. When your instructor is satisfied with your proposed testing procedures, start the test.

3. Perform on-engine inspections and tests on common rail type injection systems.
   a. List each test and your observations:

   b. Meets the manufacturer's specifications: Yes: _____ No: _____

   c. Determine any necessary action(s):

4. Discuss the findings with your instructor.

Performance Rating

CDX Tasksheet Number: H109

☐ 0 ☐ 1 ☐ 2 ☐ 3 ☐ 4

Supervisor/instructor signature ______________________________ Date__________

Student/intern information:

Name_______________ Date_______ Class_______________

Vehicle used for this activity:

Year_______ Make_______________ Model_______________

Odometer_______________ VIN _______________

◀◀ TASK Inspect high pressure injection lines, hold downs, fittings and seals; determine needed action. **NATEF 1G2.14**

Time off________

Time on________

Total time________

CDX Tasksheet Number: H110

1. Research the procedure and specifications for inspecting high-pressure injection lines, hold downs, fittings, and seals in the appropriate service information.
   a. Inspect the high-pressure injection lines.
      i. List your observations:
      ____
      ____
      ____
      ii. Meets the manufacturer's specifications: Yes: _____ No: _____
   b. Inspect the hold downs.
      i. List your observations:
      ____
      ____
      ____
      ii. Meets the manufacturer's specifications: Yes: _____ No: _____
   c. Inspect the fittings and seals.
      i. List your observations:
      ____
      ____
      ____
      ii. Meets the manufacturer's specifications: Yes: _____ No: _____
   d. Determine any necessary action(s):
      ____
      ____
      ____
2. Discuss the findings with your instructor.

Performance Rating

CDX Tasksheet Number: H110

☐	☐	☐	☐	☐
0	1	2	3	4

Supervisor/instructor signature _______________ Date_______

Diesel Fuel System: Engine Brakes

Student/intern information:

Name____________________ Date__________ Class____________________

Vehicle used for this activity:

Year__________ Make____________________ Model____________________

Odometer____________________ VIN ____________________

Learning Objective / Task	CDX Tasksheet Number	2014 NATEF Priority Level	2014 NATEF Reference Number
• Inspect and adjust engine compression/exhaust brakes; determine needed action.	H111	P-2	1H1
• Inspect, test, and adjust engine compression/exhaust brake control circuits, switches, and solenoids; repair or replace as needed.	H112	P-3	1H2
• Inspect engine compression/exhaust brake housing, valves, seals, lines and fittings; repair or replace as needed.	H113	P-3	1H3

Time off__________

Time on__________

Total time__________

Materials Required

- Vehicle with possible engine concern
- Vehicle manufacturer's service information
- Manufacturer-specific tools depending on the concern
- Vehicle lifting equipment if applicable

Some Safety Issues to Consider

- Modern diesel fuel injection systems can develop pressures as high as 30,000 psi (2068 bar); fuel can stream out at this high pressure, which will easily cut and penetrate the skin and cause serious bodily harm, and may even lead to blood poisoning. Appropriate safety equipment should be worn to prevent injury.
- Diagnosis of this fault may require test driving the vehicle on the school grounds or on a hoist, both of which carry severe risks. Attempt this task only with full permission from your supervisor/instructor and follow all the guidelines exactly.
- Caution: If you are working in an area where there could be "brake dust" present (may contain asbestos, which has been determined to cause cancer when inhaled or ingested), ensure you wear and use all OSHA-approved asbestos protective/removal equipment.
- Lifting equipment such as vehicle jacks and stands, vehicle hoists, and engine hoists are important tools that increase productivity and make the job easier. However, they can also cause severe injury or death if used improperly. Make sure you follow the manufacturer's operation procedures. Also make sure you have your supervisor/instructor's permission to use any particular type of lifting equipment.
- Comply with personal and environmental safety practices associated with clothing; eye protection; hand tools; power equipment; proper ventilation; and the handling, storage, and disposal of chemicals/materials in accordance with federal, state, and local regulations.
- Always wear the correct protective eyewear and clothing and use the appropriate safety equipment, as well as fender covers, seat protectors, and floor mat protectors.
- Make sure you understand and observe all legislative and personal safety procedures when carrying out practical assignments. If you are unsure of what these are, ask your supervisor/instructor.

Performance Standard

0–No exposure: No information or practice provided during the program; complete training required
1–Exposure only: General information provided with no practice time; close supervision needed; additional training required
2–Limited practice: Has practiced job during training program; additional training required to develop skill
3–Moderately skilled: Has performed job independently during training program; limited additional training may be required
4–Skilled: Can perform job independently with no additional training

Student/intern information:

Name________________________ Date__________ Class________________

Vehicle used for this activity:

Year__________ Make________________________ Model________________

Odometer____________________ VIN ________________________

TASK Inspect and adjust engine compression/exhaust brakes; determine needed action.

NATEF 1H1

Time off________

Time on________

Total time________

CDX Tasksheet Number: H111

1. Research the procedure and specifications to inspect and adjust engine compression/exhaust brakes in the appropriate service information.
   a. List each test or adjustment and your observations:
   ____
   ____
   ____
   ____
   ____
   ____
   ____
   ____
   b. Meets the manufacturer's specifications: Yes: _____ No: _____
   c. Determine any necessary action(s):
   ____
   ____
   ____
2. Discuss the findings with your instructor.

Performance Rating

CDX Tasksheet Number: H111

☐ 0 ☐ 1 ☐ 2 ☐ 3 ☐ 4

Supervisor/instructor signature ________________________ Date________

Student/intern information:

Name________________ Date________ Class________

Vehicle used for this activity:

Year________ Make________________ Model________

Odometer________________ VIN ________________

TASK Inspect, test, and adjust engine compression/exhaust brake control circuits, switches, and solenoids; repair or replace as needed. **NATEF 1H2**

Time off________

Time on________

Total time________

CDX Tasksheet Number: H112

1. Research the procedure and specifications to inspect, test, and adjust engine compression/exhaust brake control circuits, switches, and solenoids in the appropriate service information.
   a. List each test and your observations:

   b. Meets the manufacturer's specifications: Yes: _____ No: _____

   c. Determine any necessary action(s):

2. Discuss the findings with your instructor.

Performance Rating

CDX Tasksheet Number: H112

☐ 0 ☐ 1 ☐ 2 ☐ 3 ☐ 4

Supervisor/instructor signature ________________ Date________

Student/intern information:

Name________________________ Date____________ Class________________________

Vehicle used for this activity:

Year____________ Make________________________ Model________________

Odometer________________________ VIN ________________________

TASK Inspect engine compression/exhaust brake housing, valves, seals, lines, and fittings; repair or replace as needed. NATEF 1H3

Time off________

Time on________

Total time________

CDX Tasksheet Number: H113

1. Research the procedure and specifications to inspect engine compression/exhaust brake housing, valves, seals, lines, and fittings in the appropriate service information.
   a. Visually inspect each component and list your observations:

   b. Meets the manufacturer's specifications: Yes: _____ No: _____

   c. Determine any necessary action(s):

2. Discuss the findings with your instructor.

Performance Rating

CDX Tasksheet Number: H113

☐ 0 ☐ 1 ☐ 2 ☐ 3 ☐ 4

Supervisor/instructor signature ________________________ Date________

Heavy Duty Drive Trains, DT103

CONTENTS

Heavy Duty Drive Trains: Clutch 1

Student/intern information:

Name__________ Date__________ Class__________

Vehicle used for this activity:

Year__________ Make__________ Model__________

Odometer__________ VIN __________

Time off__________

Time on__________

Total time__________

Learning Objective / Task	CDX Tasksheet Number	2014 NATEF Priority Level	2014 NATEF Reference Number
• Identify causes of clutch noise, binding, slippage, pulsation, vibration, grabbing, dragging, and chatter problems; determine needed action.	H114	P-1	2A1
• Inspect and adjust clutch linkage, cables, levers, brackets, bushings, pivots, springs, and clutch safety switch (includes push- and pull-type assemblies); check pedal height and travel; perform needed action.	H115	P-1	2A2
• Inspect, adjust, repair, or replace hydraulic clutch slave and master cylinders, lines, and hoses; bleed system.	H116	P-2	2A3
• Inspect, adjust, lubricate, or replace release (throw-out) bearing, sleeve, bushings, springs, housing, levers, release fork, fork pads, rollers, shafts, and seals.	H117	P-1	2A4

Materials Required

- Vehicle with possible transmission concern
- Vehicle manufacturer's service information
- Manufacturer-specific tools depending on the concern
- Vehicle lifting equipment if applicable

Some Safety Issues to Consider

- Diagnosis of this fault may require test driving the vehicle on the school grounds or on a hoist, both of which carry severe risks. Attempt this task only with full permission from your supervisor/instructor and follow all the guidelines exactly.
- Caution: If you are working in an area where there could be brake dust present (may contain asbestos, which has been determined to cause cancer when inhaled or ingested), ensure you wear and use all OSHA-approved asbestos protective/removal equipment.
- Lifting equipment such as vehicle jacks and stands, vehicle hoists, and engine hoists are important tools that increase productivity and make the job easier. However, they can also cause severe injury or death if used improperly. Make sure you follow the manufacturer's operation procedures. Also make sure you have your supervisor/instructor's permission to use any particular type of lifting equipment.
- Comply with personal and environmental safety practices associated with clothing; eye protection; hand tools; power equipment; proper ventilation; and the handling, storage, and disposal of chemicals/materials in accordance with federal, state, and local regulations.
- Always wear the correct protective eyewear and clothing and use the appropriate safety equipment, as well as fender covers, seat protectors, and floor mat protectors.
- Make sure you understand and observe all legislative and personal safety procedures when carrying out practical assignments. If you are unsure of what these are, ask your supervisor/instructor.

Performance Standard

0–No exposure: No information or practice provided during the program; complete training required
1–Exposure only: General information provided with no practice time; close supervision needed; additional training required
2–Limited practice: Has practiced job during training program; additional training required to develop skill
3–Moderately skilled: Has performed job independently during training program; limited additional training may be required
4–Skilled: Can perform job independently with no additional training

Student/intern information:

Name_______________ Date_______ Class_______________

Vehicle used for this activity:

Year_______ Make_______________ Model_______________

Odometer_______________ VIN_______________

▶ TASK Identify causes of clutch noise, binding, slippage, pulsation, vibration, grabbing, dragging, and chatter problems; determine needed action. NATEF 2A1

Time off_______

Time on_______

Total time_______

CDX Tasksheet Number: H114

1. Reference the manufacturer's service information for the common causes of clutch noise.
   a. List all possible causes of clutch noise:

   b. List the necessary actions to correct the clutch noise:

2. Reference the manufacturer's service information for the common causes of binding and slippage.
   a. List all possible causes for binding and slippage:

   b. List the necessary actions to correct the binding and slippage:

3. Reference the manufacturer's service information for the common causes of pulsation and vibration.
   a. List all possible causes for pulsation and vibration:

b. List the necessary actions to correct the pulsation and vibration:

____
____
____
____
____

4. Reference the manufacturer's service information for the common causes of grabbing, dragging, and chatter problems.
   a. List all possible causes for grabbing, dragging, and chatter problems:

   ____
   ____
   ____
   ____
   ____

   b. List the necessary actions to correct the grabbing, dragging, and chatter problems:

   ____
   ____
   ____
   ____
   ____

5. Discuss the findings with your instructor.

Performance Rating

CDX Tasksheet Number: H114

☐ 0 ☐ 1 ☐ 2 ☐ 3 ☐ 4

Supervisor/instructor signature _______________ Date_______________

Student/intern information:

Name____________________ Date__________ Class____________________

Vehicle used for this activity:

Year__________ Make____________________ Model____________________

Odometer____________________ VIN ____________________

▶ TASK Inspect and adjust clutch linkage, cables, levers, brackets, bushings, pivots, springs, and clutch safety switch (includes push- and pull-type assemblies); check pedal height and travel; perform needed action. NATEF 2A2

Time off__________

Time on__________

Total time__________

CDX Tasksheet Number: H115

1. Reference the appropriate manufacturer's service information and list the following specifications.
   a. Pedal free play: ____________________
   b. Pedal height/travel: ____________________
   c. Distance between the throwout bearing and the clutch brake: ____________________
   d. Brake squeeze: ____________________
2. Using an instructor-designated truck, inspect the clutch for proper pedal free play and brake squeeze adjustment.
   a. Clutch pedal free play: ____________________ in/mm
   b. Clutch pedal height/travel: ____________________ in/mm
   c. Meets the manufacturer's specifications: Yes: _______ No: _______
   d. If no, list the necessary actions to correct the clutch adjustment.:
3. If necessary, adjust the clutch pressure plate pressure to the manufacturer's specifications.
4. Inspect and then adjust the clutch linkage, cables, levers, brackets, bushings, pivot, and springs to achieve the proper pedal free play.
   a. Meets the manufacturer's specifications: Yes: _______ No: _______
   b. List the necessary actions to correct the linkage adjustment.

5. Inspect and adjust the clutch safety switch (includes push- and pull-type assemblies).
   a. Meets the manufacturer's specifications: Yes: _______ No: _______
   b. List the necessary actions to correct the clutch safety switch adjustment.
      ____
      ____
      ____
      ____
      ____
6. Discuss the findings with your instructor.

Performance Rating

CDX Tasksheet Number: H115

☐	☐	☐	☐	☐
0	1	2	3	4

Supervisor/instructor signature ______________________________ Date__________

Student/intern information:

Name____________________ Date__________ Class________________

Vehicle used for this activity:

Year__________ Make____________________ Model________________

Odometer____________________ VIN ________________________

▶ TASK Inspect, adjust, repair, or replace hydraulic clutch slave and master cylinders, lines, and hoses; bleed system. NATEF 2A3

Time off__________

Time on__________

Total time__________

CDX Tasksheet Number: H116

1. Reference the appropriate manufacturer's service information.
   a. Inspect the hydraulic clutch slave and master cylinders. List your observations:

      i. Meets the manufacturer's specifications: Yes: _______ No: _______
      ii. List the necessary actions:

   b. If not within specifications, repair or replace the hydraulic clutch slave and master cylinders. List your observations:

   c. Inspect the hydraulic clutch lines and hoses for proper condition and routing. List your observations:

      i. Meets the manufacturer's specifications: Yes: _______ No: _______
      ii. List the necessary actions to correct the lines and hoses.

   d. If directed by your instructor, bleed the hydraulic clutch system in accordance with the specifications listed in the manufacturer's service information.
2. Discuss the findings with your instructor.

Performance Rating

CDX Tasksheet Number: H116

☐ 0 ☐ 1 ☐ 2 ☐ 3 ☐ 4

Supervisor/instructor signature ____________________ Date__________

Student/intern information:

Name____________________________________ Date___________ Class______________________

Vehicle used for this activity:

Year_____________ Make___________________________________ Model_____________________

Odometer______________________________ VIN ____

▶ TASK Inspect, adjust, lubricate, or replace release (throw-out) bearing, sleeve, bushings, springs, housing, levers, release fork, fork pads, rollers, shafts, and seals.

NATEF 2A4

Time off______________

Time on______________

Total time_____________

CDX Tasksheet Number: H117

1. Reference the appropriate manufacturer's service information.
   a. Inspect, adjust, and lubricate the release (throw-out) bearing. List your observations:

      i. Meets the manufacturer's specifications: Yes: _______ No: _______
      ii. List the necessary actions or corrections:

   b. If not within specifications, replace the release (throw-out) bearing.

   c. Inspect, adjust, and lubricate the sleeve, bushings, springs, housing, and levers. List your observations:

      i. Meets the manufacturer's specifications: Yes: _______ No: _______
      ii. List any necessary actions or corrections:

   d. If not within specifications, replace the sleeve, bushings, springs, housing, and levers.

   e. Inspect, adjust, and lubricate the release fork, fork pads, rollers, shafts, and seals. List your observations:

      i. Meets the manufacturer's specifications: Yes: _______ No: _______
      ii. List any necessary actions or corrections:

f. If not within specifications, replace the release fork, fork pads, rollers, shafts, and seals.

2. Discuss the findings with your instructor.

Performance Rating

CDX Tasksheet Number: H117

☐	☐	☐	☐	☐
0	1	2	3	4

Supervisor/instructor signature ____________________ Date__________

Heavy Duty Drive Trains: Clutch 2

Student/intern information:

Name________________________ Date____________ Class________________________

Vehicle used for this activity:

Year____________ Make________________________ Model________________

Odometer____________________ VIN ________________________

Time off________

Time on________

Total time________

Learning Objective / Task	CDX Tasksheet Number	2014 NATEF Priority Level	2014 NATEF Reference Number
• Inspect, adjust, and replace single-disc clutch pressure plate and clutch disc.	H118	P-1	2A5
• Inspect, adjust, and replace two-plate clutch pressure plate, clutch discs, intermediate plate, and drive pins/lugs.	H119	P-1	2A6
• Inspect and/or replace clutch brake assembly; inspect input shaft and bearing retainer; perform needed action.	H120	P-1	2A7
• Inspect, adjust, and replace self-adjusting/ continuous-adjusting clutch mechanisms.	H121	P-1	2A8
• Inspect and replace pilot bearing.	H122	P-1	2A9
• Remove and reinstall flywheel, inspect flywheel mounting area on crankshaft, rear main oil seal and measure crankshaft end play; determine needed action.	H123	P-1	2A10
• Inspect flywheel, starter ring gear and measure flywheel face and pilot bore runout; determine needed action.	H124	P-1	2A11
• Inspect flywheel housing(s) to transmission housing/ engine mating surface(s) and measure flywheel housing face and bore runout; determine needed action.	H125	P-2	2A12

Materials Required

- Vehicle with possible transmission concern
- Vehicle manufacturer's service information
- Manufacturer-specific tools depending on the concern
- Vehicle lifting equipment if applicable

Some Safety Issues to Consider

- Diagnosis of this fault may require test driving the vehicle on the school grounds or on a hoist, both of which carry severe risks. Attempt this task only with full permission from your supervisor/instructor and follow all the guidelines exactly.
- Caution: If you are working in an area where there could be brake dust present (may contain asbestos, which has been determined to cause cancer when inhaled or ingested), ensure you wear and use all OSHA-approved asbestos protective/removal equipment.
- Lifting equipment such as vehicle jacks and stands, vehicle hoists, and engine hoists are important tools that increase productivity and make the job easier. However, they can also cause severe injury or death if used improperly. Make sure you follow the manufacturer's operation procedures. Also make sure you have your supervisor/instructor's permission to use any particular type of lifting equipment.

- Comply with personal and environmental safety practices associated with clothing; eye protection; hand tools; power equipment; proper ventilation; and the handling, storage, and disposal of chemicals/materials in accordance with federal, state, and local regulations.
- Always wear the correct protective eyewear and clothing and use the appropriate safety equipment, as well as fender covers, seat protectors, and floor mat protectors.
- Make sure you understand and observe all legislative and personal safety procedures when carrying out practical assignments. If you are unsure of what these are, ask your supervisor/instructor.

Performance Standard

0–No exposure: No information or practice provided during the program; complete training required
1–Exposure only: General information provided with no practice time; close supervision needed; additional training required
2–Limited practice: Has practiced job during training program; additional training required to develop skill
3–Moderately skilled: Has performed job independently during training program; limited additional training may be required
4–Skilled: Can perform job independently with no additional training

Student/intern information:

Name__________ Date__________ Class__________

Vehicle used for this activity:

Year__________ Make__________ Model__________

Odometer__________ VIN __________

▶ TASK Inspect, adjust, and replace single-disc clutch pressure plate and clutch disc.

NATEF 2A5

Time off__________

Time on__________

Total time__________

CDX Tasksheet Number: H118

1. Reference the manufacturer's service information for procedures to inspect, adjust, and replace the single-disc clutch pressure plate and clutch disc.
   a. List the steps involved:

2. While referencing the manufacturer's service information and the procedures above, inspect and adjust the single-disc clutch pressure plate and clutch disc. List your observations:

   a. Meets the manufacturer's specifications: Yes: _______ No: _______

   b. List any necessary actions or corrections:

3. If directed by your instructor, replace the single-disc clutch pressure plate and clutch disc in accordance with the specifications listed in the service information.

4. Discuss the findings with your instructor.

Performance Rating

CDX Tasksheet Number: H118

☐ 0 ☐ 1 ☐ 2 ☐ 3 ☐ 4

Supervisor/instructor signature __________ Date__________

Student/intern information:

Name_________________________ Date____________ Class________________

Vehicle used for this activity:

Year____________ Make_________________________ Model________________

Odometer____________________ VIN ________________________________

▶ TASK Inspect, adjust, and replace two-plate clutch pressure plate, clutch discs, intermediate plate, and drive pins/lugs. NATEF 2A6

Time off__________

Time on__________

Total time__________

CDX Tasksheet Number: H119

1. Reference the manufacturer's service information for procedures to inspect, adjust, and replace the two-plate clutch pressure plate, clutch discs, intermediate plate, and drive pins/lugs.
   a. List the steps involved:

   ____
   ____
   ____

2. While referencing the manufacturer's service information and the procedures above, inspect and adjust the two-plate clutch pressure plate, clutch discs, intermediate plate, and drive pins/lugs. List your observations:

   ____
   ____
   ____

   a. Meets the manufacturer's specifications: Yes: _______ No: _______

   b. List any necessary actions or corrections:

   ____
   ____
   ____

3. If directed by your instructor, replace the two-plate clutch pressure plate, clutch discs, intermediate plate, and drive pins/lugs in accordance with the specifications listed in the service information.

4. Discuss the findings with your instructor.

Performance Rating

CDX Tasksheet Number: H119

☐	☐	☐	☐	☐
0	1	2	3	4

Supervisor/instructor signature _________________________ Date__________

Student/intern information:

Name______________________ Date__________ Class______________________

Vehicle used for this activity:

Year__________ Make______________________ Model______________________

Odometer______________________ VIN ______________________

▶ TASK Inspect and/or replace clutch brake assembly; inspect input shaft and bearing retainer; perform needed action. NATEF 2A7

Time off__________

Time on__________

Total time__________

CDX Tasksheet Number: H120

1. Reference the manufacturer's service information for procedures to inspect and/or replace the clutch brake assembly, input shaft, and bearing retainer. The clutch brake assembly is used to slow down and stop the input shaft rotation. This enables and assists a smooth shift when starting or stopping the vehicle, or to shift the transmission into reverse without grinding the gears.
   a. List the steps involved:

2. While referencing the manufacturer's service information and the procedures above, inspect the clutch brake assembly. List your observations:

   a. Meets the manufacturer's specifications: Yes: _______ No: _______

   b. List any necessary actions or corrections:

3. If directed by your instructor, replace the clutch brake assembly in accordance with the specifications listed in the service information.

4. While referencing the manufacturer's service information and the procedures above, inspect the input shaft and bearing retainer. List your observations:

   a. Meets the manufacturer's specifications: Yes: _______ No: _______

b. List any necessary actions or corrections:

____

____

____

5. If directed by your instructor, replace the input shaft and bearing retainer in accordance with the specifications listed in the service information.

6. Discuss the findings with your instructor.

Performance Rating

CDX Tasksheet Number: H120

☐	☐	☐	☐	☐
0	1	2	3	4

Supervisor/instructor signature _______________________________ Date_____________

Student/intern information:

Name____________________ Date__________ Class________________

Vehicle used for this activity:

Year________ Make____________________ Model________________

Odometer____________________ VIN ________________________

TASK Inspect, adjust, and replace self-adjusting/continuous-adjusting clutch mechanisms.

NATEF 2A8

Time off________

Time on________

Total time________

CDX Tasksheet Number: H121

1. Reference the manufacturer's service information for procedures to inspect, adjust, and replace the self-adjusting/continuous-adjusting clutch mechanisms.
   a. List the steps involved:

2. While referencing the manufacturer's service information and procedures above, inspect and adjust the self-adjusting/continuous-adjusting clutch mechanisms. List your observations:

   a. Meets the manufacturer's specifications: Yes: ______ No: ______

   b. List any necessary actions or corrections:

3. If directed by your instructor, replace the self-adjusting/continuous-adjusting clutch mechanisms in accordance with the specifications listed in the service information.

4. Discuss the findings with your instructor.

Performance Rating

CDX Tasksheet Number: H121

☐ 0 ☐ 1 ☐ 2 ☐ 3 ☐ 4

Supervisor/instructor signature ________________________ Date________

Student/intern information:

Name____________________ Date__________ Class________________

Vehicle used for this activity:

Year__________ Make____________________ Model________________

Odometer____________________ VIN ____________________

▶ TASK Inspect and replace pilot bearing.

NATEF 2A9

Time off__________

Time on__________

Total time__________

CDX Tasksheet Number: H122

Note: This task is performed to maintain correct alignment of the transmission input shaft. To inspect or replace the pilot bearing/bushing, the transmission must be removed along with the clutch assembly.

1. Inspect the pilot bearing for lack of lubrication; turn it by hand and feel it for roughness (there are two types of bearings, roller or ball). List your observations:

   a. Meets the manufacturer's specifications: Yes: _______ No: _______

   b. List any necessary actions or corrections:

2. If it is a brass or bronze bushing, check for wear by inserting a clutch alignment tool or old transmission input shaft; look for play or wobble. If clutch system is to be replaced, always replace the pilot bearing/bushing. List your observations:

   a. Meets the manufacturer's specifications: Yes: _______ No: _______

   b. List any necessary actions or corrections:

3. To replace the bearing/bushing, insert a pilot bearing puller and draw it out of its bore.

4. Inspect the bore for out of round by using a dial indicator or inside micrometer to make sure it is within specifications (this will ensure the bore will accept and maintain a tight fit of the new bearing/bushing). List your observations:

a. Meets the manufacturer's specifications: Yes: _______ No: _______

b. List any necessary actions or corrections:

____

____

____

5. To install the new bearing/bushing, use the appropriate driver or installer to make sure it is seated correctly.

6. Discuss the findings with your instructor.

Performance Rating

CDX Tasksheet Number: H122

☐ 0 ☐ 1 ☐ 2 ☐ 3 ☐ 4

Supervisor/instructor signature _______________________________ Date_____________

Student/intern information:

Name________________________ Date____________ Class________________________

Vehicle used for this activity:

Year____________ Make________________________ Model________________________

Odometer________________________ VIN ________________________

▶ TASK Remove and reinstall flywheel, inspect flywheel mounting area on crankshaft, rear main oil seal and measure crankshaft end play; determine needed action. NATEF 2A10

Time off________

Time on________

Total time________

CDX Tasksheet Number: H123

1. Research the following specifications in the appropriate service information:
   a. Flywheel bolt torque: ________________ ft-lb/Nm
   b. Crankshaft end play: ________________ in/mm

2. Remove flywheel by loosening the bolts that hold it to the crankshaft. Inspect bolt threads for stripping and stretching. Inspect crankshaft threads for stripping.
   a. Condition of threaded holes: Good _______ Bad _______
   b. Condition of bolts: Good _______ Bad _______

3. Inspect crankshaft mounting flange for defects or damage. List your observations:
   ____
   ____
   ____

4. Inspect rear main seal area for any type of leakage. If any type of leakage is present, replace the seal to prevent damage to new clutch disk.
   a. Leakage present Yes _______ No _______

5. Use a dial indicator and a pry bar to check crankshaft endplay by attaching the dial indicator to the crankshaft flange and the rear of the engine block. Move the crankshaft back and forth using the pry bar on the vibration damper assembly and measure the amount of movement and compare to the manufacturer's specification.
   a. Record Reading: ____________________

6. If reading is out of specification, the oil pan may need to be removed and the crankshaft thrust bearing may need to be replaced. If thrust bearing is left as is, the clutch assembly may chatter upon acceleration from a dead stop.

7. Reinstall the flywheel and torque the mounting bolts to the proper specification.
   a. Record actual torque: ____________________

   Some crankshaft mounting flanges may have bolt holes that are drilled all the way through to the crankcase. These will need to have their threads covered in Teflon tape or some type of sealant to prevent leakage onto the clutch assembly.

8. Discuss the findings with your instructor.

Performance Rating

CDX Tasksheet Number: H123

☐ 0 ☐ 1 ☐ 2 ☐ 3 ☐ 4

Supervisor/instructor signature ________________________ Date____________

Student/intern information:

Name______________________________ Date__________ Class______________________

Vehicle used for this activity:

Year__________ Make______________________________ Model______________________

Odometer__________________________ VIN ______________________________________

▶ TASK Inspect flywheel, starter ring gear and measure flywheel face and pilot bore runout; determine needed action. NATEF 2A11

Time off__________

Time on__________

Total time__________

CDX Tasksheet Number: H124

1. Research the following specifications in the appropriate service information:
   a. Flywheel face runout: ______________ in/mm
   b. Pilot bore runout: ______________ in/mm
2. Upon removal of the flywheel, inspect it for cracks, hotspots and bluing. If the flywheel is cracked, it will need to be replaced. If hotspots or bluing are present, it may need to be resurfaced. Some flywheels have weights welded on the back; check to make sure they are intact. List your observations:
3. Inspect the flywheel surface using a straight edge and a feeler gauge. Lay the feeler gauge under the straight edge in various positions and record the readings.
   a. Reading # 1: ______________
   b. Reading # 2: ______________
   c. Reading # 3: ______________
   d. Reading # 4: ______________
4. Inspect center plate lugs and holes for wear that might not allow for new ones to be installed (double disc clutches only).
   a. Pilot hole condition: Good _______ Bad _______
5. Inspect the pilot bearing bore for concentricity. Using an inside micrometer, check for run out of the bore itself.
   a. Average Reading: ______________

      Note: If the bore is out of round and will not hold a new bearing/bushing, the flywheel may need to be replaced.
6. Inspect ring gear for teeth missing or cracks. On some flywheels, the ring gear may be able to be replaced and still use the base flywheel.
   a. Ring gear condition: Good _______ Bad _______
7. Discuss the findings with your instructor.

Performance Rating

CDX Tasksheet Number: H124

☐ 0 ☐ 1 ☐ 2 ☐ 3 ☐ 4

Supervisor/instructor signature ______________________________ Date__________

Student/intern information:

Name________________ Date________ Class________________

Vehicle used for this activity:

Year________ Make________________ Model________________

Odometer________________ VIN________________

▶ TASK Inspect flywheel housing(s) to transmission housing/engine mating surface(s) and measure flywheel housing face and bore runout; determine needed action. NATEF 2A12

Time off________

Time on________

Total time________

CDX Tasksheet Number: H125

1. Upon removal of the transmission, check the transmission housing for cracks, damage, or elongation of the bolt holes.
   a. Record your findings: ________________

2. Check the flywheel housing mating surface for cracks and damage.
   a. Record your findings: ________________

3. Check the flywheel housing transmission mounting holes for stripped threads (run a thread chaser in the holes to ensure they are clean).
   a. Record your findings: ________________

4. Check the engine flywheel housing opening using a dial indicator.
   a. Connect a dial indicator base to the crankshaft flange.
   b. Connect the dial indicator pointer to the inside of the flywheel housing mating surface.
   c. Zero out the dial on the indicator.
   d. Rotate the crankshaft by using a ratchet and a socket on the vibration damper.
   e. Rotate the crankshaft 360 degrees to get a run out reading.
   f. Record the reading in a few points along the way.
      Reading # 1: ________
      Reading # 2: ________
      Reading # 3: ________
      Reading # 4: ________
   g. List the manufacturer's runout specification: ________________
   h. Determine any necessary action(s):

____

____

____

____

____

5. Discuss the findings with your instructor.

   Note: It is important to maintain perfect alignment between the transmission and the engine flywheel housing. This will ensure the clutch assembly and transmission bearings will operate smoothly and are in perfect alignment.

Performance Rating

CDX Tasksheet Number: H125

☐	☐	☐	☐	☐
0	1	2	3	4

Supervisor/instructor signature ______________________________ Date______________

Heavy Duty Drive Trains: Transmission–Introduction

Student/intern information:

Name________________________ Date____________ Class________________

Vehicle used for this activity:

Year____________ Make________________________ Model________________

Odometer____________________ VIN ________________________

Learning Objective / Task	CDX Tasksheet Number	2014 NATEF Priority Level	2014 NATEF Reference Number
• Identify causes of transmission noise, shifting concerns, lockup, jumping-out-of-gear, overheating, and vibration problems; determine needed action.	H126	P-1	2B1
• Inspect, test, repair, or replace air shift controls, lines, hoses, valves, regulators, filters, and cylinder assemblies.	H127	P-2	2B2
• Inspect and replace transmission mounts, insulators, and mounting bolts.	H128	P-1	2B3
• Inspect for leakage and replace transmission cover plates, gaskets, seals, and cap bolts; inspect seal surfaces and vents; repair as needed.	H129	P-1	2B4
• Check transmission fluid level and condition; determine needed service; add proper type of lubricant.	H130	P-1	2B5

Time off________

Time on________

Total time________

Materials Required

- Vehicle with possible transmission concern
- Vehicle manufacturer's service information
- Manufacturer-specific tools depending on the concern
- Vehicle lifting equipment if applicable

Some Safety Issues to Consider

- Diagnosis of this fault may require test driving the vehicle on the school grounds or on a hoist, both of which carry severe risks. Attempt this task only with full permission from your supervisor/instructor and follow all the guidelines exactly.
- Caution: If you are working in an area where there could be brake dust present (may contain asbestos, which has been determined to cause cancer when inhaled or ingested), ensure you wear and use all OSHA-approved asbestos protective/removal equipment.
- Lifting equipment such as vehicle jacks and stands, vehicle hoists, and engine hoists are important tools that increase productivity and make the job easier. However, they can also cause severe injury or death if used improperly. Make sure you follow the manufacturer's operation procedures. Also make sure you have your supervisor/instructor's permission to use any particular type of lifting equipment.
- Comply with personal and environmental safety practices associated with clothing; eye protection; hand tools; power equipment; proper ventilation; and the handling, storage, and disposal of chemicals/materials in accordance with federal, state, and local regulations.
- Always wear the correct protective eyewear and clothing and use the appropriate safety equipment, as well as fender covers, seat protectors, and floor mat protectors.
- Make sure you understand and observe all legislative and personal safety procedures when carrying out practical assignments. If you are unsure of what these are, ask your supervisor/instructor.

Performance Standard

0–No exposure: No information or practice provided during the program; complete training required

1–Exposure only: General information provided with no practice time; close supervision needed; additional training required

2–Limited practice: Has practiced job during training program; additional training required to develop skill

3–Moderately skilled: Has performed job independently during training program; limited additional training may be required

4–Skilled: Can perform job independently with no additional training

Student/intern information:

Name________________ Date________ Class____________

Vehicle used for this activity:

Year________ Make________________ Model____________

Odometer________________ VIN ________________

▸ TASK Identify causes of transmission noise, shifting concerns, lockup, jumping-out-of-gear, overheating, and vibration problems; determine needed action. NATEF 2B1

Time off________

Time on________

Total time________

CDX Tasksheet Number: H126

1. Reference the manufacturer's service information and/or component manufacturer's service information for causes of transmission noise.

   Note: Diagnosis of some of these concerns may require that the vehicle be operated under normal operating conditions.

   a. List all possible causes:

   b. List the necessary actions or corrections:

2. Reference the manufacturer's service information and/or component manufacturer's service information for causes of shifting concerns and lockup.

   a. List all possible causes:

   b. List the necessary actions or corrections:

3. Reference the manufacturer's service information and/or component manufacturer's service information for causes of jumping-out-of-gear.
    a. List all possible causes:

    ____
    ____
    ____
    ____
    ____

    b. List the necessary actions or corrections:

    ____
    ____
    ____
    ____
    ____

4. Reference the manufacturer's service information and/or component manufacturer's service information for causes of overheating and vibration problems.
    a. List all possible causes:

    ____
    ____
    ____
    ____
    ____

    b. List the necessary actions or corrections:

    ____
    ____
    ____
    ____
    ____

5. Discuss the findings with your instructor.

Performance Rating

CDX Tasksheet Number: H126

☐	☐	☐	☐	☐
0	1	2	3	4

Supervisor/instructor signature _______________________________ Date_____________

Student/intern information:

Name__________ Date__________ Class__________

Vehicle used for this activity:

Year__________ Make__________ Model__________

Odometer__________ VIN __________

▶ TASK Inspect, test, repair, or replace air shift controls, lines, hoses, valves, regulators, filters, and cylinder assemblies. NATEF 2B2

Time off__________

Time on__________

Total time__________

CDX Tasksheet Number: H127

1. Reference the manufacturer's service information to inspect and test the air shift controls. **Note:** Check the vehicle air system for proper operation and pressure before testing.
   a. Inspect or test the air shift controls. List your tests and your observations:
   b. Meets the manufacturer's specifications: Yes: _______ No: _______
   c. List any necessary actions or corrections:
2. If directed by your instructor, repair or replace the air shift controls in accordance with the specifications listed in the service information.
3. Reference the manufacturer's service information to inspect and test the lines, hoses, and valves.
   a. Inspect or test the lines, hoses, and valves. List your tests and your observations:
   b. Meets the manufacturer's specifications: Yes: _______ No: _______
   c. List any necessary actions or corrections:
4. If directed by your instructor, repair or replace the lines, hoses, and valves in accordance with the specifications listed in the service information.
5. Reference the manufacturer's service information to inspect and test the regulators and filters.
   a. Inspect or test the regulator and filters. List your tests and your observations:

b. Meets the manufacturer's specifications: Yes: _______ No: _______

c. List any necessary actions or corrections:

____

____

____

6. If directed by your instructor, repair or replace the regulators and filters in accordance with the specifications listed in the service information.

7. Reference the manufacturer's service information to inspect and test the cylinder assemblies.

   a. Inspect or test the cylinder assemblies. List your tests and your observations:

____

____

____

   b. Meets the manufacturer's specifications: Yes: _______ No: _______

   c. List any necessary actions or corrections:

____

____

____

8. If directed by your instructor, repair or replace the cylinder assemblies in accordance with the specifications listed in the service information.

9. Discuss the findings with your instructor.

Performance Rating

CDX Tasksheet Number: H127

☐ 0 ☐ 1 ☐ 2 ☐ 3 ☐ 4

Supervisor/instructor signature ______________________________ Date______________

Student/intern information:

Name____________________ Date__________ Class____________________

Vehicle used for this activity:

Year__________ Make____________________ Model____________________

Odometer____________________ VIN ____________________

▶ TASK Inspect and replace transmission mounts, insulators, and mounting bolts.

NATEF 2B3

Time off__________

Time on__________

Total time__________

CDX Tasksheet Number: H128

1. Reference the manufacturer's service information to inspect the transmission mounts, insulators, and mounting bolts. Check the mounts for dry rot and oil soaking. Also, check all bolts for looseness.
   a. Inspect and replace transmission mounts, insulators, and mounting bolts. List your tests and your observations:

      ____

      ____

      ____

      ____

      ____

      ____

   b. Meets the manufacturer's specifications: Yes: ______ No: ______

   c. List any necessary actions or corrections:

      ____

      ____

      ____

2. If directed by your instructor, replace the transmission mounts, insulators, and mounting bolts in accordance with the specifications listed in the service information.

3. Discuss the findings with your instructor.

Performance Rating

CDX Tasksheet Number: H128

☐	☐	☐	☐	☐
0	1	2	3	4

Supervisor/instructor signature ____________________ Date__________

Student/intern information:

Name_______________ Date_______ Class_______________

Vehicle used for this activity:

Year_______ Make_______________ Model_______________

Odometer_______________ VIN _______________

▶ TASK Inspect for leakage and replace transmission cover plates, gaskets, seals, and cap bolts; inspect seal surfaces and vents; repair as needed. NATEF 2B4

Time off_______

Time on_______

Total time_______

CDX Tasksheet Number: H129

1. Reference the manufacturer's service information for proper transmission fluid types and capacity.
   a. Manufacturer's fluid type: _______________
   b. Manufacturer's fluid capacity: _______________

2. Reference the manufacturer's service information to inspect for leakage in the transmission cover plates, gaskets, seals, and cap bolts.
   a. Inspect the transmission cover plates, gaskets, seals, and cap bolts for leakage. List your observations:
   ____
   ____
   ____
   b. Meets the manufacturer's specifications: Yes: _______ No: _______
   c. List any necessary actions or corrections:
   ____
   ____
   ____

3. If directed by your instructor, replace the transmission cover plates, gaskets, seals, and cap bolts in accordance with the specifications listed in the service information.

4. Reference the manufacturer's service information to inspect the seal surfaces and vents.
   a. Inspect the transmission seal surfaces and vents. List your observations:
   ____
   ____
   ____
   b. Meets the manufacturer's specifications: Yes: _______ No: _______
   c. List any necessary actions or corrections:
   ____
   ____
   ____

5. If directed by your instructor, repair the seal surfaces and vents in accordance with the specifications listed in the service information. List any difficulties you encountered:

____

____

____

6. Discuss the findings with your instructor.

Performance Rating

CDX Tasksheet Number: H129

☐ 0 ☐ 1 ☐ 2 ☐ 3 ☐ 4

Supervisor/instructor signature ______________________ Date__________

Student/intern information:

Name________________________ Date__________ Class________________

Vehicle used for this activity:

Year__________ Make________________________ Model______________

Odometer____________________ VIN ____________________________

▶ TASK Check transmission fluid level and condition; determine needed service; add proper type of lubricant. NATEF 2B5

Time off________

Time on________

Total time________

CDX Tasksheet Number: H130

1. Reference the manufacturer's service information for proper transmission fluid types and capacity:
   a. Manufacturer's fluid type: ________________________
   b. Manufacturer's fluid capacity: ________________________

2. Reference the manufacturer's service information to check the transmission fluid level and condition, and to determine needed service.
   a. Inspect the transmission fluid level and condition. List your observations:
   ____
   ____
   ____

   b. Meets the manufacturer's specifications: Yes: _______ No: _______

   c. List any necessary actions or corrections:
   ____
   ____
   ____
   ____
   ____

3. If directed by your instructor, add the proper type of lubricant in accordance with the specifications listed in the service information.

4. Discuss the findings with your instructor.

Performance Rating

CDX Tasksheet Number: H130

☐ 0 ☐ 1 ☐ 2 ☐ 3 ☐ 4

Supervisor/instructor signature ________________________ Date__________

Heavy Duty Drive Trains: Transmission—Mechanical Component Inspection

Student/intern information:

Name________________ Date________ Class__________

Vehicle used for this activity:

Year________ Make________________ Model__________

Odometer________________ VIN ________________

Time off________

Time on________

Total time________

Learning Objective / Task	CDX Tasksheet Number	2014 NATEF Priority Level	2014 NATEF Reference Number
• Inspect, adjust, and replace transmission shift lever, cover, rails, forks, levers, bushings, sleeves, detents, interlocks, springs, and lock bolts/safety wires.	H131	P-2	2B6
• Remove and reinstall transmission.	H132	P-1	2B7
• Inspect input shaft, gear, spacers, bearings, retainers, and slingers; determine needed action.	H133	P-3	2B8
• Inspect transmission oil filters, coolers, and related components; replace as needed.	H134	P-2	2B9
• Inspect speedometer components; determine needed action.	H135	P-2	2B10

Materials Required

- Vehicle with possible transmission concern
- Vehicle manufacturer's service information
- Manufacturer-specific tools depending on the concern
- Vehicle lifting equipment if applicable

Some Safety Issues to Consider

- Diagnosis of this fault may require test driving the vehicle on the school grounds or on a hoist, both of which carry severe risks. Attempt this task only with full permission from your supervisor/instructor and follow all the guidelines exactly.
- Caution: If you are working in an area where there could be brake dust present (may contain asbestos, which has been determined to cause cancer when inhaled or ingested), ensure you wear and use all OSHA-approved asbestos protective/removal equipment.
- Lifting equipment such as vehicle jacks and stands, vehicle hoists, and engine hoists are important tools that increase productivity and make the job easier. However, they can also cause severe injury or death if used improperly. Make sure you follow the manufacturer's operation procedures. Also make sure you have your supervisor/instructor's permission to use any particular type of lifting equipment.
- Comply with personal and environmental safety practices associated with clothing; eye protection; hand tools; power equipment; proper ventilation; and the handling, storage, and disposal of chemicals/materials in accordance with federal, state, and local regulations.
- Always wear the correct protective eyewear and clothing and use the appropriate safety equipment, as well as fender covers, seat protectors, and floor mat protectors.
- Make sure you understand and observe all legislative and personal safety procedures when carrying out practical assignments. If you are unsure of what these are, ask your supervisor/instructor.

Performance Standard

0–No exposure: No information or practice provided during the program; complete training required

1–Exposure only: General information provided with no practice time; close supervision needed; additional training required

2–Limited practice: Has practiced job during training program; additional training required to develop skill

3–Moderately skilled: Has performed job independently during training program; limited additional training may be required

4–Skilled: Can perform job independently with no additional training

Student/intern information:

Name____________________ Date__________ Class________________

Vehicle used for this activity:

Year__________ Make____________________ Model________________

Odometer____________________ VIN ____________________

▸ TASK Inspect, adjust, and replace transmission shift lever, cover, rails, forks, levers, bushings, sleeves, detents, interlocks, springs, and lock bolts/safety wires. NATEF 2B6

Time off__________

Time on__________

Total time__________

CDX Tasksheet Number: H131

1. Reference the manufacturer's service information and/or component manufacturer's service information to inspect, adjust, and replace the transmission shift lever, cover, rails, forks, levers, bushings, sleeves, detents, interlocks, springs, and lock bolts/safety wires.
   a. List, or print out and attach, the procedures:

2. Reference the appropriate service information.
   a. Inspect and adjust the transmission shift lever. List your observations:
      i. Meets the manufacturer's specifications: Yes: _____ No: _____
      ii. List any necessary actions or corrections:
   b. Inspect and adjust the lock bolts/safety wires. List your observations:
      i. Meets the manufacturer's specifications: Yes: _____ No: _____
      ii. List any necessary actions or corrections:

3. Discuss the findings with your instructor.

Performance Rating

CDX Tasksheet Number: H131

☐ 0 ☐ 1 ☐ 2 ☐ 3 ☐ 4

Supervisor/instructor signature ____________________ Date__________

Student/intern information:

Name________________ Date________ Class____________

Vehicle used for this activity:

Year________ Make________________ Model____________

Odometer________________ VIN ________________

▸ TASK Remove and reinstall transmission. NATEF 2B7

Time off________

Time on________

Total time________

CDX Tasksheet Number: H132

1. Reference the manufacturer's service information to list the steps involved in removing and replacing the vehicle's transmission.
   a. List, or print out and attach, the steps involved in removal:

   b. List, or print out and attach, the steps involved in reinstallation:

2. If directed by your instructor, remove the transmission in accordance with the specifications listed in the service information.
   a. Use all the recommended lifting and supporting devices and follow all safety procedures in the removal process.

3. Visually inspect the transmission for any damage or worn parts. List your observations:

4. Have your instructor verify removal. Supervisor's/instructor's initials: ________

5. If directed by your instructor, reinstall the transmission in accordance with the specifications listed in the service information.
   a. Use all the recommended lifting and supporting devices and follow all safety procedures in the reinstallation process.

6. Discuss the findings with your instructor.

Performance Rating

CDX Tasksheet Number: H132

☐	☐	☐	☐	☐
0	1	2	3	4

Supervisor/instructor signature ________________ Date________

Student/intern information:

Name________________ Date________ Class________________

Vehicle used for this activity:

Year________ Make________________ Model________________

Odometer________________ VIN ________________

▸ TASK Inspect input shaft, gear, spacers, bearings, retainers, and slingers; determine needed action. NATEF 2B8

Time off________

Time on________

Total time________

CDX Tasksheet Number: H133

1. Reference the manufacturer's service information to inspect the input shaft, gear, spacers, bearings, retainers, and slingers.
   a. List, or print off and attach, the steps involved:

2. Reference the appropriate service information.
   a. Inspect the input shaft, gear, spacers, bearings, retainers, and slingers as outlined above. List your observations for each component:

      i. Meets the manufacturer's specifications: Yes: _____ No: _____
      ii. List any necessary actions or corrections:

3. Discuss the findings with your instructor.

Performance Rating

CDX Tasksheet Number: H133

☐ 0 ☐ 1 ☐ 2 ☐ 3 ☐ 4

Supervisor/instructor signature ________________ Date________

Student/intern information:

Name________________ Date________ Class____________

Vehicle used for this activity:

Year________ Make________________ Model____________

Odometer________________ VIN ________________

▸ TASK Inspect transmission oil filters, coolers, and related components; replace as needed.

NATEF 2B9

Time off________

Time on________

Total time________

CDX Tasksheet Number: H134

1. Reference the appropriate service information.
   a. Inspect the transmission oil filters. List your observations:

      i. Meets the manufacturer's specifications: Yes: _____ No: _____
      ii. List any necessary actions or corrections:

   b. Inspect the transmission oil coolers. List your observations:

      i. Meets the manufacturer's specifications: Yes: _____ No: _____
      ii. List any necessary actions or corrections:

2. If directed by your instructor, replace the transmission oil filters and/or coolers in accordance with the specifications listed in the service information.

3. Discuss the findings with your instructor.

Performance Rating

CDX Tasksheet Number: H134

☐ 0 ☐ 1 ☐ 2 ☐ 3 ☐ 4

Supervisor/instructor signature ________________ Date________

Student/intern information:

Name__________ Date__________ Class__________

Vehicle used for this activity:

Year__________ Make__________ Model__________

Odometer__________ VIN __________

▸ TASK Inspect speedometer components; determine needed action. NATEF 2B10

Time off__________

Time on__________

Total time__________

CDX Tasksheet Number: H135

1. Reference the appropriate service information.
   a. Inspect the speedometer components. List the components and your observations:

      i. Meets the manufacturer's specifications: Yes: _____ No: _____
      ii. List any necessary actions or corrections:

2. Discuss the findings with your instructor.

Performance Rating

CDX Tasksheet Number: H135

☐	☐	☐	☐	☐
0	1	2	3	4

Supervisor/instructor signature __________ Date__________

Heavy Duty Drive Trains: Transmission—Power Take-Offs and Shift Controls

Student/intern information:

Name__________ Date__________ Class__________

Vehicle used for this activity:

Year__________ Make__________ Model__________

Odometer__________ VIN __________

Learning Objective / Task	CDX Tasksheet Number	2014 NATEF Priority Level	2014 NATEF Reference Number
• Inspect and adjust power take-off (P.T.O.) assemblies, controls, and shafts; determine needed action.	H136	P-3	2B11
• Inspect and test function of reverse light, neutral start, and warning device circuits; determine needed action.	H137	P-1	2B12
• Inspect and test transmission temperature gauge, wiring harnesses and sensor/sending unit; determine needed action.	H138	P-2	2B13
• Inspect and test operation of automated mechanical transmission and manual electronic shift controls, shift, range and splitter solenoids, shift motors, indicators, speed and range sensors, electronic/transmission control units (ECU/TCU), neutral/in gear and reverse switches, and wiring harnesses; determine needed action.	H139	P-2	2B14

Time off__________

Time on__________

Total time__________

Materials Required

- Vehicle with possible transmission concern
- Vehicle manufacturer's service information
- Manufacturer-specific tools depending on the concern
- Vehicle lifting equipment if applicable

Some Safety Issues to Consider

- Diagnosis of this fault may require test driving the vehicle on the school grounds or on a hoist, both of which carry severe risks. Attempt this task only with full permission from your supervisor/instructor and follow all the guidelines exactly.
- Caution: If you are working in an area where there could be brake dust present (may contain asbestos, which has been determined to cause cancer when inhaled or ingested), ensure you wear and use all OSHA-approved asbestos protective/removal equipment.
- Lifting equipment such as vehicle jacks and stands, vehicle hoists, and engine hoists are important tools that increase productivity and make the job easier. However, they can also cause severe injury or death if used improperly. Make sure you follow the manufacturer's operation procedures. Also make sure you have your supervisor/instructor's permission to use any particular type of lifting equipment.
- Comply with personal and environmental safety practices associated with clothing; eye protection; hand tools; power equipment; proper ventilation; and the handling, storage, and disposal of chemicals/materials in accordance with federal, state, and local regulations.
- Always wear the correct protective eyewear and clothing and use the appropriate safety equipment, as well as fender covers, seat protectors, and floor mat protectors.
- Make sure you understand and observe all legislative and personal safety procedures when carrying out practical assignments. If you are unsure of what these are, ask your supervisor/instructor.

Performance Standard

0–No exposure: No information or practice provided during the program; complete training required
1–Exposure only: General information provided with no practice time; close supervision needed; additional training required
2–Limited practice: Has practiced job during training program; additional training required to develop skill
3–Moderately skilled: Has performed job independently during training program; limited additional training may be required
4–Skilled: Can perform job independently with no additional training

Student/intern information:

Name____________________ Date__________ Class____________________

Vehicle used for this activity:

Year__________ Make____________________ Model____________________

Odometer____________________ VIN ____________________

▶ TASK Inspect and adjust power take-off (P.T.O.) assemblies, controls, and shafts; determine needed action. NATEF 2B11

Time off__________

Time on__________

Total time__________

CDX Tasksheet Number: H136

1. Reference the appropriate workshop service information to inspect and adjust the power take-off (P.T.O.) assemblies, controls, and shafts.

   Note: P.T.O. is used as a parasitic component to run various components off of the transmission for different types of trucks such as dump trucks, trash trucks, and oil tanker pumps.

   a. Inspect and adjust the P.T.O. assembly, controls, and shaft. List your observations:

   b. Meets the manufacturer's specifications: Yes: _____ No: _____

   c. List any necessary actions or corrections:

2. Discuss the findings with your instructor.

Performance Rating

CDX Tasksheet Number: H136

☐	☐	☐	☐	☐
0	1	2	3	4

Supervisor/instructor signature ____________________ Date__________

Student/intern information:

Name______________________ Date__________ Class______________

Vehicle used for this activity:

Year__________ Make______________________ Model______________

Odometer__________________ VIN ______________________

▶ TASK Inspect and test function of reverse light, neutral start, and warning device circuits; determine needed action. NATEF 2B12

Time off________

Time on________

Total time________

CDX Tasksheet Number: H137

1. Reference the appropriate service information.
   a. Inspect and test the function of the reverse light. List your observations:
      ____
      ____
      ____
      i. Meets the manufacturer's specifications: Yes: _____ No: _____
      ii. If no, list the necessary actions or corrections:
      ____
      ____
   b. Inspect and test the function of the neutral start circuit. List your observations:
      ____
      ____
      ____
      i. Meets the manufacturer's specifications: Yes: _____ No: _____
      ii. If no, list the necessary actions or corrections:
      ____
      ____
   c. Inspect and test the function of the warning device circuits. List your observations:
      ____
      ____
      ____
      i. Meets the manufacturer's specifications: Yes: _____ No: _____
      ii. If no, list the necessary actions or corrections:
      ____
      ____

2. Inspect various wiring and connectors for burnt or frayed wiring or broken or loose connections.
    a. Condition of wiring and connectors: Good ______ Bad_____

3. Discuss the findings with your instructor.

Performance Rating

CDX Tasksheet Number: H137

☐ 0 ☐ 1 ☐ 2 ☐ 3 ☐ 4

Supervisor/instructor signature ________________________________ Date________________

Student/intern information:

Name____________________ Date__________ Class__________

Vehicle used for this activity:

Year__________ Make____________________ Model__________

Odometer____________________ VIN ____________________

▶ TASK Inspect and test transmission temperature gauge, wiring harnesses and sensor/sending unit; determine needed action. NATEF 2B13

Time off__________

Time on__________

Total time__________

CDX Tasksheet Number: H138

1. Reference the appropriate manufacturer's service information to inspect and test the transmission temperature gauge, wiring harnesses and sensor/sending unit.
   a. Inspect and test the transmission temperature gauge, wiring harness, and sensor/sending unit. List your observations for each:

   ____

   ____

   ____

   ____

   ____

   ____

   b. Meets the manufacturer's specifications: Yes: _____ No: _____
   c. List any necessary actions or corrections:

   ____

   ____

   ____

2. Discuss the findings with your instructor.

Performance Rating

CDX Tasksheet Number: H138

☐	☐	☐	☐	☐
0	1	2	3	4

Supervisor/instructor signature ____________________ Date__________

Student/intern information:

Name______________________________ Date____________ Class______________________

Vehicle used for this activity:

Year______________ Make________________________________ Model____________________

Odometer__________________________ VIN ______________________________________

▶ TASK Inspect and test operation of automated mechanical transmission and manual electronic shift controls, shift, range and splitter solenoids, shift motors, indicators, speed and range sensors, electronic/transmission control units (ECU/TCU), neutral/in gear and reverse switches, and wiring harnesses; determine needed action. NATEF 2B14

Time off________

Time on________

Total time________

CDX Tasksheet Number: H139

1. Reference the appropriate service information.
   a. Inspect and test the operation of the automated mechanical transmission and manual electronic shift controls. List your observations:

      ____
      ____
      ____
      ____

      i. Meets the manufacturer's specifications: Yes: _____ No: _____
      ii. If no, list the necessary actions or corrections:

      ____
      ____
      ____

   b. Inspect and test the operation of the automated mechanical transmission and manual electronic shift, range and splitter solenoids, and shift motors. List your observations:

      ____
      ____
      ____
      ____

      i. Meets the manufacturer's specifications: Yes: _____ No: _____
      ii. If no, list the necessary actions or corrections:

      ____
      ____
      ____

   c. Inspect and test the operation of the automated mechanical transmission and manual electronic indicators and speed and range sensors. List your observations:

      ____
      ____
      ____

      i. Meets the manufacturer's specifications: Yes: _____ No: _____
      ii. If no, list the necessary actions or corrections:

      ____
      ____
      ____

d. Inspect and test the operation of the automated mechanical transmission and manual electronic electronic/transmission control units (ECU/TCU), neutral/in gear and reverse switches, and wiring harnesses. List your observations:

____

____

____

____

____

i. Meets the manufacturer's specifications: Yes: _____ No: _____

ii. If no, list the necessary actions or corrections:

____

____

____

2. Discuss the findings with your instructor.

Performance Rating

CDX Tasksheet Number: H139

☐ 0 ☐ 1 ☐ 2 ☐ 3 ☐ 4

Supervisor/instructor signature ______________________ Date__________

Heavy Duty Drive Trains: Transmission–Electronic Control Diagnosis

Student/intern information:

Name________________ Date________ Class____________

Vehicle used for this activity:

Year________ Make________________ Model____________

Odometer________________ VIN ________________

Time off________

Time on________

Total time________

Learning Objective / Task	CDX Tasksheet Number	2014 NATEF Priority Level	2014 NATEF Reference Number
• Inspect and test operation of automated mechanical transmission electronic shift selectors, air and electrical switches, displays and indicators, wiring harnesses, and air lines; determine needed action.	H140	P-2	2B15
• Use appropriate electronic service tools and procedures to diagnose automated mechanical transmission problems; check and record diagnostic codes, clear codes, and interpret digital multimeter (DMM) readings; determine needed action.	H141	P-1	2B16
• Inspect and test operation of automatic transmission electronic shift controls, shift solenoids, shift motors, indicators, speed and range sensors, electronic/transmission control units (ECU/TCU), neutral/in gear and reverse switches, and wiring harnesses.	H142	P-2	2B17
• Inspect and test operation of automatic transmission electronic shift selectors, switches, displays, indicators, and wiring harnesses.	H143	P-2	2B18
• Use appropriate electronic service tools and procedures to diagnose automatic transmission problems; check and record diagnostic codes, clear codes, and interpret digital multimeter (DMM) readings; determine needed action.	H144	P-3	2B19

Materials Required

- Vehicle with possible transmission concern
- Vehicle manufacturer's service information
- Manufacturer-specific tools depending on the concern
- Vehicle lifting equipment if applicable

Some Safety Issues to Consider

- Diagnosis of this fault may require test driving the vehicle on the school grounds or on a hoist, both of which carry severe risks. Attempt this task only with full permission from your supervisor/instructor and follow all the guidelines exactly.
- Caution: If you are working in an area where there could be brake dust present (may contain asbestos, which has been determined to cause cancer when inhaled or ingested), ensure you wear and use all OSHA-approved asbestos protective/removal equipment.
- Lifting equipment such as vehicle jacks and stands, vehicle hoists, and engine hoists are important tools that increase productivity and make the job easier. However, they can also cause severe injury or death if used improperly. Make sure you follow the manufacturer's operation procedures. Also make sure you have your supervisor/instructor's permission to use any particular type of lifting equipment.

- Comply with personal and environmental safety practices associated with clothing; eye protection; hand tools; power equipment; proper ventilation; and the handling, storage, and disposal of chemicals/materials in accordance with federal, state, and local regulations.
- Always wear the correct protective eyewear and clothing and use the appropriate safety equipment, as well as fender covers, seat protectors, and floor mat protectors.
- Make sure you understand and observe all legislative and personal safety procedures when carrying out practical assignments. If you are unsure of what these are, ask your supervisor/instructor.

Performance Standard

0–No exposure: No information or practice provided during the program; complete training required

1–Exposure only: General information provided with no practice time; close supervision needed; additional training required

2–Limited practice: Has practiced job during training program; additional training required to develop skill

3–Moderately skilled: Has performed job independently during training program; limited additional training may be required

4–Skilled: Can perform job independently with no additional training

Student/intern information:

Name____________________ Date__________ Class____________________

Vehicle used for this activity:

Year__________ Make____________________ Model____________________

Odometer____________________ VIN ____________________

▶ TASK Inspect and test operation of automated mechanical transmission electronic shift selectors, air and electrical switches, displays and indicators, wiring harnesses, and air lines; determine needed action. NATEF 2B15

Time off__________

Time on__________

Total time__________

CDX Tasksheet Number: H140

1. Reference the appropriate service information.
   a. Inspect and test the operation of the automated mechanical transmission electronic shift selectors. List your observations:

      i. Meets the manufacturer's specifications: Yes: _____ No: _____
      ii. If no, list the necessary actions or corrections:

   b. Inspect and test the operation of the air and electrical switches. List your observations:

      i. Meets the manufacturer's specifications: Yes: _____ No: _____
      ii. If no, list the necessary actions or corrections:

   c. Inspect and test the operation of the displays and indicators, wiring harnesses, and air lines. List your observations:

i. Meets the manufacturer's specifications: Yes: _____ No: _____
ii. If no, list the necessary actions or corrections:

____

____

____

2. Discuss the findings with your instructor.

Performance Rating

CDX Tasksheet Number: H140

☐	☐	☐	☐	☐
0	1	2	3	4

Supervisor/instructor signature ______________________________ Date ____________

Student/intern information:

Name________________ Date________ Class____________

Vehicle used for this activity:

Year________ Make________________ Model____________

Odometer______________ VIN ________________

▶ TASK Use appropriate electronic service tools and procedures to diagnose automated mechanical transmission problems; check and record diagnostic codes, clear codes, and interpret digital multimeter (DMM) readings; determine needed action.

NATEF 2B16

Time off________

Time on________

Total time________

CDX Tasksheet Number: H141

1. Reference the appropriate service information and use appropriate electronic service tools and procedures to diagnose the automated mechanical transmission problems.
   a. List the scan tool and DMM you will be using for this task:

2. Check and record the diagnostic codes present and their descriptions:
   a. Code #1: ________________
   b. Code #2: ________________
   c. Code #3: ________________
   d. Code #4: ________________
   e. Determine any necessary actions or corrections:

3. Clear the codes.

4. Perform and interpret the digital multimeter (DMM) readings. List your tests and conclusions:

a. Meets the manufacturer's specifications: Yes: _____ No: _____
b. List any necessary actions or corrections:

____

____

____

5. Discuss the findings with your instructor.

Performance Rating

CDX Tasksheet Number: H141

☐ 0 ☐ 1 ☐ 2 ☐ 3 ☐ 4

Supervisor/instructor signature ______________________________ Date______________

Student/intern information:

Name________________________________ Date__________ Class____________________

Vehicle used for this activity:

Year__________ Make____________________________ Model____________________

Odometer________________________ VIN ____________________________________

▶ TASK Inspect and test operation of automatic transmission electronic shift controls, shift solenoids, shift motors, indicators, speed and range sensors, electronic/transmission control units (ECU/TCU), neutral/in gear and reverse switches, and wiring harnesses.

NATEF 2B17

Time off__________

Time on__________

Total time__________

CDX Tasksheet Number: H142

1. Reference the appropriate service information.
    a. Inspect and test the operation of the automatic transmission electronic shift controls. List your observations:

        i. Meets the manufacturer's specifications: Yes: _____ No: _____
        ii. Determine any necessary actions or corrections:

    b. Inspect and test the operation of the shift solenoids, shift motors, and indicators. List your observations:

        i. Meets the manufacturer's specifications: Yes: _____ No: _____
        ii. Determine any necessary actions or corrections:

    c. Inspect and test the operation of the speed and range sensors and electronic/transmission control units (ECT/TCU). List your observations:

i. Meets the manufacturer's specifications: Yes: _____ No: _____

ii. Determine any necessary actions or corrections:

____

____

____

d. Inspect and test the operation of the neutral/in gear and reverse switches and wiring harnesses. List your observations:

____

____

____

____

i. Meets the manufacturer's specifications: Yes: _____ No: _____

ii. Determine any necessary actions or corrections:

____

____

____

2. Discuss the findings with your instructor.

Performance Rating

CDX Tasksheet Number: H142

☐ 0 ☐ 1 ☐ 2 ☐ 3 ☐ 4

Supervisor/instructor signature _______________________________ Date_____________

Student/intern information:

Name________________ Date________ Class________

Vehicle used for this activity:

Year________ Make________________ Model________

Odometer________________ VIN ________________

▶ TASK Inspect and test operation of automatic transmission electronic shift selectors, switches, displays, indicators, and wiring harnesses. NATEF 2B18

Time off________

Time on________

Total time________

CDX Tasksheet Number: H143

1. Reference the appropriate service information.
   a. Inspect and test the operation of the automatic transmission electronic shift selectors. List your observations:

      i. Meets the manufacturer's specifications: Yes: _____ No: _____
      ii. Determine any necessary actions or corrections:

   b. Inspect and test the operation of the automatic transmission switches, displays, and indicators. List your observations:

      i. Meets the manufacturer's specifications: Yes: _____ No: _____
      ii. Determine any necessary actions or corrections:

   c. Inspect the condition of the wiring harness. Test the operation of the wiring harnesses. List your observations:

i. Meets the manufacturer's specifications: Yes: _____ No: _____
ii. Determine any necessary actions or corrections:

____

____

____

2. Discuss the findings with your instructor.

Performance Rating

CDX Tasksheet Number: H143

☐	☐	☐	☐	☐
0	1	2	3	4

Supervisor/instructor signature _______________________________ Date_____________

Student/intern information:

Name________________ Date________ Class____________

Vehicle used for this activity:

Year________ Make________________ Model____________

Odometer________________ VIN ____________________

▶ TASK Use appropriate electronic service tools and procedures to diagnose automatic transmission problems; check and record diagnostic codes, clear codes, and interpret digital multimeter (DMM) readings; determine needed action. NATEF 2B19

Time off________

Time on________

Total time________

CDX Tasksheet Number: H144

1. Reference the appropriate service information and use appropriate electronic service tools and procedures to diagnose the automatic transmission problems; to check and record the diagnostic codes and clear codes; and to interpret digital multimeter (DMM) readings.
   a. Diagnose the automatic transmission problems and check and record any codes present and their descriptions:
      i. Code #1: ________________
      ii. Code #2: ________________
      iii. Code #3: ________________
      iv. Code #4: ________________
      v. Determine any necessary actions or corrections:

   b. Clear the codes.

   c. Test and interpret the digital multimeter (DMM) readings. List your tests and their readings:

      i. Meets the manufacturer's specifications: Yes: _____ No: _____
      ii. Determine any necessary actions or corrections:

2. Discuss the findings with your instructor.

Performance Rating

CDX Tasksheet Number: H144

☐	☐	☐	☐	☐
0	1	2	3	4

Supervisor/instructor signature ____________________ Date________

Heavy Duty Drive Trains: Transmission–Driveshaft and Universal Joint

Student/intern information:

Name________________ Date________ Class____________

Vehicle used for this activity:

Year________ Make________________ Model____________

Odometer________________ VIN ________________

Time off________

Time on________

Total time________

Learning Objective / Task	CDX Tasksheet Number	2014 NATEF Priority Level	2014 NATEF Reference Number
• Identify causes of driveshaft and universal joint noise and vibration problems; determine needed action.	H145	P-1	2C1
• Inspect, service, or replace driveshaft, slip joints, yokes, drive flanges, and universal joints, driveshaft boots and seals, and retaining hardware; check phasing of all shafts.	H146	P-1	2C2
• Inspect driveshaft center support bearings and mounts; determine needed action.	H147	P-1	2C3
• Measure driveline angles; determine needed action.	H148	P-1	2C4

Materials Required

- Vehicle with possible transmission concern
- Vehicle manufacturer's service information
- Manufacturer-specific tools depending on the concern
- Vehicle lifting equipment if applicable

Some Safety Issues to Consider

- Diagnosis of this fault may require test driving the vehicle on the school grounds or on a hoist, both of which carry severe risks. Attempt this task only with full permission from your supervisor/instructor and follow all the guidelines exactly.
- Caution: If you are working in an area where there could be brake dust present (may contain asbestos, which has been determined to cause cancer when inhaled or ingested), ensure you wear and use all OSHA-approved asbestos protective/removal equipment.
- Lifting equipment such as vehicle jacks and stands, vehicle hoists, and engine hoists are important tools that increase productivity and make the job easier. However, they can also cause severe injury or death if used improperly. Make sure you follow the manufacturer's operation procedures. Also make sure you have your supervisor/instructor's permission to use any particular type of lifting equipment.
- Comply with personal and environmental safety practices associated with clothing; eye protection; hand tools; power equipment; proper ventilation; and the handling, storage, and disposal of chemicals/materials in accordance with federal, state, and local regulations.
- Always wear the correct protective eyewear and clothing and use the appropriate safety equipment, as well as fender covers, seat protectors, and floor mat protectors.
- Make sure you understand and observe all legislative and personal safety procedures when carrying out practical assignments. If you are unsure of what these are, ask your supervisor/instructor.

Performance Standard

0–No exposure: No information or practice provided during the program; complete training required

1–Exposure only: General information provided with no practice time; close supervision needed; additional training required

2–Limited practice: Has practiced job during training program; additional training required to develop skill

3–Moderately skilled: Has performed job independently during training program; limited additional training may be required

4–Skilled: Can perform job independently with no additional training

Student/intern information:

Name__________ Date__________ Class__________

Vehicle used for this activity:

Year__________ Make__________ Model__________

Odometer__________ VIN __________

▸ TASK Identify causes of driveshaft and universal joint noise and vibration problems; determine needed action. NATEF 2C1

Time off__________

Time on__________

Total time__________

CDX Tasksheet Number: H145

1. Reference the manufacturer's service information for the common causes of driveshaft and universal joint noise and vibration problems.
   a. List all possible causes of driveshaft and universal joint noise and vibration problems:
   b. Determine what action will be required to correct the driveshaft and universal joint noise and vibration problems:
2. Discuss the findings with your instructor.

Performance Rating

CDX Tasksheet Number: H145

☐ 0 ☐ 1 ☐ 2 ☐ 3 ☐ 4

Supervisor/instructor signature __________ Date__________

Student/intern information:

Name________________ Date________ Class________________

Vehicle used for this activity:

Year__________ Make________________ Model__________

Odometer________________ VIN________________

▶ TASK Inspect, service, or replace driveshaft, slip joints, yokes, drive flanges, and universal joints, driveshaft boots and seals, and retaining hardware; check phasing of all shafts.

NATEF 2C2

Time off________

Time on________

Total time________

CDX Tasksheet Number: H146

1. Reference the appropriate service information.
   a. Inspect and service the driveshaft, slip joints, yokes, and drive flanges. List your observations for each:

      ____
      ____
      ____
      ____
      ____

      i. Meets the manufacturer's specifications: Yes: _____ No: _____
      ii. Determine any necessary actions or corrections:

      ____
      ____
      ____

   b. If directed by your instructor, replace the driveshaft, slip joints, yokes, and drive flanges in accordance with the specifications listed in the service information.

   c. Inspect and service the universal joints, driveshaft boots and seals, and retaining hardware. List your observations for each:

      ____
      ____
      ____
      ____
      ____

      i. Meets the manufacturer's specifications: Yes: _____ No: _____
      ii. Determine any necessary actions or corrections:

      ____
      ____
      ____

   d. If directed by your instructor, replace the universal joints, driveshaft boots and seals, and retaining hardware in accordance with the specifications listed in the service information.

e. Check the phasing of all shafts. List your observations for each joint:

____

____

____

____

____

i. Meets the manufacturer's specifications: Yes: _____ No: _____

ii. Determine any necessary actions or corrections:

____

____

____

2. Discuss the findings with your instructor.

Performance Rating

CDX Tasksheet Number: H146

☐	☐	☐	☐	☐
0	1	2	3	4

Supervisor/instructor signature ______________________ Date__________

Student/intern information:

Name________________ Date________ Class____________

Vehicle used for this activity:

Year________ Make________________ Model____________

Odometer______________ VIN ________________

▶ TASK Inspect driveshaft center support bearings and mounts; determine needed action.

NATEF 2C3

Time off________

Time on________

Total time________

CDX Tasksheet Number: H147

1. Reference the appropriate service information.

   Note: Center support bearings are required when driveshaft lengths exceed five and a half feet. If driveshaft lengths are exceeded, premature failure or catastrophic failure will occur.

   a. Inspect the driveshaft center support bearings.

      i. List your observations:

      ____

      ____

      ____

      ii. Meets the manufacturer's specifications: Yes: _____ No: _____

      iii. Determine any necessary actions or corrections:

      ____

      ____

      ____

   b. Inspect the drive shaft mounts. List your observations:

      ____

      ____

      ____

      i. Meets the manufacturer's specifications: Yes: _____ No: _____

      ii. Determine any necessary actions or corrections:

      ____

      ____

      ____

2. Discuss the findings with your instructor.

Performance Rating

CDX Tasksheet Number: H147

☐	☐	☐	☐	☐
0	1	2	3	4

Supervisor/instructor signature ____________________ Date________

Student/intern information:

Name____________________ Date__________ Class____________________

Vehicle used for this activity:

Year__________ Make____________________ Model____________________

Odometer____________________ VIN ____________________

▶ TASK Measure driveline angles; determine needed action. NATEF 2C4

Time off__________

Time on__________

Total time__________

CDX Tasksheet Number: H148

1. Reference the appropriate service information for the correct procedure to measure driveline angles.

   Note: Measuring driveline angles ensures that all universal joints operate at the proper angle to prevent driveline premature wear or a catastrophic failure.

2. Utilizing an inclinometer or a dial protractor, measure the angles of the universal joint by placing it on the flat surface of each driveline component. Drive components include transmission, driveshaft(s) and differential. Make sure the driveline components have a clean flat surface to enable a measuring tool to be used.

   Note: Always stay on one side of the vehicles driveline while recording readings. Start with the transmission flat surface then proceed to the first driveshaft and then to the next shaft or component in the drivetrain. Any angle that runs downhill from the front to the back of the vehicle is considered a positive angle. Negative angles can be present when driveline components are running uphill from front to back of the vehicle.

3. Measure and record the angle for each component below. The number of readings will vary depending on the number of components. See Figure 1.
   a. Measure component angle # 1: ____________________

   b. Measure component angle # 2: ____________________

   c. Measure component angle # 3: ____________________

   d. Measure component angle # 4: ____________________

   e. Measure component angle # 5: ____________________

   f. Measure component angle # 6: ____________________

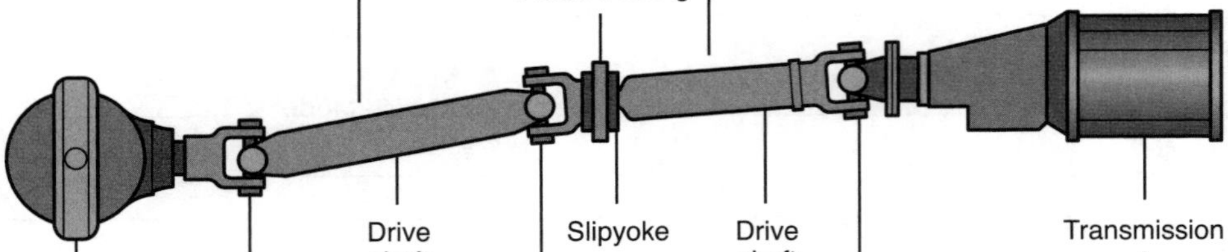

Figure 1

4. Compute angles by adding or subtracting two readings depending on whether they are positive or negative to get the operating angle of each u-joint. See Figure 2.

   Note: See example for computation of angle measurement:
   Measuring the transmission reads 2 degrees positive, while measuring the first driveshaft reads -1 degrees negative. A plus 2 reading minus a negative 1 reading will result in a plus or positive 1 reading for the operating angle of joint # 1.

   Note: Depending on how many shafts and drive components are involved will result in more driveline operating angles. All joints should have a computed operating angle of .5 degrees below 3500 rpm and 1 degree above 3500 rpm.

   a. Computed angle measurement result #1: ______________________________

   b. Computed angle measurement result #2: ______________________________

   c. Computed angle measurement result #3: ______________________________

   d. Computed angle measurement result #4: ______________________________

5. Compute operating angles of each driveshaft. See Figure 2.

   a. Computed operating angle of driveshaft #1: _________________________

   b. Computed operating angle of driveshaft #2: _________________________

Center bearing

Computed angle measurements # 2 and # 3

Computed angle measurements # 1 and # 2

Computed angle measurements # 3 and # 4

U-joint operating angle # 2

U-joint operating angle # 1

U-joint operating angle # 3

Computed operating angle of driveshaft # 1

Computed operating angle of driveshaft # 2

Operating angle of shaft # 1

Operating angle of shaft # 2

Figure 2

c. Depending on the reading outcomes, angles may have to be adjusted.

d. If adjustments are necessary, record the procedure to correct any angles that are not in operating parameters.

____

____

____

____

Performance Rating

CDX Tasksheet Number: H148

☐	☐	☐	☐	☐
0	1	2	3	4

Supervisor/instructor signature ____________________ Date__________

Heavy Duty Drive Trains: Drive Axle 1

Student/intern information:

Name__________ Date__________ Class__________

Vehicle used for this activity:

Year__________ Make__________ Model__________

Odometer__________ VIN __________

Time off__________

Time on__________

Total time__________

Learning Objective / Task	CDX Tasksheet Number	2014 NATEF Priority Level	2014 NATEF Reference Number
• Identify causes of drive axle(s) drive unit noise and overheating problems; determine needed action.	H149	P-2	2D1
• Check and repair fluid leaks; inspect and replace drive axle housing cover plates, gaskets, sealants, vents, magnetic plugs, and seals.	H150	P-1	2D2
• Check drive axle fluid level and condition; determine needed service; add proper type of lubricant.	H151	P-1	2D3
• Remove and replace differential carrier assembly.	H152	P-2	2D4
• Inspect and replace differential case assembly including spider gears, cross shaft, side gears, thrust washers, case halves, and bearings.	H153	P-3	2D5
• Inspect and replace components of locking differential case assembly.	H154	P-3	2D6
• Inspect differential carrier housing and caps, side bearing bores, and pilot (spigot, pocket) bearing bore; determine needed action.	H155	P-3	2D7

Materials Required

- Vehicle with possible transmission concern
- Vehicle manufacturer's service information
- Manufacturer-specific tools depending on the concern
- Vehicle lifting equipment if applicable

Some Safety Issues to Consider

- Diagnosis of this fault may require test driving the vehicle on the school grounds or on a hoist, both of which carry severe risks. Attempt this task only with full permission from your supervisor/instructor and follow all the guidelines exactly.
- Caution: If you are working in an area where there could be brake dust present (may contain asbestos, which has been determined to cause cancer when inhaled or ingested), ensure you wear and use all OSHA-approved asbestos protective/removal equipment.
- Lifting equipment such as vehicle jacks and stands, vehicle hoists, and engine hoists are important tools that increase productivity and make the job easier. However, they can also cause severe injury or death if used improperly. Make sure you follow the manufacturer's operation procedures. Also make sure you have your supervisor/instructor's permission to use any particular type of lifting equipment.
- Comply with personal and environmental safety practices associated with clothing; eye protection; hand tools; power equipment; proper ventilation; and the handling, storage, and disposal of chemicals/materials in accordance with federal, state, and local regulations.

- Always wear the correct protective eyewear and clothing and use the appropriate safety equipment, as well as fender covers, seat protectors, and floor mat protectors.
- Make sure you understand and observe all legislative and personal safety procedures when carrying out practical assignments. If you are unsure of what these are, ask your supervisor/instructor.

Performance Standard

0–No exposure: No information or practice provided during the program; complete training required
1–Exposure only: General information provided with no practice time; close supervision needed; additional training required
2–Limited practice: Has practiced job during training program; additional training required to develop skill
3–Moderately skilled: Has performed job independently during training program; limited additional training may be required
4–Skilled: Can perform job independently with no additional training

Student/intern information:

Name__________________ Date__________ Class______________

Vehicle used for this activity:

Year__________ Make__________________ Model______________

Odometer__________________ VIN ________________________

▸ TASK Identify causes of drive axle(s) drive unit noise and overheating problems; determine needed action.

NATEF 2D1

Time off________

Time on________

Total time________

CDX Tasksheet Number: H149

1. Reference the manufacturer's service information for the common causes of driveshaft and universal joint noise and vibration problems.
   a. List all possible causes:

   ____

   b. List possible corrections:

   ____

2. Discuss the findings with your instructor.

Performance Rating

CDX Tasksheet Number: H149

☐ 0 ☐ 1 ☐ 2 ☐ 3 ☐ 4

Supervisor/instructor signature ________________________ Date__________

Student/intern information:

Name____________________ Date__________ Class________________

Vehicle used for this activity:

Year__________ Make____________________ Model________________

Odometer____________________ VIN ____________________

▶ TASK Check and repair fluid leaks; inspect and replace drive axle housing cover plates, gaskets, sealants, vents, magnetic plugs, and seals. NATEF 2D2

Time off________

Time on________

Total time________

CDX Tasksheet Number: H150

1. Reference the manufacturer's service information.
   a. Check for fluid leaks. List your observations:

      ____

      i. Meets the manufacturer's specifications: Yes: _____ No: _____
      ii. If no, list the necessary actions or corrections:

      ____

   b. If directed by your instructor, repair the fluid leaks in accordance with the specifications listed in the service information.

   c. Inspect the drive axle housing cover plates, gaskets, sealants, vents, magnetic plugs, and seals. It is extremely important to pay attention to the drive axle vents. Overfilling of the axle can create internal axle pressure and damage wheel seals and differential seals. List your observations:

      ____

      i. Meets the manufacturer's specifications: Yes: _____ No: _____
      ii. If no, list the necessary actions or corrections:

      ____

   d. If directed by your instructor, repair the drive axle housing cover plates, gaskets, sealants, vents, magnetic plugs, and seals in accordance with the specifications listed in the service information.

2. Discuss the findings with your instructor.

Performance Rating

CDX Tasksheet Number: H150

☐	☐	☐	☐	☐
0	1	2	3	4

Supervisor/instructor signature ____________________ Date__________

Student/intern information:

Name__________ Date__________ Class__________

Vehicle used for this activity:

Year__________ Make__________ Model__________

Odometer__________ VIN __________

▶ TASK Check drive axle fluid level and condition; determine needed service; add proper type of lubricant. NATEF 2D3

Time off__________

Time on__________

Total time__________

CDX Tasksheet Number: H151

1. Reference the manufacturer's service information. List the manufacturer's fluid type and fluid capacity:
   a. Specified fluid type: __________
   b. Specified fluid quantity: __________

2. Check the drive axle fluid level and condition. List your observations:

   a. Meets the manufacturer's specifications: Yes: _____ No: _____
   b. Determine any necessary actions or corrections:

3. If directed by your instructor, add the proper type of lubricant in accordance with the specifications listed in the service information. Certain types of differential carriers (locking differentials) require special fluid.

4. Discuss the findings with your instructor.

Performance Rating

CDX Tasksheet Number: H151

☐ 0 ☐ 1 ☐ 2 ☐ 3 ☐ 4

Supervisor/instructor signature __________ Date__________

Student/intern information:

Name__________ Date__________ Class__________

Vehicle used for this activity:

Year__________ Make__________ Model__________

Odometer__________ VIN __________

▶ TASK Remove and replace differential carrier assembly. NATEF 2D4

Time off__________

Time on__________

Total time__________

CDX Tasksheet Number: H152

1. Reference the manufacturer's service information and/or component manufacturer's service information.
   a. List the procedures for removing and replacing the differential carrier assembly:

2. Reference the manufacturer's service information and/or component manufacturer's service information plus the above procedures to remove the differential carrier assembly.
   a. List any difficulties you faced during removal:

   b. Determine any necessary actions:

   c. Have your instructor verify removal and your answers.
   Supervisor's/instructor's initials: __________

3. If directed by your instructor, replace the differential carrier assembly in accordance with the specifications listed in the service information. List any difficulties you had during reassembly:

4. Discuss the findings with your instructor.

Performance Rating

CDX Tasksheet Number: H152

☐ 0 ☐ 1 ☐ 2 ☐ 3 ☐ 4

Supervisor/instructor signature __________ Date__________

Student/intern information:

Name________________ Date________ Class____________

Vehicle used for this activity:

Year________ Make________________ Model____________

Odometer________________ VIN ________________

▶ TASK Inspect and replace differential case assembly including spider gears, cross shaft, side gears, thrust washers, case halves, and bearings. NATEF 2D5

Time off________

Time on________

Total time________

CDX Tasksheet Number: H153

1. Reference the appropriate service information.
   a. Inspect the differential case assembly including spider gears, cross shaft, side gears, thrust washers, case halves, and bearings. List your observations:

      i. Meets the manufacturer's specifications: Yes: _____ No: _____
      ii. Determine any necessary actions or corrections:

   b. If directed by your instructor, replace the differential case assembly including spider gears, cross shaft, side gears, thrust washers, case halves, and bearings in accordance with the specifications listed in the service information. List any difficulties you experienced during reassembly:

2. Discuss the findings with your instructor.

Performance Rating

CDX Tasksheet Number: H153

☐ 0 ☐ 1 ☐ 2 ☐ 3 ☐ 4

Supervisor/instructor signature ________________ Date________

Student/intern information:

Name____________________ Date__________ Class____________________

Vehicle used for this activity:

Year__________ Make____________________ Model____________________

Odometer____________________ VIN ____________________

TASK Inspect and replace components of locking differential case assembly. NATEF 2D6

Time off__________

Time on__________

Total time__________

CDX Tasksheet Number: H154

1. Reference the appropriate service information.
   a. Inspect the components of the locking differential case assembly. List your observations:
      i. Meets the manufacturer's specifications: Yes: _____ No: _____
      ii. Determine any necessary actions or corrections:
   b. If directed by your instructor, replace the components of the locking differential case assembly in accordance with the specifications listed in the service information. List any difficulties you experienced during reassembly:
2. Discuss the findings with your instructor.

Performance Rating

CDX Tasksheet Number: H154

☐ 0 ☐ 1 ☐ 2 ☐ 3 ☐ 4

Supervisor/instructor signature ____________________ Date__________

Student/intern information:

Name__________________ Date________ Class________________

Vehicle used for this activity:

Year__________ Make__________________ Model______________

Odometer__________________ VIN ________________________

▸ TASK Inspect differential carrier housing and caps, side bearing bores, and pilot (spigot, pocket) bearing bore; determine needed action. NATEF 2D7

Time off________

Time on________

Total time________

CDX Tasksheet Number: H155

1. Reference the appropriate service information service information.
   a. Inspect the differential carrier housing and caps. List your observations:

      i. Meets the manufacturer's specifications: Yes: _____ No: _____
      ii. Determine any necessary actions or corrections:

   b. Inspect the side bearing bores. List your observations:

      i. Meets the manufacturer's specifications: Yes: _____ No: _____
      ii. Determine any necessary actions or corrections:

   c. Inspect the pilot (spigot, pocket) bearing bore. List your observations:

      i. Meets the manufacturer's specifications: Yes: _____ No: _____
      ii. Determine any necessary actions or corrections:

2. Discuss the findings with your instructor.

Performance Rating

CDX Tasksheet Number: H155

☐	☐	☐	☐	☐
0	1	2	3	4

Supervisor/instructor signature ________________________ Date________

Heavy Duty Drive Trains: Drive Axle 2

Student/intern information:

Name__________ Date__________ Class__________

Vehicle used for this activity:

Year__________ Make__________ Model__________

Odometer__________ VIN __________

Time off__________

Time on__________

Total time__________

Learning Objective / Task	CDX Tasksheet Number	2014 NATEF Priority Level	2014 NATEF Reference Number
• Measure ring gear runout; determine needed action.	H156	P-2	2D8
• Inspect and replace ring and drive pinion gears, spacers, sleeves, bearing cages, and bearings.	H157	P-3	2D9
• Measure and adjust drive pinion bearing preload.	H158	P-3	2D10
• Measure and adjust drive pinion depth.	H159	P-3	2D11
• Measure and adjust side bearing preload and ring gear backlash.	H160	P-2	2D12
• Check and interpret ring gear and pinion tooth contact pattern; determine needed action.	H161	P-2	2D13
• Inspect, adjust, or replace ring gear thrust block/screw.	H162	P-3	2D14
• Inspect power divider (inter-axle differential) assembly; determine needed action.	H163	P-3	2D15

Materials Required

- Vehicle with possible transmission concern
- Vehicle manufacturer's service information
- Manufacturer-specific tools depending on the concern
- Vehicle lifting equipment if applicable

Some Safety Issues to Consider

- Diagnosis of this fault may require test driving the vehicle on the school grounds or on a hoist, both of which carry severe risks. Attempt this task only with full permission from your supervisor/instructor and follow all the guidelines exactly.
- Caution: If you are working in an area where there could be brake dust present (may contain asbestos, which has been determined to cause cancer when inhaled or ingested), ensure you wear and use all OSHA-approved asbestos protective/removal equipment.
- Lifting equipment such as vehicle jacks and stands, vehicle hoists, and engine hoists are important tools that increase productivity and make the job easier. However, they can also cause severe injury or death if used improperly. Make sure you follow the manufacturer's operation procedures. Also make sure you have your supervisor/instructor's permission to use any particular type of lifting equipment.
- Comply with personal and environmental safety practices associated with clothing; eye protection; hand tools; power equipment; proper ventilation; and the handling, storage, and disposal of chemicals/materials in accordance with federal, state, and local regulations.

- Always wear the correct protective eyewear and clothing and use the appropriate safety equipment, as well as fender covers, seat protectors, and floor mat protectors.
- Make sure you understand and observe all legislative and personal safety procedures when carrying out practical assignments. If you are unsure of what these are, ask your supervisor/instructor.

Performance Standard

0–No exposure: No information or practice provided during the program; complete training required
1–Exposure only: General information provided with no practice time; close supervision needed; additional training required
2–Limited practice: Has practiced job during training program; additional training required to develop skill
3–Moderately skilled: Has performed job independently during training program; limited additional training may be required
4–Skilled: Can perform job independently with no additional training

Student/intern information:

Name____________________ Date__________ Class______________

Vehicle used for this activity:

Year__________ Make____________________ Model______________

Odometer__________________ VIN ________________________

▶ TASK Measure ring gear runout; determine needed action. NATEF 2D8

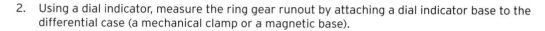

Time off________

Time on________

Total time________

CDX Tasksheet Number: H156

1. Research the procedure and specifications for inspecting and measuring ring gear runout in the appropriate service information.
   a. Record the manufacturer's specified maximum ring gear runout: __________ in/mm

2. Using a dial indicator, measure the ring gear runout by attaching a dial indicator base to the differential case (a mechanical clamp or a magnetic base).

   Attach the dial pointer to ring gear outer flat edge (see image):

Note: Make sure ring gear outer surface is clean and free of anything that could result in a false reading.

   a. Zero the dial indicator out.
   b. Obtain a ratchet and a socket to mount on the front of the pinion gear retaining nut.
   c. Rotate the pinion slowly in the direction of drive to obtain a reading.
   d. Record the reading and compare to the manufacturer's specification.
      Reading: __________ ft-lb/Nm

3. Consult the manufacturer's service information and record the procedure for adjusting the ring gear runout:

____
____
____
____
____

4. Discuss the findings with your instructor.

Performance Rating

CDX Tasksheet Number: H156

☐ 0 ☐ 1 ☐ 2 ☐ 3 ☐ 4

Supervisor/instructor signature _______________________ Date_________

Student/intern information:

Name_______________ Date_______ Class_______________

Vehicle used for this activity:

Year_______ Make_______________ Model_______________

Odometer_______________ VIN _______________

▶ TASK Inspect and replace ring and drive pinion gears, spacers, sleeves, bearing cages, and bearings. NATEF 2D9

Time off_______

Time on_______

Total time_______

CDX Tasksheet Number: H157

1. Reference the manufacturer's service information.
   a. Inspect the ring and drive pinion gears. List your observations:

      ____
      ____
      ____

      i. Meets the manufacturer's specifications: Yes: _____ No: _____
      ii. Determine any necessary actions or corrections:

         ____
         ____
         ____

   b. If directed by your instructor, replace the ring and drive pinion gears in accordance with the specifications listed in the service information.
   c. Inspect the spacers and sleeves. List your observations:

      ____
      ____
      ____

      i. Meets the manufacturer's specifications: Yes: _____ No: _____
      ii. Determine any necessary actions or corrections:

         ____
         ____
         ____

   d. If directed by your instructor, replace the spacers and sleeves in accordance with the specifications listed in the service information.
   e. Inspect the bearing cages and bearings. List your observations:

      ____
      ____
      ____

      i. Meets the manufacturer's specifications: Yes: _____ No: _____
      ii. Determine any necessary actions or corrections:

         ____
         ____
         ____

f. If directed by your instructor, replace the bearing cages and bearings in accordance with the specifications listed in the service information.

2. Discuss the findings with your instructor.

Performance Rating

CDX Tasksheet Number: H157

☐	☐	☐	☐	☐
0	1	2	3	4

Supervisor/instructor signature _______________ Date_______

Student/intern information:

Name____________________ Date__________ Class________________

Vehicle used for this activity:

Year__________ Make____________________ Model________________

Odometer____________________ VIN ____________________________

▶ TASK Measure and adjust drive pinion bearing preload. NATEF 2D10

Time off__________

Time on__________

Total time__________

CDX Tasksheet Number: H158

1. Research the procedure and specifications for measuring and adjusting drive pinion bearing preload in the appropriate service information.
    a. Record manufacturer's specified drive pinion preload: __________ in-lb/Nm

2. Following the specified procedure, measure the drive pinion bearing preload.

    Note: The purpose of pinion bearing preload is to make sure all bearings are loaded correctly. This will ensure proper operation of the pinion drive gear. If it is adjusted too tight or too loose, premature wear or catastrophic failure could occur.

    a. Utilizing a torque wrench, connect the socket end to the pinion flange retaining nut.

    b. Utilizing the torque wrench, rotate the pinion. Record the torque reading on the dial portion of the wrench: __________ ft-lb/Nm

        Note: If necessary, repeat this step to make sure you have an accurate reading.

3. Compare the reading to the manufacturer specification. Are the readings comparable?
    Yes____ No____

4. If the reading is not comparable, list the procedure from the manufacturer service information to correct the reading.

    ____

    ____

    ____

    ____

    ____

5. If directed by your instructor, adjust the drive pinion bearing preload in accordance with the specifications listed in the service information.

6. Discuss the findings with your instructor.

Performance Rating

CDX Tasksheet Number: H158

☐ 0 ☐ 1 ☐ 2 ☐ 3 ☐ 4

Supervisor/instructor signature ____________________________ Date__________

Student/intern information:

Name____________________ Date__________ Class________________

Vehicle used for this activity:

Year__________ Make____________________ Model________________

Odometer____________________ VIN ____________________

▸ TASK Measure and adjust drive pinion depth. NATEF 2D11

Time off__________

Time on__________

Total time__________

CDX Tasksheet Number: H159

1. Research the following specifications and procedures in the appropriate service information:
   a. Drive pinion depth: ________________ in/mm
2. Make sure all components are free from dirt or debris that could cause premature wear or failure.
3. Place the pinion gear into the differential housing with the bearings installed.
   Note: Pay attention to the etching number on the bottom of the pinion drive gear; compare to the old one.
   a. Record the number that is etched on the bottom of the pinion drive gear for future reference: __________
   b. Prior to this, all bearing races should have been replaced along with the new bearings.
   c. If there were shims under one of the races, paying attention to the thickness of the shims, these should also have been reinstalled.
      Note: The thickness of the shims will determine how far the pinion will be sitting into the ring gear. Adjust as necessary. If pinion housing is separate from the differential case, measure old shims and replace as necessary.
4. Utilizing a pinion depth gauge, measure and record the actual depth reading: ________ in/mm
   Note: The purpose of measuring drive pinion depth is to ensure that the drive gear is in perfect alignment with the ring gear and is in correct contact with the ring gear teeth.
5. Is the measurement within manufacturer's specifications? Yes____ No ____
6. If adjustments are necessary, record the steps necessary to bring the pinion to manufacturer's specification.

____

____

____

Performance Rating

CDX Tasksheet Number: H159

☐	☐	☐	☐	☐
0	1	2	3	4

Supervisor/instructor signature ____________________ Date__________

Student/intern information:

Name____________________ Date__________ Class________________

Vehicle used for this activity:

Year__________ Make____________________ Model________________

Odometer____________________ VIN ________________________

▶ TASK Measure and adjust side bearing preload and ring gear backlash. NATEF 2D12

Time off__________

Time on__________

Total time__________

CDX Tasksheet Number: H160

1. Research the following specifications and procedures in the appropriate service information:
    a. Side bearing preload: ____________________
    b. Ring gear backlash: _______________ in/mm
    c. Side bearing saddle bolt torque: _______________ ft-lb/Nm
2. Make sure all components are clean and free of dirt or debris that could cause a false reading and adjustment.
3. Install the ring gear into the differential housing with the bearing races. Prior to this action, the pinion should have been installed and adjusted as necessary.
4. Install the main bearing caps onto the housing and thread the bolts through the caps and into the housing.
5. Thread the side bearing adjusters into the bearing caps(see Figure 1 below).

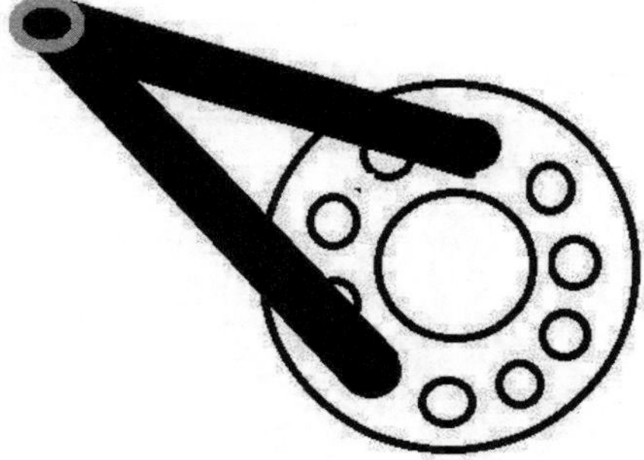

Figure 1

6. Torque the bolts to the proper manufacturer's specification.
    a. Record the torque specification: ___________ft-lb/Nm
7. Thread the side bearing adjusters into the caps until they make contact with the side bearings, allowing for some backlash play to be present.

8. Attach a dial indicator base to the differential case housing, and the dial pointer onto one of the ring gear teeth (see Figure 2 below).

9. Utilizing a spanner wrench or equivalent, rotate one of the side bearing adjusters until the backlash starts to change (see Figure 2 below).

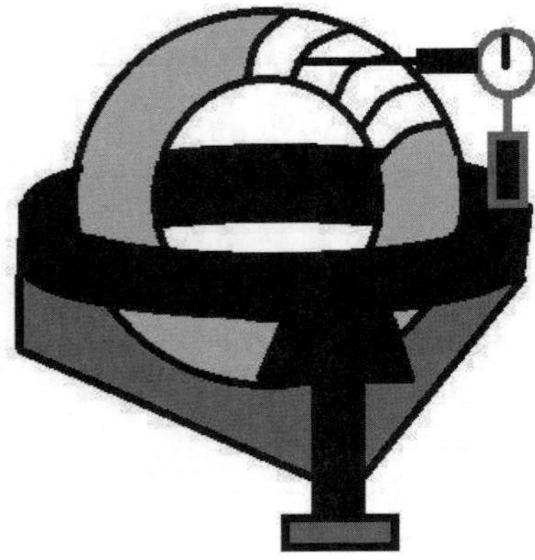

Figure 2

10. Always alternate the side bearing adjusters to keep the ring gear stable in the housing.

11. Zero out the dial indicator.

12. Rock the ring gear back and forth to achieve a reading on the dial indicator.
    a. Record the reading on the indicator and compare to manufacturer's specification: ___________ in/mm

13. Depending on the type of differential, record the procedure from the manufacturer's service information to correct and bring the reading into specification.

____

____

____

____

____

Performance Rating

CDX Tasksheet Number: H160

☐ 0　☐ 1　☐ 2　☐ 3　☐ 4

Supervisor/instructor signature _______________________ Date_________

Student/intern information:

Name_______________ Date_______ Class_______________

Vehicle used for this activity:

Year_______ Make_______________ Model_______________

Odometer_______________ VIN _______________

▸ TASK Check and interpret ring gear and pinion tooth contact pattern; determine needed action. NATEF 2D13

Time off___________

Time on___________

Total time___________

CDX Tasksheet Number: H161

1. Upon overhaul of the differential, it is necessary to check tooth contact patterns to assess if all parts are in their proper positions and adjusted correctly.
2. Mount differential in an overhaul stand with the ring gear (crown gear) facing towards the top.
3. Obtain a tube of Prussion blue or equivalent to use for this process.
4. Paint six to eight of the ring gear (crown gear) teeth with the Prussion blue or equivalent.
5. Utilizing a ratchet and socket on the pinion gear retainer nut, slowly rotate the ring gear to the drive side direction one full turn or 360 degrees.
6. Rotate the ring in the reverse direction a full turn or 360 degrees.

   Note: It may be wise to wedge a piece of wood or equivalent between the ring gear and carrier housing to create a drag on the ring gear simulating a drive condition.

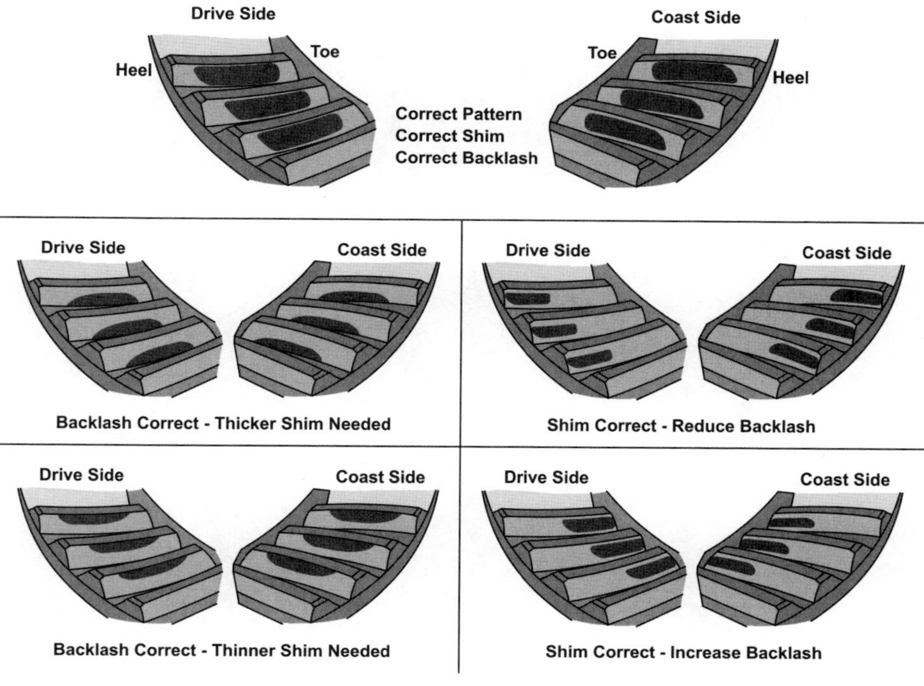

Figure 1

7. Compare the gear tooth pattern to the chart shown on page 349 (see Figure 1). List the pattern obtained for both the drive and coast sides of the ring gear:

____
____
____
____
____

8. If the gear tooth patterns do not match the chart, list and record the manufacturer's service information procedure to adjust and/or correct the pattern to specification.

____
____
____
____
____

9. Discuss the findings with your instructor. List your instructor's comments or recommendations:

____
____
____
____
____

Performance Rating

CDX Tasksheet Number: H161

☐	☐	☐	☐	☐
0	1	2	3	4

Supervisor/instructor signature _______________________________ Date__________

Student/intern information:

Name______________________________ Date__________ Class____________________

Vehicle used for this activity:

Year____________ Make______________________________ Model____________________

Odometer__________________________ VIN ____

▶ TASK Inspect, adjust, or replace ring gear thrust block/screw. NATEF 2D14

Time off__________

Time on__________

Total time__________

CDX Tasksheet Number: H162

Note: Some of the differential carriers do not come with a thrust block adjuster.

1. Mount the carrier assembly in the overhaul stand with the back surface of the ring gear (Crown gear) toward the top.
2. Install the thrust block on the back side of the ring gear (Crown gear).
3. The thrust block must be on center between the backside of the ring gear (Crown gear) and the differential case.
4. Turn the ring gear (Crown gear) until the thrust block and the hole for the thrust screw and the carrier housing are lined up.
5. Thread the thrust screw lock nut onto the thrust screw about half way down the threads.
6. Thread the thrust screw into the carrier housing until the thrust screw makes contact with the backside of the ring gear (Crown gear) or thrust block.
7. Unscrew the thrust screw one half turn or 180 degrees.
8. Tighten the thrust screw lock nut to manufacturer specifications. Record the torque specification: ______________ ft-lb/Nm (see Figure 1).

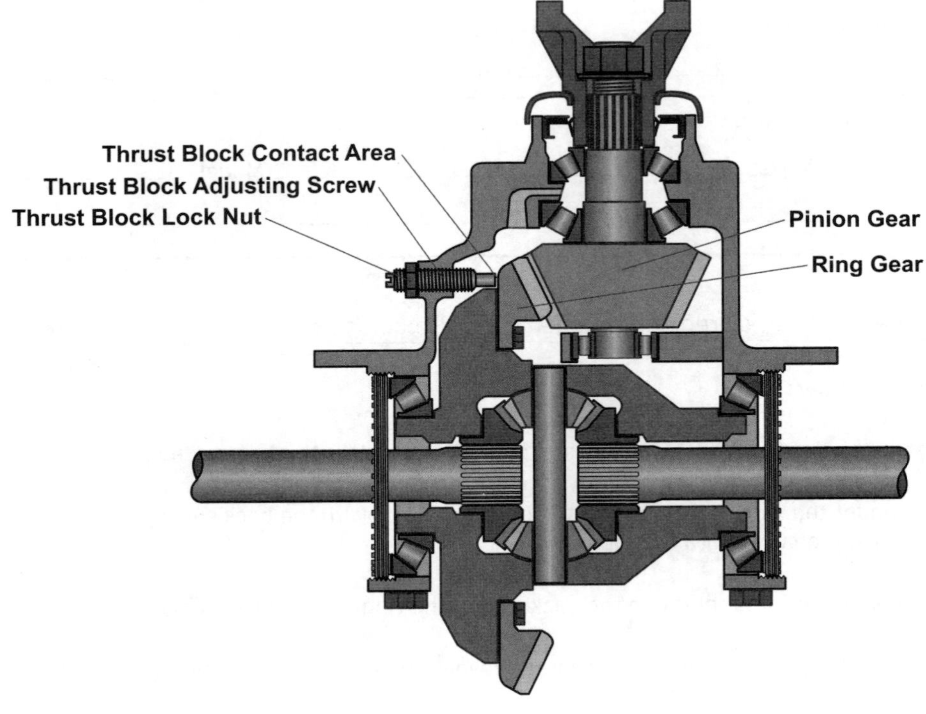

Figure 1

9. If adjustment is not within specification, record the procedure that is outlined in the manufacturer's service information to correct the problem.

____

____

____

____

____

10. Discuss the findings with your instructor. List your instructor's comments:

____

____

____

____

____

Performance Rating

CDX Tasksheet Number: H162

☐	☐	☐	☐	☐
0	1	2	3	4

Supervisor/instructor signature _______________________________ Date__________

Student/intern information:

Name__________________ Date__________ Class__________

Vehicle used for this activity:

Year__________ Make__________________ Model__________

Odometer__________________ VIN__________________

▶ TASK Inspect power divider (inter-axle differential) assembly; determine needed action.

NATEF 2D15

Time off________

Time on________

Total time________

CDX Tasksheet Number: H163

1. Reference the manufacturer's service information.
   a. Inspect the power divider (inter-axle differential) assembly. List your observations:

      ____
      ____
      ____
      ____
      ____

      i. Meets the manufacturer's specifications: Yes: _____ No: _____
      ii. Determine any necessary actions or corrections:

      ____
      ____
      ____

2. Discuss the findings with your instructor.

Performance Rating

CDX Tasksheet Number: H163

☐ 0 ☐ 1 ☐ 2 ☐ 3 ☐ 4

Supervisor/instructor signature ______________________________ Date __________

Heavy Duty Drive Trains: Drive Axle 3

Student/intern information:

Name__________ Date__________ Class__________

Vehicle used for this activity:

Year__________ Make__________ Model__________

Odometer__________ VIN __________

Time off__________

Time on__________

Total time__________

Learning Objective / Task	CDX Tasksheet Number	2014 NATEF Priority Level	2014 NATEF Reference Number
• Inspect, adjust, repair, or replace air operated power divider (inter-axle differential) lockout assembly including diaphragms, seals, springs, yokes, pins, lines, hoses, fittings, and controls.	H164	P-2	2D16
• Inspect, repair, or replace drive axle lubrication system: pump, troughs, collectors, slingers, tubes, and filters.	H165	P-3	2D17
• Inspect and replace drive axle shafts.	H166	P-1	2D18
• Remove and replace wheel assembly; check rear wheel seal and axle flange gasket for leaks; perform needed action.	H167	P-1	2D19

Materials Required

- Vehicle with possible transmission concern
- Vehicle manufacturer's service information
- Manufacturer-specific tools depending on the concern
- Vehicle lifting equipment if applicable

Some Safety Issues to Consider

- Diagnosis of this fault may require test driving the vehicle on the school grounds or on a hoist, both of which carry severe risks. Attempt this task only with full permission from your supervisor/instructor and follow all the guidelines exactly.
- Caution: If you are working in an area where there could be brake dust present (may contain asbestos, which has been determined to cause cancer when inhaled or ingested), ensure you wear and use all OSHA-approved asbestos protective/removal equipment.
- Lifting equipment such as vehicle jacks and stands, vehicle hoists, and engine hoists are important tools that increase productivity and make the job easier. However, they can also cause severe injury or death if used improperly. Make sure you follow the manufacturer's operation procedures. Also make sure you have your supervisor/instructor's permission to use any particular type of lifting equipment.
- Comply with personal and environmental safety practices associated with clothing; eye protection; hand tools; power equipment; proper ventilation; and the handling, storage, and disposal of chemicals/materials in accordance with federal, state, and local regulations.
- Always wear the correct protective eyewear and clothing and use the appropriate safety equipment, as well as fender covers, seat protectors, and floor mat protectors.
- Make sure you understand and observe all legislative and personal safety procedures when carrying out practical assignments. If you are unsure of what these are, ask your supervisor/instructor.

Performance Standard

0–No exposure: No information or practice provided during the program; complete training required

1–Exposure only: General information provided with no practice time; close supervision needed; additional training required

2–Limited practice: Has practiced job during training program; additional training required to develop skill

3–Moderately skilled: Has performed job independently during training program; limited additional training may be required

4–Skilled: Can perform job independently with no additional training

Student/intern information:

Name________________________ Date____________ Class________________

Vehicle used for this activity:

Year____________ Make________________________ Model________________

Odometer____________________ VIN ________________________

▶ TASK Inspect, adjust, repair, or replace air operated power divider (inter-axle differential) lockout assembly including diaphragms, seals, springs, yokes, pins, lines, hoses, fittings, and controls. NATEF 2D16

Time off________

Time on________

Total time________

CDX Tasksheet Number: H164

1. Reference the manufacturer's service information.
   a. Inspect the air operated power divider (inter-axle differential) lockout assembly including diaphragms, seals, springs, yokes, pins, lines, hoses, fittings, and controls. List your observations:

      ____
      ____
      ____
      ____
      ____

      i. Meets the manufacturer's specifications: Yes: _____ No: _____
      ii. Determine any necessary actions or corrections:

      ____
      ____
      ____

2. If directed by your instructor, adjust, repair, or replace the air operated power divider (inter-axle differential) lockout assembly including diaphragms, seals, springs, yokes, pins, lines, hoses, fittings, and controls in accordance with the specifications listed in the service information. List any difficulties you experienced during the replacement of these parts:

   ____
   ____
   ____
   ____
   ____

3. Discuss the findings with your instructor.

Performance Rating

CDX Tasksheet Number: H164

☐	☐	☐	☐	☐
0	1	2	3	4

Supervisor/instructor signature ________________________________ Date____________

Student/intern information:

Name____________________ Date__________ Class________________

Vehicle used for this activity:

Year__________ Make____________________ Model________________

Odometer__________________ VIN ________________________

▶ TASK Inspect, repair, or replace drive axle lubrication system: pump, troughs, collectors, slingers, tubes, and filters. NATEF 2D17

Time off__________

Time on__________

Total time__________

CDX Tasksheet Number: H165

1. Reference the manufacturer's service information.
   a. Inspect the drive axle lubrication system including the pump, troughs, collectors, slingers, tubes, and filters. List your observations:
      i. Meets the manufacturer's specifications: Yes: _____ No: _____
      ii. Determine any necessary actions or corrections:
2. If directed by your instructor, repair or replace the drive axle lubrication system including the pump, troughs, collectors, slingers, tubes, and filters in accordance with the specifications listed in the service information. List any difficulties that you experienced during the repair or replacement of these parts:
3. Discuss the findings with your instructor.

Performance Rating

CDX Tasksheet Number: H165

☐ 0 ☐ 1 ☐ 2 ☐ 3 ☐ 4

Supervisor/instructor signature ________________________ Date__________

Student/intern information:

Name________________ Date________ Class________________

Vehicle used for this activity:

Year__________ Make________________ Model________________

Odometer________________ VIN ________________

▶ TASK Inspect and replace drive axle shafts. NATEF 2D18

Time off________

Time on________

Total time________

CDX Tasksheet Number: H166

1. Remove drive axle shaft bolts or nuts (depends on type of axle arrangement).
2. Remove axle(s) from the differential carrier housing.
3. Inspect axle flange for distortion or rust build-up and mounting holes for ovality or elongation.
   a. Describe the condition of the axle flange: ________________
   b. Describe the condition of the mounting holes: ________________
4. If reusing the axle, clean any gasket material from the axle flange.
5. Inspect axle housing hub for damage to threaded holes or stripped or broken studs.
6. Inspect axle shaft for cracks and straightness.
   a. Describe the condition of the axle shaft: ________________
7. Inspect axle splines for damage or twisting (see Figure 1).
   a. Describe the condition of the axle splines: ________________

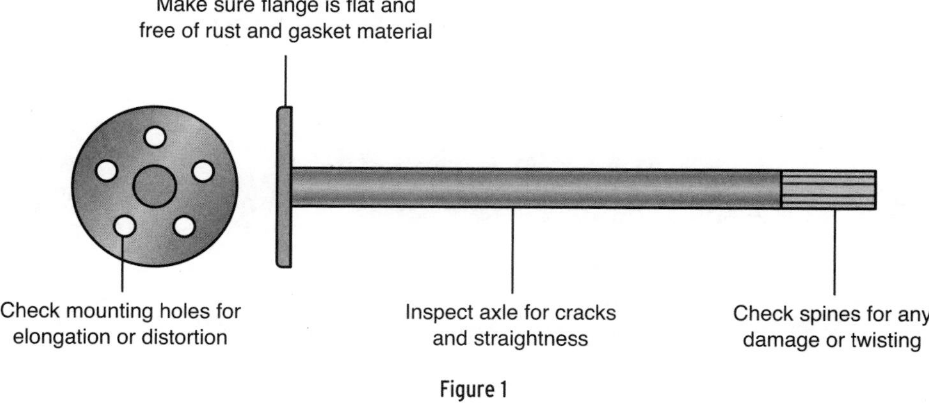
Make sure flange is flat and free of rust and gasket material
Check mounting holes for elongation or distortion
Inspect axle for cracks and straightness
Check spines for any damage or twisting

Figure 1

8. Reinstall axle and gasket with correct bolts or nuts and record torque specification according to manufacturer's service information.
    a. Torque specified: ________________ ft-lb/Nm

9. Refill differential with manufacturer's specified fluid to proper level.

10. If the axle is not within specification, list the procedure from the manufacturer's service information to correct the problem:
    ____
    ____
    ____
    ____

11. Discuss the findings with your instructor.

Performance Rating

CDX Tasksheet Number: H166

☐ 0 ☐ 1 ☐ 2 ☐ 3 ☐ 4

Supervisor/instructor signature ______________________________ Date ______________

Student/intern information:

Name____________________ Date________ Class____________

Vehicle used for this activity:

Year________ Make____________________ Model____________

Odometer__________________ VIN ________________________

▶ TASK Remove and replace wheel assembly; check rear wheel seal and axle flange gasket for leaks; perform needed action. NATEF 2D19

Time off________

Time on________

Total time________

CDX Tasksheet Number: H167

1. Reference the manufacturer's service information.
   a. Remove the wheel assembly.
   b. Check the rear wheel seal and axle flange gasket for leaks. List your observations:

      ____

      i. Meets the manufacturer's specifications: Yes: _____ No: _____
      ii. Determine any necessary actions or corrections:

      ____

2. If directed by your instructor, replace the wheel assembly in accordance with the specifications listed in the service information. List any difficulties you experienced during this task:

   ____

3. Discuss the findings with your instructor.

Performance Rating

CDX Tasksheet Number: H167

☐	☐	☐	☐	☐
0	1	2	3	4

Supervisor/instructor signature ________________________ Date________

Heavy Duty Drive Trains: Drive Axle 4

Student/intern information:

Name________________ Date________ Class____________

Vehicle used for this activity:

Year________ Make________________ Model____________

Odometer________________ VIN ________________

Time off________

Time on________

Total time________

Learning Objective / Task	CDX Tasksheet Number	2014 NATEF Priority Level	2014 NATEF Reference Number
• Identify causes of drive axle wheel bearing noise and check for damage; perform needed action.	H168	P-1	2D20
• Inspect and test drive axle temperature gauge, wiring harnesses, and sending unit/sensor; determine needed action.	H169	P-2	2D21
• Clean, inspect, lubricate, and replace wheel bearings; replace seals and wear rings; inspect and replace retaining hardware; adjust drive axle wheel bearings. Verify end play with dial indicator method.	H170	P-1	2D22

Materials Required

- Vehicle with possible transmission concern
- Vehicle manufacturer's service information
- Manufacturer-specific tools depending on the concern
- Vehicle lifting equipment if applicable

Some Safety Issues to Consider

- Diagnosis of this fault may require test driving the vehicle on the school grounds or on a hoist, both of which carry severe risks. Attempt this task only with full permission from your supervisor/instructor and follow all the guidelines exactly.
- Caution: If you are working in an area where there could be brake dust present (may contain asbestos, which has been determined to cause cancer when inhaled or ingested), ensure you wear and use all OSHA-approved asbestos protective/removal equipment.
- Lifting equipment such as vehicle jacks and stands, vehicle hoists, and engine hoists are important tools that increase productivity and make the job easier. However, they can also cause severe injury or death if used improperly. Make sure you follow the manufacturer's operation procedures. Also make sure you have your supervisor/instructor's permission to use any particular type of lifting equipment.
- Comply with personal and environmental safety practices associated with clothing; eye protection; hand tools; power equipment; proper ventilation; and the handling, storage, and disposal of chemicals/materials in accordance with federal, state, and local regulations.
- Always wear the correct protective eyewear and clothing and use the appropriate safety equipment, as well as fender covers, seat protectors, and floor mat protectors.
- Make sure you understand and observe all legislative and personal safety procedures when carrying out practical assignments. If you are unsure of what these are, ask your supervisor/instructor.

Performance Standard

0–No exposure: No information or practice provided during the program; complete training required
1–Exposure only: General information provided with no practice time; close supervision needed; additional training required
2–Limited practice: Has practiced job during training program; additional training required to develop skill
3–Moderately skilled: Has performed job independently during training program; limited additional training may be required
4–Skilled: Can perform job independently with no additional training

Student/intern information:

Name____________________ Date________ Class______________

Vehicle used for this activity:

Year________ Make____________________ Model____________

Odometer________________ VIN ____________________

▸ TASK Identify causes of drive axle wheel bearing noise and check for damage; perform needed action. NATEF 2D20

Time off________

Time on________

Total time________

CDX Tasksheet Number: H168

1. Reference the manufacturer's service information and/or component manufacturer's service information to identify the causes of drive axle wheel bearing noise.
   a. List all possible causes:

   b. List possible corrections:

2. Reference the manufacturer's service information.
   a. Check the drive axle wheel bearing for damage. List your observations:

      i. Meets the manufacturer's specifications: Yes: _____ No: _____
      ii. Determine any necessary actions or corrections:

3. Discuss the findings with your instructor.

Performance Rating

CDX Tasksheet Number: H168

☐ 0 ☐ 1 ☐ 2 ☐ 3 ☐ 4

Supervisor/instructor signature ____________________ Date________

Student/intern information:

Name_______________ Date_______ Class_______________

Vehicle used for this activity:

Year_______ Make_______________ Model_______________

Odometer_______________ VIN _______________

▶ TASK Inspect and test drive axle temperature gauge, wiring harnesses, and sending unit/sensor; determine needed action. NATEF 2D21

Time off_______

Time on_______

Total time_______

CDX Tasksheet Number: H169

1. Reference the manufacturer's service information.
   a. Inspect and test drive the axle temperature gauge, wiring harnesses, and sending unit/sensor. List your observations:

      i. Meets the manufacturer's specifications: Yes: _____ No: _____
      ii. Determine any necessary actions or corrections:

2. Discuss the findings with your instructor.

Performance Rating

CDX Tasksheet Number: H169

☐ 0 ☐ 1 ☐ 2 ☐ 3 ☐ 4

Supervisor/instructor signature _______________ Date_______

Student/intern information:

Name____________________ Date__________ Class________________

Vehicle used for this activity:

Year__________ Make____________________ Model________________

Odometer____________________ VIN ____________________

TASK Clean, inspect, lubricate, and replace wheel bearings; replace seals and wear rings; inspect and replace retaining hardware; adjust drive axle wheel bearings. Verify end play with dial indicator method. NATEF 2D22

Time off________

Time on________

Total time________

CDX Tasksheet Number: H170

1. Reference the manufacturer's service information.
   a. Remove, clean, inspect, and lubricate the wheel bearings. List your observations:

      i. Meets the manufacturer's specifications: Yes: _____ No: _____
      ii. Determine any necessary actions or corrections:

   b. If directed by your instructor, replace the wheel bearings, seals, and wear rings in accordance with the specifications listed in the service information.

   c. Inspect the retaining hardware. List your observations:

      i. Meets the manufacturer's specifications: Yes: _____ No: _____
      ii. Determine any necessary actions or corrections:

   d. If directed by your instructor, replace the retaining hardware in accordance with the specifications listed in the service information.

      i. List the procedure for adjusting the drive axle wheel bearings:

e. Adjust the drive axle wheel bearings to the manufacturer's specifications.

f. Verify end play with dial indicator method.

g. Have your instructor verify the wheel bearing end play.
Supervisor's/instructor's initials: ______________

2. Discuss the findings with your instructor.

Performance Rating

CDX Tasksheet Number: H170

☐ 0 ☐ 1 ☐ 2 ☐ 3 ☐ 4

Supervisor/instructor signature ______________________________ Date______________

Truck Electrical & Electronics, DT108

CONTENTS

Truck Electrical & Electronics: General Electric Systems

Student/intern information:

Name________ Date________ Class________

Vehicle used for this activity:

Year________ Make________ Model________

Odometer________ VIN ________

Learning Objective/Task	CDX Tasksheet Number	2014 NATEF Priority Level	2014 NATEF Reference Number
• Read and interpret electrical/electronic circuits using wiring diagrams.	H271	P-1	5A1
• Check continuity in electrical/electronic circuits using appropriate test equipment.	H272	P-1	5A2
• Check applied voltages, circuit voltages, and voltage drops in electrical/electronic circuits using appropriate test equipment.	H273	P-1	5A3
• Check current flow in electrical/electronic circuits and components using appropriate test equipment.	H274	P-1	5A4
• Check resistance in electrical/electronic circuits and components using appropriate test equipment.	H275	P-1	5A5
• Locate shorts, grounds, and opens in electrical/electronic circuits.	H276	P-1	5A6
• Identify parasitic (key-off) battery drain problems; perform tests; determine needed action.	H277	P-1	5A7
• Inspect and test fusible links, circuit breakers, relays, solenoids, and fuses; replace as needed.	H278	P-1	5A8
• Inspect and test spike suppression devices; replace as needed.	H279	P-3	5A9
• Check frequency and pulse width signal in electrical/electronic circuits using appropriate test equipment.	H280	P-3	5A10

Time off________

Time on________

Total time________

Materials Required

- Vehicle or simulator with electrical circuit concerns
- Vehicle manufacturer's service information including schematic wiring diagrams
- Digital volt-ohmmeter (DVOM), ammeter, current clamp, graphing multimeter (GMM), or digital storage oscilloscope (DSO)
- Electrical spare parts, including fuses, circuit breakers, relays, and solenoids
- Manufacturer-specific tools depending on the concern
- Vehicle lifting equipment, if applicable

Some Safety Issues to Consider

- Activities require you to measure electrical values. Always ensure that the instructor/supervisor checks test instrument connections prior to connecting power or taking measurements. High current flows can be dangerous; avoid accidental short circuits or grounding a battery's positive connections.
- Activities may require test driving the vehicle on the school grounds or on a hoist, both of which carry severe risks. Attempt this task only with full permission from your supervisor/instructor, and follow all the guidelines exactly.
- Lifting equipment such as vehicle jacks and stands, vehicle hoists, and engine hoists are important tools that increase productivity and make the job easier. However, they can also cause severe injury or death if used improperly. Make sure you follow the manufacturer's operation procedures. Also make sure you have your supervisor/instructor's permission to use any particular type of lifting equipment.
- Comply with personal and environmental safety practices associated with clothing; eye protection; hand tools; power equipment; proper ventilation; and the handling, storage, and disposal of chemicals/materials in accordance with federal, state, and local regulations.
- Always wear the correct protective eyewear and clothing and use the appropriate safety equipment, as well as fender covers, seat protectors, and floor mat protectors.
- Make sure you understand and observe all legislative and personal safety procedures when carrying out practical assignments. If you are unsure of what these are, ask your supervisor/instructor.

Performance Standard

0—No exposure: No information or practice provided during the program; complete training required
1—Exposure only: General information provided with no practice time; close supervision needed; additional training required
2—Limited practice: Has practiced job during training program; additional training required to develop skill
3—Moderately skilled: Has performed job independently during training program; limited additional training may be required
4—Skilled: Can perform job independently with no additional training

Student/intern information:

Name________________________ Date____________ Class________________________

Vehicle used for this activity:

Year______________ Make________________________ Model________________

Odometer________________________ VIN ________________________________

▸ TASK Read and interpret electrical/electronic circuits using wiring diagrams. **NATEF 5A1**

Time off________

Time on________

Total time________

CDX Tasksheet Number: H271

1. Ask your instructor to provide a wiring diagram or assign a circuit so you can print its wiring diagram. If your instructor has no preference, print a wiring diagram of your choice.
2. Using a red crayon or highlighter, trace all of the wires that are connected directly to power.
3. Using an orange crayon or highlighter, trace all of the wires that are switched to power.
4. Using a green crayon or highlighter, trace all of the wires that are connected directly to ground.
5. Using a yellow crayon or highlighter, trace all of the wires that are switched to ground.
6. Using a blue crayon or highlighter, trace all of the wires that are variable wires, such as sensor outputs.
7. If any wires switch polarity (such as a power window motor), trace those wires with alternating orange and yellow.
8. Have your supervisor/instructor verify satisfactory completion of this procedure.

Performance Rating

CDX Tasksheet Number: H271

☐	☐	☐	☐	☐
0	1	2	3	4

Supervisor/instructor signature ________________________________ Date________

Student/intern information:

Name____________________ Date__________ Class________________

Vehicle used for this activity:

Year__________ Make____________________ Model________________

Odometer____________________ VIN ____________________

▶ TASK Check continuity in electrical/electronic circuits using appropriate test equipment.

NATEF 5A2

Time off________

Time on________

Total time________

CDX Tasksheet Number: H272

Note: This tasksheet may require the use of a vehicle or simulator with electrical faults. Ask your instructor which vehicle or simulator you are to use.

1. Prepare the DVOM to measure continuity. Continuity is measured using the ohms scale on the DVOM.
   a. What are the steps necessary in preparing your DVOM to measure continuity?

   b. Explain how to connect the meter leads to a component in a circuit:

   c. What readings would you expect the DVOM to indicate when the circuit has:
      i. Good continuity: __________
      ii. Poor continuity: __________
      iii. No continuity: __________

2. Using the appropriate service information, check for circuit continuity in electrical/electronic circuits. Ask your instructor/supervisor for a vehicle and circuits to check continuity.
   a. Circuit 1:
      i. Name the component with the concern: __________
      ii. What is the component specification? __________
      iii. What is the actual resistance reading of the component? __________
      iv. Is the reading within the manufacturer's specification? Yes: _____ No: _____
      v. If no, determine any necessary action(s):

   b. Circuit 2:
      i. Name the component with the concern: __________
      ii. What is the component specification? __________
      iii. What is the actual resistance reading of the component? __________
      iv. Is the reading within the manufacturer's specification? Yes: _____ No: _____
      v. If no, determine any necessary action(s):

c. Circuit 3:
   i. Name the component with the concern: ______
   ii. What is the component specification? ______
   iii. What is the actual resistance reading of the component? ______
   iv. Is the reading within the manufacturer's specification? Yes: _____ No: _____
   v. If no, determine any necessary action(s):
      ______
      ______
      ______

3. Return the vehicle to its beginning condition, and return any tools you used to their proper locations.

4. Discuss the findings with the instructor.

Performance Rating

CDX Tasksheet Number: H272

☐ 0 ☐ 1 ☐ 2 ☐ 3 ☐ 4

Supervisor/instructor signature ______ Date______

Student/intern information:

Name______________________________ Date__________ Class______________________

Vehicle used for this activity:

Year__________ Make______________________________ Model__________________

Odometer______________________ VIN ______________________________

▶ TASK Check applied voltages, circuit voltages, and voltage drops in electrical/electronic circuits using appropriate test equipment. **NATEF 5A3**

Time off__________

Time on__________

Total time__________

CDX Tasksheet Number: H273

Note: This tasksheet may require the use of a vehicle or simulator with electrical faults. Ask your instructor which vehicle or simulator you are to use.

1. Using the appropriate service information for the vehicle you are working on, research how to check applied voltages, circuit voltages, and voltage drops in electrical/electronic circuits. List the circuit or circuits that your instructor indicates you should check.
   a. Applied voltages:
   ____
   ____
   b. Circuit voltages:
   ____
   ____
   c. Voltage drops:
   ____
   ____
2. Prepare the DVOM to measure DC volts.
   a. What are the steps necessary in preparing your DVOM to measure voltage?
   ____
   ____
   ____
3. Have your supervisor/instructor verify your research.
   Supervisor/instructor's initials: __________
4. Using the appropriate service information, check applied voltages, circuit voltages, and voltage drops in electrical/electronic circuits. Ask your instructor/supervisor for a vehicle and circuits to check.
   a. Applied voltages: On the assigned circuit listed in 1a above, measure the applied voltages at each of the loads in the circuit. List the name of each load and measured voltage:
   ____
   ____
   ____
      i. Is the above reading within specifications? Yes: _____ No: _____
      ii. Determine any necessary action(s):
      ____
      ____
      ____

b. Circuit voltages: On the assigned circuit listed in 1b on the previous page, measure the circuit voltages at the input of each of the components in the circuit. List the name of each component and measured voltage:

____
____
____

   i. Is the above reading within specifications? Yes: _____ No: _____
   ii. Determine any necessary action(s):

   ____
   ____
   ____

c. Voltage drops: On the assigned circuit listed in 1c on the previous page, measure the voltage drop across each of the loads in the circuit. List the name of each load and voltage measured:

____
____
____

   i. Is the above reading within specifications? Yes: _____ No: _____
   ii. Determine any necessary action(s):

   ____
   ____
   ____

5. Return the vehicle or simulator to its beginning condition, and return any tools you used to their proper locations.

6. Discuss the findings with the instructor.

Performance Rating

CDX Tasksheet Number: H273

☐	☐	☐	☐	☐
0	1	2	3	4

Supervisor/instructor signature ______________________________ Date__________

Student/intern information:

Name____________________ Date__________ Class____________________

Vehicle used for this activity:

Year__________ Make____________________ Model____________________

Odometer____________________ VIN ____________________

▶ TASK Check current flow in electrical/electronic circuits and components using appropriate test equipment.

NATEF 5A4

Time off__________

Time on__________

Total time__________

CDX Tasksheet Number: H274

Note: This tasksheet may require the use of a vehicle or simulator with electrical faults. Ask your instructor which vehicle or simulator you are to use. Be sure to follow the correct steps for connecting your DVOM or ammeter to check for amperage/current flow. Have your supervisor/instructor check your connections. Improper connection of the DVOM may damage your meter.

1. Using the appropriate service information for the vehicle you are working on, research how to measure current flow in electrical/electronic circuits. List the three circuits that your instructor indicates you should check.

   Circuit #1: ____________________
   Circuit #2: ____________________
   Circuit #3: ____________________

   a. Describe how the leads must be connected in the circuit to measure current flow:

   b. DVOM current measurements:
   Draw a diagram showing the lead connection and circuit.

   c. DVOM with inductive clamp current measurements:
   Draw a diagram showing the lead connection and circuit.

2. Prepare the DVOM to measure DC current.
   a. What are the steps necessary in preparing your DVOM to measure current?

3. Have your supervisor/instructor verify your research.
   Supervisor/instructor's initials: __________

4. Using the appropriate service information, check current flow in electrical/electronic circuits and components. Ask your instructor/supervisor for a vehicle and circuits to check.

   Caution: Ensure that the meter is connected correctly when measuring current draw. Damage may occur to circuits and the test equipment if connections are made incorrectly.

   a. On Circuit #1 from the previous page, measure the current flow in the circuit. List the name of the circuit and current flow measured:

      ____

      i. Is the above reading within specifications? Yes: _____ No: _____
      ii. Determine any necessary action(s):

      ____
      ____
      ____

   b. On Circuit #2 from the previous page, measure the current flow in the circuit. List the name of the circuit and current flow measured:

      ____

      i. Is the above reading within specifications? Yes: _____ No: _____
      ii. Determine any necessary action(s):

      ____
      ____
      ____

   c. On Circuit #3 from the previous page, measure the current flow in the circuit. List the name of the circuit and current flow measured:

      ____

      i. Is the above reading within specifications? Yes: _____ No: _____
      ii. Determine any necessary action(s):

      ____
      ____
      ____

5. Return the vehicle or simulator to its beginning condition, and return any tools you used to their proper locations.

6. Discuss the findings with the instructor.

Performance Rating

CDX Tasksheet Number: H274

☐	☐	☐	☐	☐
0	1	2	3	4

Supervisor/instructor signature ______________________________ Date__________

Student/intern information:

Name________________________ Date__________ Class________________

Vehicle used for this activity:

Year__________ Make____________________ Model________________

Odometer________________________ VIN ________________________

▸ TASK Check resistance in electrical/electronic circuits and components using appropriate test equipment. **NATEF 5A5**

Time off__________

Time on__________

Total time__________

CDX Tasksheet Number: H275

Note: This tasksheet may require the use of a vehicle or simulator with electrical faults. Ask your instructor which vehicle or simulator you are to use.

1. Using the appropriate service information for the vehicle you are working on, research how to check resistance in electrical/electronic circuits and components. List the three components that your instructor indicates you should check.
   Component #1 ________________________
   Component #2 ________________________
   Component #3 ________________________

   a. DVOM resistance measurements:
      Draw a diagram showing the lead connection and circuit.

2. Prepare the DVOM to measure resistance.
   a. What are the steps necessary in preparing your DVOM to measure resistance?
      ____
      ____
      ____

3. Explain why resistance measurements should only be made with power disconnected from the circuit.
   ____
   ____
   ____

4. Have your supervisor/instructor verify your research.
   Supervisor/instructor's initials: __________

5. Using the appropriate service information, check resistance in electrical/electronic circuits and components. Ask your instructor/supervisor for a vehicle and circuits to check.

   Caution: Ensure that the meter is correctly connected and no power is applied to the circuit under test when measuring resistance.

   a. On Component #1 from the previous page, measure the resistance in the component. List the name of the component and resistance measured:

      ____

      i. Is the above reading within specifications? Yes: _____ No: _____
      ii. Determine any necessary action(s):

      ____
      ____
      ____

   b. On Component #2 from the previous page, measure the resistance in the component. List the name of the component and resistance measured:

      ____

      i. Is the above reading within specifications? Yes: _____ No: _____
      ii. Determine any necessary action(s):

      ____
      ____
      ____

   c. On Component #3 from the previous page, measure the resistance in the component. List the name of the component and resistance measured:

      ____

      i. Is the above reading within specifications? Yes: _____ No: _____
      ii. Determine any necessary action(s):

      ____
      ____
      ____

6. Return the vehicle to its beginning condition, and return any tools you used to their proper locations.

7. Discuss the findings with the instructor.

Performance Rating

CDX Tasksheet Number: H275

☐ 0 ☐ 1 ☐ 2 ☐ 3 ☐ 4

Supervisor/instructor signature ______________________________ Date__________

Student/intern information:

Name__________ Date__________ Class__________

Vehicle used for this activity:

Year__________ Make__________ Model__________

Odometer__________ VIN__________

▶ TASK Locate shorts, grounds, and opens in electrical/electronic circuits. **NATEF 5A6**

Time off__________

Time on__________

Total time__________

CDX Tasksheet Number: H276

Note: This tasksheet may require the use of a vehicle or simulator with electrical faults. Ask your instructor which vehicle or simulator you are to use.

1. What is the customer concern for this tasksheet?

2. Identify or isolate the circuit or circuits involved.
   a. What circuit component(s) is (are) not working as designed?

3. Using the appropriate service information, locate the wiring diagram for the circuit(s) you identified in Step 2.

4. Test the circuit to locate the fault.
   a. List the cause of the fault and the steps you took to identify it.

5. Determine any necessary actions to repair the fault:

6. Return the vehicle to its beginning condition, and return any tools you used to their proper locations.

7. Discuss the findings with the instructor.

Performance Rating

CDX Tasksheet Number: H276

☐ 0 ☐ 1 ☐ 2 ☐ 3 ☐ 4

Supervisor/instructor signature__________ Date__________

Student/intern information:

Name____________________ Date________ Class____________

Vehicle used for this activity:

Year________ Make____________________ Model____________

Odometer__________________ VIN ____________________

▶ TASK Identify parasitic (key-off) battery drain problems; perform tests; determine needed action. **NATEF 5A7**

Time off________

Time on________

Total time________

CDX Tasksheet Number: H277

Note: Be sure to follow the correct steps for connecting your DVOM to check for amperage/current flow. Have your supervisor/instructor check your connections. Improper connection of the DVOM may damage your meter.

1. Research key-off battery drain (parasitic drain) checks in the appropriate service information.
   a. List the maximum allowable key-off battery drain (parasitic drain) for the vehicle/simulator that has been assigned to you. What is the maximum allowable drain? __________ mA
   b. What is the specified time for the last module to go to sleep? __________ sec/min
2. List the appropriate steps to measure the key-off battery drain (parasitic drain):

   ____

   ____

   ____
3. Using the steps listed, measure the key-off battery drain (parasitic drain).
   a. What is the actual drain? __________ mA
   b. Is this reading within specifications? Yes: _____ No: _____
      i. If no, identify the faulty circuit by pulling and replacing fuses one at a time. Watch the amps reading on the meter to see if it drops. If it drops substantially, you should investigate that circuit further by disconnecting the loads and tracing the wires.
4. If pulling the fuses does not identify the faulty circuit, disconnect unfused wires one at a time, such as the alternator output wire and the ignition switch feed wire.
5. List the steps you took to diagnose the cause of the parasitic draw and their results:

   ____

   ____

   ____

   ____

   ____
6. Determine any necessary action(s):

   ____

   ____

   ____

7. What would the customer concern be that would require you to perform this test?

8. Have your supervisor/instructor verify satisfactory completion of this procedure, any observations found, and any necessary action(s) recommended.

Performance Rating

CDX Tasksheet Number: H277

☐ 0 ☐ 1 ☐ 2 ☐ 3 ☐ 4

Supervisor/instructor signature __________ Date__________

Student/intern information:

Name________________________________ Date__________ Class______________________

Vehicle used for this activity:

Year____________ Make________________________________ Model______________________

Odometer__________________________ VIN ________________________________

Time off________

Time on________

Total time________

▸ TASK Inspect and test fusible links, circuit breakers, relays, solenoids, and fuses; replace as needed. **NATEF 5A8**

CDX Tasksheet Number: H278

Note: This tasksheet may require the use of a vehicle or simulator with electrical faults. Ask your instructor which vehicle or simulator you are to use.

1. Using the appropriate service information, locate the fuse panel(s), circuit breakers, fusible links, relays, and solenoids for the vehicle/simulator you are assigned to.

    a. List the fuse panel, circuit breaker, fusible link, relay, and solenoid locations for this vehicle/simulator.

2. Determine and list any circuit protection devices that are defective (open).

    Note: Circuit protection devices do not normally wear out. If a circuit protection device is found to be faulty, too much current was/is present. You should determine the reason for the fault.

3. What is the rating (size) of the circuit protection device for this circuit?

4. Is the correct size installed? Yes: _____ No: _____

5. Determine the cause for the circuit protection device to fail. List your findings.

6. Determine and list any relay or solenoids that are defective.

7. Determine the cause for the relay or solenoid to fail. List your findings.

____

____

____

____

8. Return the vehicle to its beginning condition, and return any tools you used to their proper locations.

9. Discuss the findings with the instructor.

Performance Rating

CDX Tasksheet Number: H278

☐ 0 ☐ 1 ☐ 2 ☐ 3 ☐ 4

Supervisor/instructor signature ____________________ Date__________

Student/intern information:

Name________________ Date________ Class____________

Vehicle used for this activity:

Year________ Make________________ Model____________

Odometer________________ VIN ________________

▶ TASK Inspect and test spike suppression devices; replace as needed. **NATEF 5A9**

Time off________

Time on________

Total time________

CDX Tasksheet Number: H279

Note: This tasksheet may require the use of a vehicle or simulator with electrical faults. Ask your instructor which vehicle or simulator you are to use.

1. Using the appropriate service information for the vehicle/simulator you are working on, research how to inspect and test spike suppression devices.
   a. List the types of spike suppression used on the vehicle/simulator.
   b. What test would be used for each type of suppression device?
2. Have your supervisor/instructor verify your research.
   Supervisor/instructor's initials: ________
3. Test the suppression devices. List your findings.
   Note: Suppression devices do not normally wear out. If a suppression device is found to be faulty, you should determine the reason for the fault.
4. Determine any necessary action(s):
5. Return the vehicle to its beginning condition, and return any tools you used to their proper locations.
6. Discuss the findings with the instructor.

Performance Rating

CDX Tasksheet Number: H279

☐ 0 ☐ 1 ☐ 2 ☐ 3 ☐ 4

Supervisor/instructor signature ________________ Date________

Student/intern information:

Name________________ Date________ Class____________

Vehicle used for this activity:

Year________ Make________________ Model____________

Odometer________________ VIN ________________

▸ TASK Check frequency and pulse width signal in electrical/electronic circuits using appropriate test equipment. **NATEF 5A10**

Time off________

Time on________

Total time________

CDX Tasksheet Number: H280

Note: This tasksheet may require the use of a vehicle or simulator with electrical faults. Ask your instructor which vehicle or simulator you are to use.

1. Prepare the vehicle and/or circuit for the tests to be carried out.

2. Using the appropriate service information, research the correct procedures for measuring frequency and pulse width, and list the steps.

3. Carry out the tests using a graphing multimeter (GMM) or digital storage oscilloscope (DSO). The tests should include:
   - Frequency data
   - Pulse width
   - Output signal

   a. What are the frequency and pulse width?
      Frequency: ________
      Pulse width: ________

   b. Is this within the manufacturer's specifications?
      Yes: ____ No: ____

4. Determine any necessary action(s):

5. Return the vehicle to its beginning condition, and return any tools you used to their proper locations.

6. Discuss the findings with the instructor.

Performance Rating

CDX Tasksheet Number: H280

☐ 0 ☐ 1 ☐ 2 ☐ 3 ☐ 4

Supervisor/instructor signature ________________ Date________

Truck Electrical & Electronics: Battery

Student/intern information:

Name__________ Date__________ Class__________

Vehicle used for this activity:

Year__________ Make__________ Model__________

Odometer__________ VIN __________

Time off__________

Time on__________

Total time__________

Learning Objective/Task	CDX Tasksheet Number	2014 NATEF Priority Level	2014 NATEF Reference Number
• Identify battery type; perform appropriate battery load test; determine needed action.	H281	P-1	5B1
• Determine battery state of charge using an open circuit voltage test.	H282	P-1	5B2
• Inspect, clean, and service battery; replace as needed.	H283	P-1	5B3
• Inspect and clean battery boxes, mounts, and hold downs; repair or replace as needed.	H284	P-1	5B4
• Charge battery using appropriate method for battery type.	H285	P-1	5B5
• Inspect, test, and clean battery cables and connectors; repair or replace as needed.	H286	P-1	5B6
• Jump start a vehicle using jumper cables and a booster battery or appropriate auxiliary power supply using proper safety procedures.	H287	P-1	5B7
• Perform battery capacitance test; determine needed action.	H288	P-2	5B8
• Identify and test low voltage disconnect (LVD) systems; determine needed repair.	H289	P-2	5B9

Materials Required

- Vehicle(s) with possible battery concern
- Vehicle manufacturer's service information
- Battery hydrometer, digital volt-ohmmeter (DVOM), conductance/capacitance tester, slow and fast chargers, jumper cables, booster battery
- Manufacturer-specific tools depending on the concern
- Personal protective equipment (PPE)

Some Safety Issues to Consider

- Diagnosis of this fault may require running the engine and managing an environment of dangerous gases and chemicals that carry severe risks. Attempt this task only with full permission from your supervisor/instructor, and follow all the guidelines exactly.
- Use extreme caution when working around batteries. Immediately remove any electrolyte that may come in contact with you. Electrolyte is a mixture of sulphuric acid and water. Batteries may produce explosive mixtures of gas containing hydrogen; avoid creating any sparks around batteries. Please consult with the shop safety and emergency procedures when working with or around batteries.
- Make sure you follow the manufacturer's operation procedures. Also make sure you have your supervisor/instructor's permission to use any particular type of lifting equipment.

- Comply with personal and environmental safety practices associated with clothing; eye protection; hand tools; power equipment; proper ventilation; and the handling, storage, and disposal of chemicals/materials in accordance with federal, state, and local regulations.
- Always wear the correct protective eyewear and clothing, and use the appropriate safety equipment, as well as fender covers, seat protectors, and floor mat protectors.
- Make sure you understand and observe all legislative and personal safety procedures when carrying out practical assignments. If you are unsure of what these are, ask your supervisor/instructor.

Performance Standard

0–No exposure: No information or practice provided during the program; complete training required

1–Exposure only: General information provided with no practice time; close supervision needed; additional training required

2–Limited practice: Has practiced job during training program; additional training required to develop skill

3–Moderately skilled: Has performed job independently during training program; limited additional training may be required

4–Skilled: Can perform job independently with no additional training

Student/intern information:

Name____________________ Date__________ Class________________

Vehicle used for this activity:

Year__________ Make____________________ Model________________

Odometer____________________ VIN ____________________

▶ TASK Identify battery type; perform appropriate battery load test; determine needed action.

NATEF 5B1

Time off________

Time on________

Total time________

CDX Tasksheet Number: H281

1. Using the appropriate service information, research and confirm proper battery capacity for the vehicle application. List the specified battery size and ratings.
2. List the rating of the battery you are testing: __________ CCAs
3. Perform the battery load test following the testing equipment's test instructions. List the test results:

   Note: Battery load testing is used to determine if the battery has the capacity to handle all of the electrical requirements while the vehicle is being operated.
4. Does the battery meet the manufacturer's specifications? Yes: _____ No: _____
5. Determine any necessary action(s):
6. Return the vehicle to its beginning condition, and return any tools you used to their proper locations.
7. Discuss the findings with the instructor.

Performance Rating

CDX Tasksheet Number: H281

☐ 0 ☐ 1 ☐ 2 ☐ 3 ☐ 4

Supervisor/instructor signature ____________________ Date__________

Student/intern information:

Name____________________ Date__________ Class____________________

Vehicle used for this activity:

Year__________ Make____________________ Model____________________

Odometer____________________ VIN ____________________

▶ TASK Determine battery state of charge using an open circuit voltage test. NATEF 5B2

Time off__________

Time on__________

Total time__________

CDX Tasksheet Number: H282

Note: This tasksheet may require the use of a vehicle or simulator with electrical faults. Ask your instructor which vehicle or simulator you are to use.

1. Locate "Open Circuit Voltage Test" in the appropriate service information. List the steps for this procedure.

   Note: Open circuit voltage testing should not be used to make a final determination for battery replacement.

   ____

   ____

   ____

   ____

2. Make sure the engine is off and the battery is stabilized. If the battery has just been recharged, you must remove the surface charge. Turning the headlights on for 30 seconds can be used to remove the surface charge of a battery. Wait at least 10 minutes after removing the surface charge before measuring the open circuit voltage. Follow the manufacturer's recommendations closely.

3. Prepare the DVOM to measure voltage.

4. Measure the battery voltage with the meter. Place the red lead on the positive post/terminal and the black lead on the negative post/terminal.

   a. What is the measured voltage (open circuit voltage) of the battery? __________ volts

5. The chart below represents the open circuit voltage of the battery. Please mark the state of charge of the battery as it relates to the voltage measured.

12.6V or greater	100% charge	
12.4-12.6V	75-100% charge	
12.2-12.4V	50-75% charge	
12.0-12.2V	25-50% charge	
11.7-12.0V	0-25% charge	
11.7-0.0V	0% or no charge	

6. Determine any necessary action(s): ____________________

7. Return the vehicle to its beginning condition, and return any tools you used to their proper locations.

8. Discuss the findings with the instructor.

Performance Rating

CDX Tasksheet Number: H282

☐ 0 ☐ 1 ☐ 2 ☐ 3 ☐ 4

Supervisor/instructor signature ____________________ Date ____________

Student/intern information:

Name____________________ Date________ Class______________

Vehicle used for this activity:

Year________ Make____________________ Model______________

Odometer__________________ VIN ________________________

▸ TASK Inspect, clean, and service battery; replace as needed.

NATEF 5B3

Time off________

Time on________

Total time________

CDX Tasksheet Number: H283

1. Prepare the vehicle for the task.
2. Research the recommended process for servicing the battery in the appropriate service information or other available data. List the steps.
3. Inspect, clean, fill, and/or replace battery, as required. Note your observations.
4. Determine any necessary further action(s).
5. Return the vehicle to its beginning condition, and return any tools you used to their proper locations.
6. Discuss the findings with the instructor.

Performance Rating

CDX Tasksheet Number: H283

☐ 0 ☐ 1 ☐ 2 ☐ 3 ☐ 4

Supervisor/instructor signature ________________________ Date________

Student/intern information:

Name_______________ Date_______ Class_______________

Vehicle used for this activity:

Year_______ Make_______________ Model_______________

Odometer_______________ VIN _______________

TASK Inspect and clean battery boxes, mounts, and hold downs; repair or replace as needed.

NATEF 5B4

Time off_______

Time on_______

Total time_______

CDX Tasksheet Number: H284

1. Research inspecting and cleaning battery boxes, mounts, and hold-downs.
2. List the steps for inspecting and cleaning battery boxes, mounts, and hold-downs.

   ____

   ____

   ____
3. Determine whether the battery should be removed to allow this task to be performed. Follow the manufacturer's recommendations.
4. Inspect the battery hold-down hardware and the battery tray. List your findings and any necessary actions:

   ____

   ____

   ____
5. Clean the battery, battery tray, and hold-down hardware with a suitable cleaner or by mixing baking soda and water. Be careful when using baking soda as it is a acid neutralizer if introduced into the cells.

   Note: The consistency of the baking soda and water should be like a paste. The use of a small brush will help the cleaning process.
6. Rinse the components with clean water. Wipe the components dry. Do not use compressed air.
   a. Have your supervisor/instructor check your work.
      Supervisor/instructor's initials: ________
7. Install the battery (if removed) and hold-down hardware. Reconnect the cables as outlined in the service information.
8. Return any tools you used to their proper locations.
9. Discuss the findings with the instructor.

Performance Rating

CDX Tasksheet Number: H284

☐ 0 ☐ 1 ☐ 2 ☐ 3 ☐ 4

Supervisor/instructor signature _______________ Date_______

Student/intern information:

Name________________________ Date__________ Class________________

Vehicle used for this activity:

Year__________ Make________________________ Model________________

Odometer____________________ VIN ________________________

▶ TASK Charge battery using appropriate method for battery type. **NATEF 5B5**

Time off________

Time on________

Total time________

CDX Tasksheet Number: H285

Note: You may use either a vehicle with a discharged battery or an assigned battery that is out of a vehicle. Recharging a battery differs from manufacturer to manufacturer. It is important that you follow the recharging steps recommended by the manufacturer of the battery that is assigned to you. Be careful when attempting to charge a battery. Hooking the charger up incorrectly could cause injury to eyes and skin.

1. Using the appropriate service information, research slow and/or fast battery charging for this vehicle. Follow all directions.
   a. List the steps for recharging the battery.
   ____
   ____
   ____

2. List the voltage of each battery that you will be charging: ______________ V

3. What method is required for recharging the battery: slow charge or fast charge?
   ____

4. List the steps for charging at the rate determined in Step 2.
   ____
   ____
   ____

5. Have your supervisor/instructor check your steps for recharging the battery.
   Supervisor/instructor's initials: __________

6. Charge the battery according to the manufacturer's recommendations.
   a. How long did the battery take to charge? ______________________
   b. What was the highest amperage reading during charging?______________ amps
   c. What was the lowest amperage reading during charging? ______________ amps
   d. How did you determine the battery was fully charged?
   ____
   ____
   ____
   ____

7. Determine any necessary action(s):
____
____
____
____

8. Return any tools you used to their proper locations.

9. Discuss the findings with the instructor.

Performance Rating

CDX Tasksheet Number: H285

☐	☐	☐	☐	☐
0	1	2	3	4

Supervisor/instructor signature _______________ Date_______________

Student/intern information:

Name________________ Date________ Class____________

Vehicle used for this activity:

Year________ Make________________ Model____________

Odometer________________ VIN ________________

Time off________

Time on________

Total time________

▶ TASK Inspect, test, and clean battery cables and connectors; repair or replace as needed.

NATEF 5B6

CDX Tasksheet Number: H286

1. Research inspecting, testing, cleaning, and repair or replacement of battery cables and connectors. List the steps.

2. Determine whether the battery should be removed to allow this task to be performed. Follow the manufacturer's recommendations.

3. Inspect the battery cables and connectors. List your findings and determine any necessary actions:

4. Clean the battery cables and connectors with a suitable cleaner or by mixing baking soda and water.

   Note: The consistency of the baking soda and water should be like a paste. The use of a small brush will help the cleaning process.

5. Use a battery terminal tool to scrape both the battery posts and mating battery cable connections clean. When finished, there should be no black lead oxide (which is an insulator) remaining.

6. Have your supervisor/instructor check your work.
   Supervisor/instructor's initials: ________

7. Install the battery (if removed) and hold-down hardware. Reconnect the cables as outlined in the service information.

8. Return any tools you used to their proper locations.

9. Discuss the findings with the instructor.

Performance Rating

CDX Tasksheet Number: H286

☐ 0 ☐ 1 ☐ 2 ☐ 3 ☐ 4

Supervisor/instructor signature ________________ Date________

Student/intern information:

Name____________________ Date__________ Class________________

Vehicle used for this activity:

Year__________ Make____________________ Model________________

Odometer____________________ VIN ________________________

▶ TASK Jump start a vehicle using jumper cables and a booster battery or appropriate auxiliary power supply using proper safety procedures. **NATEF 5B7**

Time off__________

Time on__________

Total time__________

CDX Tasksheet Number: H287

1. Locate "starting a vehicle with a dead battery" or "jump-starting procedures" in the appropriate service information for the vehicle you are working on.
   Caution: Some vehicle manufacturers prohibit jump-starting of their vehicles. If this is the case, inform your supervisor/instructor.
2. List the steps as outlined in the service information.
3. List the voltage of the starting system on the vehicle being jumped: __________ V
4. Have your supervisor/instructor verify the steps for the vehicle assigned to you. Supervisor/instructor's initials: __________
5. Connect the jumper cables as outlined in the service information or connect the auxiliary power supply (jump box) as was outlined in the service information.
6. Explain why the last connection to the dead battery is away from the battery, preferably on a solid, non-painted metal component on the engine.
7. Start the engine.
8. Remove the cables in the reverse order as they were installed.
9. Return the vehicle to its beginning condition, and return any tools you used to their proper locations.
10. Discuss the findings with the instructor.

Performance Rating

CDX Tasksheet Number: H287

☐ 0 ☐ 1 ☐ 2 ☐ 3 ☐ 4

Supervisor/instructor signature ________________________ Date__________

Student/intern information:

Name________________ Date________ Class________

Vehicle used for this activity:

Year________ Make________________ Model________

Odometer________________ VIN ________________

▶ TASK Perform battery capacitance test; determine needed action. **NATEF 5B8**

Time off________

Time on________

Total time________

CDX Tasksheet Number: H288

1. Describe the customer concern, if known:

2. Using the appropriate service information, research and confirm proper battery capacity for the vehicle application. List the specified size and ratings:

3. Perform the battery conductance test, following the testing equipment's test instructions. List your observations. Always be mindful of safety when working in or around the battery area. Wear appropriate clothing and eye protection.

    a. CCA or CA rating of battery in vehicle: ________ CCA or CA

    b. Measured CCA or CA of battery: ________ CCA or CA

    c. Does the battery meet specifications? Yes: ____ No: ____

4. Determine any necessary action(s):

5. Return the vehicle to its beginning condition, and return any tools you used to their proper locations.

6. Discuss the findings with the instructor.

Performance Rating

CDX Tasksheet Number: H288

☐ 0 ☐ 1 ☐ 2 ☐ 3 ☐ 4

Supervisor/instructor signature ________________ Date________

Student/intern information:

Name__________ Date__________ Class__________

Vehicle used for this activity:

Year__________ Make__________ Model__________

Odometer__________ VIN __________

▶ TASK Identify and test low voltage disconnect (LVD) systems; determine needed repair.

NATEF 5B9

Time off__________

Time on__________

Total time__________

CDX Tasksheet Number: H289

Note: Low voltage disconnects (LVDs) are designed to protect batteries from excessive voltage draw.

1. Check to make sure that a corrosion inhibitor is present to prevent battery acid from corroding the connections. The corrosion inhibitor is usually mounted in the battery box.
    a. Inhibitor present? Yes: _____ No: _____
    b. If the inhibitor is not present, consult manufacturer guidelines for the correct inhibitor to use.
2. Connect a DVOM or voltmeter to the sense terminal (depending on the model of the LVD) and the ground terminal.
3. Connect a carbon pile or some way of creating a parasitic load to the battery. Monitor the voltage for a decrease and observe the set point indicator light.
4. When the indicator light switches from off to on, record the reading of the set point.
    a. Voltage recorded: __________ volts
    b. Manufacturer recommended set point voltage: __________ volts
    c. If adjustment is necessary, consult and record manufacturer guidelines for adjusting to the proper set point voltage.

    ____

    ____

    ____
5. Discuss your findings with your instructor.

Performance Rating

CDX Tasksheet Number: H289

☐	☐	☐	☐	☐
0	1	2	3	4

Supervisor/instructor signature __________ Date__________

Truck Electrical & Electronics: Starting System

Student/intern information:

Name__________ Date__________ Class__________

Vehicle used for this activity:

Year__________ Make__________ Model__________

Odometer__________ VIN __________

Learning Objective/Task	CDX Tasksheet Number	2014 NATEF Priority Level	2014 NATEF Reference Number
• Perform starter circuit cranking voltage and voltage drop tests; determine needed action.	H290	P-1	5C1
• Inspect and test components (key switch, push button, and/or magnetic switch) and wires and harnesses in the starter control circuit; replace as needed.	H291	P-2	5C2
• Inspect and test starter relays and solenoids/switches; replace as needed.	H292	P-1	5C3
• Remove and replace starter; inspect flywheel ring gear or flex plate.	H293	P-1	5C4

Time off__________

Time on__________

Total time__________

Materials Required

- Vehicle(s) with possible starter concern
- Vehicle manufacturer's service information
- Digital volt-ohmmeter (DVOM), ammeter for starter circuits, test lamp, starter circuit spare parts
- Manufacturer-specific tools depending on the concern
- Personal protective equipment (PPE)

Some Safety Issues to Consider

- Activities may require running the engine and managing an environment of rotating equipment and large current draw, which carry severe risks. Attempt this task only with full permission from your supervisor/instructor, and follow all the guidelines exactly.
- Use extreme caution when working around batteries. Immediately remove any electrolyte that may come in contact with you. Electrolyte is a mixture of sulphuric acid and water. Batteries may produce explosive mixtures of gas containing hydrogen; avoid creating any sparks around batteries. Consult with the shop safety and emergency procedures when working with or around batteries.
- Make sure you follow the manufacturer's operation procedures. Also make sure you have your supervisor/instructor's permission to use any particular type of lifting equipment.
- Comply with personal and environmental safety practices associated with clothing; eye protection; hand tools; power equipment; proper ventilation; and the handling, storage, and disposal of chemicals/materials in accordance with federal, state, and local regulations.
- Always wear the correct protective eyewear and clothing, and use the appropriate safety equipment, as well as fender covers, seat protectors, and floor mat protectors.
- Make sure you understand and observe all legislative and personal safety procedures when carrying out practical assignments. If you are unsure of what these are, ask your supervisor/instructor.

Performance Standard

0–No exposure: No information or practice provided during the program; complete training required

1–Exposure only: General information provided with no practice time; close supervision needed; additional training required

2–Limited practice: Has practiced job during training program; additional training required to develop skill

3–Moderately skilled: Has performed job independently during training program; limited additional training may be required

4–Skilled: Can perform job independently with no additional training

Student/intern information:

Name____________________ Date________ Class____________

Vehicle used for this activity:

Year________ Make____________________ Model____________

Odometer________________ VIN ____________________

▶ TASK Perform starter circuit cranking voltage and voltage drop tests; determine needed action.

NATEF 5C1

Time off________

Time on________

Total time________

CDX Tasksheet Number: H290

1. Locate "cranking voltage test" in the appropriate service information and list the steps for this procedure.

____
____
____
____
____
____

2. Prepare the DVOM to measure voltage.

3. Measure the battery voltage at the starter motor (high current circuit) with the meter while the engine is cranking. Place the red lead on the main battery terminal of the starter and the black lead on the ground terminal of the starter motor. If the main battery terminal on the starter is inaccessible, use the battery terminal on the solenoid.

   Note: If the starter is not easily accessible, cranking voltage may be measured at the battery. Remember that any voltage drop between the battery and the starter may affect the test results.

   a. What is the measured voltage (cranking circuit voltage) of the battery?
   ________ volts

   b. Does the system meet the manufacturer's specifications?
   Yes: _____ No: _____

4. Determine any necessary actions:

____
____
____
____
____
____

   a. Have your supervisor/instructor verify these steps.
   Supervisor/instructor's initials: ________

5. Using the appropriate service information for the vehicle you are working on, locate starter circuit (low current circuit) voltage drop tests. List the steps outlined.

____
____
____
____
____

6. What is the maximum voltage drop specification(s) for this test?

   a. Positive side: ____________________volts

   b. Negative side, if specified: ___________________ volts

7. To conduct this test, it will be required that the engine cranks but does not start. Follow the manufacturer's recommendations for disabling the engine so it does not start. Identify the steps you will take to prevent the engine from starting.

   ____
   ____
   ____
   ____
   ____

   a. Have your supervisor/instructor verify these steps.
      Supervisor/instructor's initials: ____________

8. Starter circuit voltage drop test: Positive/feed side

   a. List the voltmeter connection points in the circuit.

      i. Black lead: ____

      ii. Red lead: ____

   b. Conduct the starter circuit voltage drop test.

      i. What is the voltage drop on the positive side? ________ volts

      ii. Is this reading within specifications? Yes: _____ No: _____

9. Starter circuit voltage drop test: Ground side

   a. List the voltmeter connection points in the circuit.

      i. Black lead: ____

      ii. Red lead: ____

   b. Conduct the starter circuit voltage drop test.

      i. What is the voltage drop on the negative side?________ volts

      ii. Is this reading within specifications? Yes: _____ No: _____

      iii. Determine any necessary action(s):

      ____
      ____
      ____

10. Return the vehicle engine to normal operating condition.

11. Start the vehicle and verify proper operation of the starting system and engine.

12. Return any tools you used to their proper locations.

13. Discuss the findings with the instructor.

Performance Rating

CDX Tasksheet Number: H290

☐ 0 ☐ 1 ☐ 2 ☐ 3 ☐ 4

Supervisor/instructor signature _______________ Date_______

Student/intern information:

Name____________________ Date__________ Class________________

Vehicle used for this activity:

Year__________ Make____________________ Model________________

Odometer____________________ VIN ____________________

▶ TASK Inspect and test components (key switch, push button, and/or magnetic switch) and wires and harnesses in the starter control circuit; replace as needed. **NATEF 5C2**

Time off________

Time on________

Total time________

CDX Tasksheet Number: H291

1. Locate the wiring diagram for the starter motor control circuit.
2. Write a short description of the purpose and operation of the components.
   Note: Understanding how a component is designed to operate within a circuit will make problems easier to diagnose.
3. Using the appropriate service information, determine the steps necessary for testing the components. List the suggested steps for diagnosing the components in question.
4. Test the starter motor control circuit components. List your tests and observations:
5. Determine any necessary action(s):
6. Return the vehicle to its beginning condition, and return any tools you used to their proper locations.
7. Discuss the findings with the instructor.

Performance Rating

CDX Tasksheet Number: H291

☐	☐	☐	☐	☐
0	1	2	3	4

Supervisor/instructor signature ____________________ Date__________

Student/intern information:

Name____________________ Date__________ Class____________________

Vehicle used for this activity:

Year__________ Make____________________ Model____________________

Odometer____________________ VIN ____________________

▶ TASK Inspect and test starter relays and solenoids/switches; replace as needed. NATEF 5C3

Time off__________

Time on__________

Total time__________

CDX Tasksheet Number: H292

1. Using the appropriate service information for the vehicle you are working on, locate the starter relay and/or solenoid testing procedure.
2. List the steps as outlined in the service information.
   a. What is the maximum voltage drop specification for this test? __________ V
3. To conduct this test, it will be required that the engine cranks but does not start. Follow the manufacturer's recommendations on disabling the engine so it does not start. Identify the steps you will take to prevent the engine from starting.
   a. Have your supervisor/instructor verify these steps.
      Supervisor/instructor's initials: __________
4. List the voltmeter connection points for checking the voltage drop across the starter solenoid.
   a. Red lead: ____________________
   b. Black lead: ____________________
5. Conduct the test.
   a. What is the voltage drop across the solenoid contacts: __________ V
   b. Is this reading within specifications? Yes: _____ No: _____
6. List the voltmeter connection points for measuring the voltage drop across the starter relay, if equipped.
   a. Red lead: ____________________
   b. Black lead: ____________________
7. Conduct the test.
   a. List the voltage drop across the relay contacts: __________ V
   b. Is this reading within specifications? Yes: _____ No: _____

8. Determine any necessary further action(s).

____
____
____
____

9. Return the vehicle engine to its normal operating condition.

10. Start the vehicle and verify proper operation of the starting system and engine.

11. Return the vehicle to a satisfactory condition, and return any tools you used to their proper locations.

12. Discuss the findings with the instructor.

Performance Rating

CDX Tasksheet Number: H292

☐ 0 ☐ 1 ☐ 2 ☐ 3 ☐ 4

Supervisor/instructor signature ______________________________ Date ____________

Student/intern information:

Name____________________ Date__________ Class________________

Vehicle used for this activity:

Year__________ Make____________________ Model________________

Odometer____________________ VIN ____________________

▸ TASK Remove and replace starter; inspect flywheel ring gear or flex plate. NATEF 5C4

Time off________

Time on________

Total time________

CDX Tasksheet Number: H293

1. Using the appropriate service information, research the starter removal and installation procedure for this vehicle.
   a. List the procedures and tools required to perform this task.

   b. List the starter mounting bolt torque: ________________ ft-lb (Nm)

   c. Have your supervisor/instructor verify this information.
   Supervisor/instructor's initials: ________

2. Remove the starter following the manufacturer's procedures.
   Note: Manufacturers may require that the vehicle cab or hood be lifted to remove the starter. Follow the manufacturer's recommendations regarding the correct procedure.

   a. Have your supervisor/instructor verify the starter removal.
   Supervisor/instructor's initials: ________

3. Using the appropriate service information, research the manufacturer's procedure for inspection of the flywheel ring gear or flex plate for this vehicle.
   a. List the checks that should be made.

   b. List the result of the inspection.

   c. Have your supervisor/instructor verify this information.
   Supervisor/instructor's initials: ________

4. Install the starter following the manufacturer's procedures.
    a. Have your supervisor/instructor verify the starter installation.
    Supervisor/instructor's initials: ________

5. Return the vehicle to its beginning condition, and return any tools you used to their proper locations.

6. Discuss the findings with the instructor.

Performance Rating

CDX Tasksheet Number: H293

☐ 0 ☐ 1 ☐ 2 ☐ 3 ☐ 4

Supervisor/instructor signature ________________________________ Date____________

Truck Electrical & Electronics: Charging System Diagnosis and Repair

Student/intern information:

Name__________ Date__________ Class__________

Vehicle used for this activity:

Year__________ Make__________ Model__________

Odometer__________ VIN __________

Time off__________

Time on__________

Total time__________

Learning Objective/Task	CDX Tasksheet Number	2014 NATEF Priority Level	2014 NATEF Reference Number
• Test instrument panel mounted voltmeters and/or indicator lamps; determine needed action.	H294	P-1	5D1
• Identify causes of no charge, low charge, or overcharge problems; determine needed action.	H295	P-1	5D2
• Inspect and replace alternator drive belts, pulleys, fans, tensioners, and mounting brackets; adjust drive belts and check alignment.	H296	P-1	5D3
• Perform charging system voltage and amperage output tests; perform AC ripple test; determine needed action.	H297	P-1	5D4
• Perform charging circuit voltage drop tests; determine needed action.	H298	P-1	5D5
• Remove and replace alternator.	H299	P-1	5D6
• Inspect, repair, or replace cables, wires, and connectors in the charging circuit.	H300	P-1	5D7

Materials Required

- Vehicle(s) with possible alternator concern, including cable, wiring, or connector faults
- Vehicle manufacturer's service information
- Digital volt-ohmmeter (DVOM), ammeters, test lamp, alternator testing equipment such as load banks, oscilloscope, wire, cable connectors, electrical hand tools
- Manufacturer-specific tools depending on the concern
- Exhaust hoses
- Personal protective equipment (PPE)

Some Safety Issues to Consider

- Activities may require running the engine and managing an environment of rotating equipment and large current draw, which carry severe risks. Attempt this task only with full permission from your supervisor/instructor, and follow all the guidelines exactly.
- Ensure that your supervisor/instructor checks connectors of any test equipment.
- Do not run the alternator without a load connected or allow the output voltage to exceed the manufacturer's specified maximum.
- Use extreme caution when working around batteries. Immediately remove any electrolyte that may come in contact with you. Electrolyte is a mixture of sulphuric acid and water. Batteries may produce explosive mixtures of gas containing hydrogen; avoid creating any sparks around batteries. Consult with the shop safety and emergency procedures when working with or around batteries.

- Make sure you follow the manufacturer's operation procedures. Also make sure you have your supervisor/instructor's permission to use any particular type of lifting equipment.
- Comply with personal and environmental safety practices associated with clothing; eye protection; hand tools; power equipment; proper ventilation; and the handling, storage, and disposal of chemicals/materials in accordance with federal, state, and local regulations.
- Always wear the correct protective eyewear and clothing, and use the appropriate safety equipment, as well as fender covers, seat protectors, and floor mat protectors.
- Make sure you understand and observe all legislative and personal safety procedures when carrying out practical assignments. If you are unsure of what these are, ask your supervisor/instructor.

Performance Standard

0–No exposure: No information or practice provided during the program; complete training required
1–Exposure only: General information provided with no practice time; close supervision needed; additional training required
2–Limited practice: Has practiced job during training program; additional training required to develop skill
3–Moderately skilled: Has performed job independently during training program; limited additional training may be required
4–Skilled: Can perform job independently with no additional training

Student/intern information:

Name_______________ Date_______ Class_______________

Vehicle used for this activity:

Year_______ Make_______________ Model_______________

Odometer_______________ VIN _______________

TASK Test instrument panel mounted voltmeters and/or indicator lamps; determine needed action. **NATEF 5D1**

Time off_______

Time on_______

Total time_______

CDX Tasksheet Number: H294

1. Using the appropriate service information for the vehicle you are working on, locate the test for panel-mounted voltmeters and/or indicator lamps.
2. List the inspection and test procedures for panel-mounted voltmeters and/or indicator lamps.
3. Check your documented procedures with your supervisor/instructor. Supervisor/instructor's initials: _______
4. Using the appropriate service information, inspect and test panel-mounted voltmeters and/or indicator lamps.
   a. List the tests and results:
   b. Determine any necessary corrective action(s):
5. Check corrective actions with your supervisor/instructor. Supervisor/instructor's initials: _______
6. Return the vehicle to its beginning condition, and return any tools you used to their proper locations.
7. Discuss the findings with the instructor.

Performance Rating

CDX Tasksheet Number: H294

☐ 0 ☐ 1 ☐ 2 ☐ 3 ☐ 4

Supervisor/instructor signature _______________ Date_______

Student/intern information:

Name________________ Date________ Class____________

Vehicle used for this activity:

Year________ Make________________ Model____________

Odometer______________ VIN ________________

▸ TASK Identify causes of no charge, low charge, or overcharge problems; determine needed action.

NATEF 5D2

Time off________

Time on________

Total time________

CDX Tasksheet Number: H295

1. Using the appropriate service information for the instructor designated vehicle you are working on, research the identification of causes and repair action of no-charge, low-charge, or overcharge problems.
   a. Potential causes and repair action of no charge are:
   b. Potential causes and repair action of low charge are:
   c. Potential causes and repair action of overcharge are:
2. Have your supervisor/instructor verify your research.
   Supervisor/instructor's initials: ________
3. Ask your supervisor for a vehicle to check. Install exhaust hose(s), set the parking brake, and lift the cabin or hood as necessary.
4. Test the system to determine the cause of the concern: List your observations.
5. Compare your results to the manufacturer's specifications. List your observations.

6. Determine any necessary action(s):

____
____
____
____

7. Return the vehicle to its beginning condition, and return any tools you used to their proper locations.

8. Discuss the findings with the instructor.

Performance Rating

CDX Tasksheet Number: H295

☐ 0 ☐ 1 ☐ 2 ☐ 3 ☐ 4

Supervisor/instructor signature ______________________________ Date__________

Student/intern information:

Name____________________ Date________ Class____________

Vehicle used for this activity:

Year________ Make____________________ Model____________

Odometer________________ VIN ____________________

Time off________

Time on________

Total time________

▶ TASK Inspect and replace alternator drive belts, pulleys, fans, tensioners, and mounting brackets; adjust drive belts and check alignment. **NATEF 5D3**

CDX Tasksheet Number: H296

1. Using the appropriate service information for the vehicle you are working on, locate "inspecting, adjusting, and/or replacing alternator drive belts, pulleys, fans, tensioners, and mounting brackets; check pulley and belt alignment."
   a. Write down the specified tension of the alternator drive belt:
   b. List faults to look for when inspecting drive belts, pulleys, tensioners, and mounting brackets.
   c. Describe how to check correct pulley and belt alignment.
2. Visually check for correct pulley, tensioner, and drive belt alignment. List your observations:
3. Remove the vehicle drive belt(s).
4. Inspect the vehicle drive belts, pulleys, tensioners, and mounting brackets for faults.
   a. List any faults identified on the vehicle drive belt(s), pulleys, tensioners, and mounting brackets.
5. Have your instructor verify removal of the belts and your answers.
   Supervisor/instructor's initials: __________
6. Refit the vehicle drive belts using appropriate service information.
7. Re-tension the drive belt(s) using appropriate service information.

8. Check for correct pulley, tensioner, and drive belt alignment.

9. Return the vehicle to a satisfactory condition, and return any tools you used to their proper locations.

10. Discuss the findings with the instructor.

Performance Rating

CDX Tasksheet Number: H296

☐ 0 ☐ 1 ☐ 2 ☐ 3 ☐ 4

Supervisor/instructor signature ______________________ Date ____________

Student/intern information:

Name________________________ Date__________ Class________________

Vehicle used for this activity:

Year__________ Make____________________ Model____________

Odometer________________ VIN ________________________

▶ TASK Perform charging system voltage and amperage output tests; perform AC ripple test; determine needed action. **NATEF 5D4**

Time off________

Time on________

Total time________

CDX Tasksheet Number: H297

1. List the steps to test for system voltage, amperage, and AC ripple as outlined in the service information.
   ____
   ____
   ____
   a. What is the specified charging system output?
      __________ amps at __________ volts at __________ rpm
      AC ripple: ____________________________
2. Install exhaust hose(s), set the parking brake, and lift the cabin or hood as necessary.
3. Connect the test instruments as outlined in the appropriate service information or as listed in Step 1.
4. Have your supervisor/instructor verify your test procedure and connections.
   Supervisor/instructor's initials: ________
5. Conduct the charging system output test. List the measured results at the maximum output:
   __________ amps at __________ volts at __________ rpm
   AC ripple: ____________________________
6. Compare your results to the manufacturer's specifications. List your observations.
   ____
   ____
   ____
7. Determine any necessary action(s):
   ____
   ____
8. Return the vehicle to its beginning condition, and return any tools you used to their proper locations.
9. Discuss the findings with the instructor.

Performance Rating

CDX Tasksheet Number: H297

☐ 0 ☐ 1 ☐ 2 ☐ 3 ☐ 4

Supervisor/instructor signature ________________________ Date________

Student/intern information:

Name____________________ Date__________ Class____________________

Vehicle used for this activity:

Year__________ Make____________________ Model____________________

Odometer____________________ VIN ____________________

▶ TASK Perform charging circuit voltage drop tests; determine needed action. **NATEF 5D5**

Time off__________

Time on__________

Total time__________

CDX Tasksheet Number: H298

1. Locate "perform charging circuit voltage drop tests; determine necessary action" in the service information for the vehicle you are working on.
   a. List the procedure as outlined in the service information to perform charging circuit voltage drop tests.

   ____

   ____

   ____

   ____

   ____

   b. List the maximum specified charging circuit voltage drop allowable, positive side: ________________ V
   c. List the maximum specified charging circuit voltage drop allowable, negative side: ________________ V
2. Prepare the vehicle, attach exhaust hose(s), tilt cabin or lift hood, and set the parking brake.
3. Connect the tester as outlined in the appropriate service information or as listed in Step 1a.
4. Have your supervisor/instructor verify your test procedure and connections. Supervisor/instructor initials: ____________
5. Conduct the charging system voltage drop test. Repeat the tests as many times as required to test all parts of the charging circuit as described in Step 1. List the measured results.
   a. Voltage drop on the positive side, between __________ and __________ is __________ volts at __________ amps.
   b. Voltage drop on the negative side, between __________ and __________ is __________ volts at __________ amps.
   c. List the total voltage drop for both sides of the charging circuit: ________________ V
6. Compare your results to the manufacturer's specifications.
   a. List your observations.

   ____

   ____

   ____

   ____

   ____

7. Determine any necessary corrective action(s):

____

____

____

8. Return any tools you used to their proper locations.

9. Discuss the findings with the instructor.

Performance Rating

CDX Tasksheet Number: H298

☐	☐	☐	☐	☐
0	1	2	3	4

Supervisor/instructor signature ______________________ Date__________

Student/intern information:

Name________________ Date________ Class____________

Vehicle used for this activity:

Year________ Make________________ Model____________

Odometer________________ VIN ____________________

▶ TASK Remove and replace alternator. **NATEF 5D6**

Time off________

Time on________

Total time________

CDX Tasksheet Number: H299

1. Locate "remove and replace alternator" in the appropriate service information for the vehicle you are working on.
    a. List the steps outlined in the service information to remove the alternator.

2. Remove the alternator as per the service information.

3. Visually inspect the alternator for damage and wear. List your observations:

4. Have your instructor verify removal of the alternator.
   Supervisor/instructor initials: __________

5. List the steps outlined in the service information to install the alternator.

6. Install the alternator as per the service information.

7. Start the vehicle and check the alternator output and voltage.
    a. Voltage output: __________ V
    b. Amperage output: ______ amps

8. Return any tools you used to their proper locations.

9. Discuss the findings with the instructor.

Performance Rating

CDX Tasksheet Number: H299

☐ 0 ☐ 1 ☐ 2 ☐ 3 ☐ 4

Supervisor/instructor signature ____________________ Date________

Student/intern information:

Name________________ Date________ Class____________

Vehicle used for this activity:

Year________ Make________________ Model____________

Odometer________________ VIN ________________

▶ TASK Inspect, repair, or replace cables, wires, and connectors in the charging circuit.

NATEF 5D7

Time off________

Time on________

Total time________

CDX Tasksheet Number: H300

1. Locate the wiring diagram for the charging system that you are testing.
2. Research "inspect, repair, or replace wires and connectors as needed" for this vehicle in the appropriate service information.
   a. List the steps outlined in the service information to inspect, repair, or replace cables, wires, and connectors.
3. Prepare the vehicle, tilt the cabin or lift the hood, and set the parking brake.
4. Inspect the wires, cables, and connectors for the charging circuit as outlined in the appropriate service information or as listed in Step 2a. List your observations:
5. Determine any necessary corrective action(s).
6. Repair or replace wires, cables, and connectors for the charging circuit as outlined in the appropriate service information or as listed in Step 2a.
   a. Have your supervisor/instructor check your work.
      Supervisor/instructor's initials: ________
7. Return the vehicle to its beginning condition, and return any tools you used to their proper locations.
8. Discuss the findings with the instructor.

Performance Rating

CDX Tasksheet Number: H300

☐ 0 ☐ 1 ☐ 2 ☐ 3 ☐ 4

Supervisor/instructor signature ________________ Date________

Truck Electrical & Electronics: Lighting Systems

Student/intern information:

Name____________________ Date__________ Class________________

Vehicle used for this activity:

Year__________ Make____________________ Model________________

Odometer____________________ VIN ____________________

Learning Objective/Task	CDX Tasksheet Number	2014 NATEF Priority Level	2014 NATEF Reference Number
• Interface with vehicle's on-board computer; perform diagnostic procedures using recommended electronic service tool(s) (including PC-based software and/or data scan tools); determine needed action.	H301	P-1	5E1
• Identify causes of brighter than normal, intermittent, dim, or no headlight and daytime running light (DRL) operation.	H302	P-1	5E2
• Test, aim, and replace headlights.	H303	P-1	5E3
• Test headlight and dimmer circuit switches, relays, wires, terminals, connectors, sockets, and control components/modules; repair or replace as needed.	H304	P-1	5E4
• Inspect and test switches, bulbs/LEDs, sockets, connectors, terminals, relays, wires, and control components/modules of parking, clearance, and taillight circuits; repair or replace as needed.	H305	P-1	5E5
• Inspect and test instrument panel light circuit switches, relays, bulbs/LEDs, sockets, connectors, terminals, wires, and printed circuits/control modules; repair or replace as needed.	H306	P-2	5E6
• Inspect and test interior cab light circuit switches, bulbs/LEDs, sockets, low voltage disconnect (LVD), connectors, terminals, wires, and control components/modules; repair or replace as needed.	H307	P-2	5E7
• Inspect and test tractor-to-trailer multiwire connector(s); repair or replace as needed.	H308	P-1	5E8
• Inspect, test, and adjust stoplight circuit switches, bulbs/LEDs, sockets, connectors, terminals, wires, and control components/modules; repair or replace as needed.	H309	P-1	5E9
• Inspect and test turn signal and hazard circuit flasher(s), switches, relays, bulbs/LEDs, sockets, connectors, terminals, wires, and control components/modules; repair or replace as needed.	H310	P-1	5E10
• Inspect and test reverse lights and warning device circuit switches, bulbs/LEDs, sockets, horns, buzzers, connectors, terminals, wires, and control components/modules; repair or replace as needed.	H311	P-1	5E11

Time off________

Time on________

Total time________

Materials Required

- Vehicle or simulator with electrical lighting concern(s)
- Vehicle manufacturer's service information including schematic wiring diagrams
- Digital volt-ohmmeter (DVOM), ammeter, current clamp, PC-based software and/or data scan tools, headlight aiming equipment, tractor-to-trailer multiwire connector(s)
- Electrical spare parts, including fuses, circuit breakers, relays, connectors, wires, bulbs, sockets
- Manufacturer-specific tools depending on the concern
- Refer to the sample Diagnostics Procedure chart at the end of this section.

Some Safety Issues to Consider

- Activities require you to measure electrical values. Always ensure that the instructor/supervisor checks test instrument connections prior to connecting power or taking measurements. High current flows can be dangerous; avoid accidental short circuits or grounding the battery's positive connections.
- Activities may require test driving the vehicle on the school grounds or on a hoist, both of which carry severe risks. Attempt this task only with full permission from your supervisor/instructor and follow all the guidelines exactly.
- Comply with personal and environmental safety practices associated with clothing; eye protection; hand tools; power equipment; proper ventilation; and the handling, storage, and disposal of chemicals/materials in accordance with federal, state, and local regulations.
- Always wear the correct protective eyewear and clothing, and use the appropriate safety equipment, as well as fender covers, seat protectors, and floor mat protectors.
- Make sure you understand and observe all legislative and personal safety procedures when carrying out practical assignments. If you are unsure of what these are, ask your supervisor/instructor.

Performance Standard

0–No exposure: No information or practice provided during the program; complete training required
1–Exposure only: General information provided with no practice time; close supervision needed; additional training required
2–Limited practice: Has practiced job during training program; additional training required to develop skill
3–Moderately skilled: Has performed job independently during training program; limited additional training may be required
4–Skilled: Can perform job independently with no additional training

Student/intern information:

Name____________________ Date__________ Class____________________

Vehicle used for this activity:

Year__________ Make____________________ Model____________________

Odometer____________________ VIN ____________________

▶ TASK Interface with vehicle's on-board computer; perform diagnostic procedures using recommended electronic service tool(s) (including PC-based software and/or data scan tools); determine needed action. **NATEF 5E1**

Time off__________

Time on__________

Total time__________

CDX Tasksheet Number: H301

1. Describe the customer concern:

2. Research how to interface with the vehicle's on-board computer. List the procedure and type of PC-based software and/or data scan tools that will be used for the vehicle.

3. Connect the PC-based software and/or data scan tool to the vehicle's data link connector (DLC), and retrieve any diagnostic trouble codes (DTCs). List any stored DTCs:

4. If the computer system has freeze frame capability, copy the data here.

5. Research the DTCs for this vehicle in the appropriate service information.
   a. List the DTC code description(s) for each code stored.

   b. Print out the procedure for diagnosing each code and attach a copy to this sheet.

6. Have your supervisor/instructor verify satisfactory completion of this section of the procedure. Supervisor/instructor's initials: __________

7. Follow the vehicle service information procedure to diagnose the specific cause of the DTC, and use the PC-based software and/or data scan tool to assist in the diagnosis of the problem. List the data related to this DTC.

____
____
____
____
____

8. Compare the above data to the service information specifications and list your interpretations.

____
____
____
____
____

9. Determine any necessary action(s):

____
____
____
____
____

10. Have your supervisor/instructor verify satisfactory completion of this section of the procedure. If instructed, carry out any rectification required.
Supervisor/instructor's initials: _______________

11. Return the vehicle to its beginning condition, and return any tools you used to their proper locations.

12. Discuss the findings with the instructor.

Performance Rating

CDX Tasksheet Number: H301

☐ 0 ☐ 1 ☐ 2 ☐ 3 ☐ 4

Supervisor/instructor signature _______________ Date_______________

Student/intern information:

Name____________________ Date__________ Class________________

Vehicle used for this activity:

Year__________ Make____________________ Model________________

Odometer____________________ VIN ________________________

▶ TASK Identify causes of brighter than normal, intermittent, dim, or no headlight and daytime running light (DRL) operation. **NATEF 5E2**

Time off__________

Time on__________

Total time__________

CDX Tasksheet Number: H302

1. List the customer concern regarding the lighting system fault.

2. If the lights are dim or do not operate, go to step 3. If the lights are too bright, go to step 9.

3. Research the affected lighting system troubleshooting section and the wiring diagram(s) in the appropriate service information for the vehicle you are working on.

4. Turn on the affected lights(s), measure the battery voltage, and list it here: __________volts

5. Measure the voltage drop across the power and ground at the light while illuminated. List the voltage: __________ volts
   a. Calculate the total voltage drop in the circuit and list it here: __________ voltage drop
   b. Is the voltage drop excessive? Yes: ______ No: ______
   c. If Yes, go to step 7. If No, go to step 6.

6. Inspect the bulb and connection for any faults (wrong bulb, corroded, or loose connection). List your observations below.

7. Measure the voltage drop from the battery positive post to the input terminal of the light.
   a. List the voltage drop: __________ volts
   b. Is this within specifications? Yes: ______ No: ______
   c. Determine any necessary actions and list them below:

8. Measure the voltage drop from the bulb ground to the battery negative post.
   a. List the voltage drop: __________ volts
   b. Is this within specification? Yes: ______ No: ______
   c. Determine any necessary actions and list them below:

9. Install an exhaust hose(s) and wheel chocks, and set the parking brake. Start the vehicle.

10. Measure the charging system voltage at the battery, with the engine running at 1000 rpm. If the battery voltage is too high, you will need to perform charging system checks to determine the cause of the overcharge. __________________ volts

    a. Is this within specification? Yes: ______ No: ______

11. List your observations:
____
____
____

12. Determine any necessary action(s):
____
____
____

13. Discuss your findings with your instructor.

Performance Rating

CDX Tasksheet Number: H302

☐	☐	☐	☐	☐
0	1	2	3	4

Supervisor/instructor signature ________________________________ Date__________

Student/intern information:

Name__________ Date__________ Class__________

Vehicle used for this activity:

Year__________ Make__________ Model__________

Odometer__________ VIN __________

▶ TASK Test, aim, and replace headlights.

NATEF 5E3

Time off__________

Time on__________

Total time__________

CDX Tasksheet Number: H303

1. Research the headlight aiming procedure in the exterior lighting section in the appropriate service information for the vehicle you are working on.
    a. Type of headlights the vehicle is equipped with: __________
    b. High-beam bulb number: __________
    c. Low beam bulb number: __________

2. Research the headlamp aiming process in the appropriate service information for the vehicle you are working on. List (or print off and attach) the steps that are required to aim these headlights:

    Note: Do not touch the bulb with your fingers. Some bulbs will fail prematurely due to the oils from your skin.

3. Aim the headlights following the specified procedure.

4. List any problems you encountered performing this task:

5. Discuss your findings with your instructor.

Performance Rating

CDX Tasksheet Number: H303

☐ 0 ☐ 1 ☐ 2 ☐ 3 ☐ 4

Supervisor/instructor signature __________ Date__________

Student/intern information:

Name_______________ Date_______ Class_______________

Vehicle used for this activity:

Year_______ Make_______________ Model_______________

Odometer_______________ VIN _______________

▶ TASK Test headlight and dimmer circuit switches, relays, wires, terminals, connectors, sockets, and control components/modules; repair or replace as needed. **NATEF 5E4**

Time off_______

Time on_______

Total time_______

CDX Tasksheet Number: H304

1. Locate the wiring diagram for the headlight and dimmer circuit that you are testing. Determine purpose and operation of the components.

   Note: Knowledge of how to read a wiring diagram is critical in diagnosing malfunctions in any given circuit. Understanding how components are designed to operate within a circuit will make problems easier to diagnose.

2. Test the headlight switch by moving the switch through all of its positions to make sure it is operating as it should.
   a. Operation of the switch: Pass ______ Fail ______

3. If the switch fails to operate as designed, test the switch and list your observations:

   ____
   ____
   ____

4. Test the dimmer switch by turning the headlights on and operating the dimmer switch up or down, depending on design (older vehicle dimmer switches are on the driver side floor towards the kick panel; newer models are usually on the turn signal switch).
   a. Operation of the switch: Pass ______ Fail ______

5. If the switch fails to operate as designed, test the switch and list your observations:

   ____
   ____
   ____

6. Check all connectors to relays and control modules for looseness, cracking and burn marks that may cause the system to malfunction. Any burn marks or discoloration of the connectors may indicate excessive amperage running through them.
   a. Condition of connectors: Good: ______ Bad: ______

7. If the connectors are bad, determine any necessary actions:

   ____
   ____
   ____

8. Test relay(s) and modules for proper operation.
   a. Consult the service information and test them for proper operation. List your observations:

      ____
      ____
      ____

9. Check all wiring that is present to that circuit for bare spots, cracked insulation, and no connection to connector or component. Perform voltage drop tests to the circuit if necessary.
    a. Condition of wiring: Good: ______ Bad: ______

10. If the condition of the wiring is bad, determine any necessary actions:
    ____
    ____
    ____

11. Return the vehicle to its beginning condition, and return any tools to their proper locations.

12. Discuss your findings with your instructor.

Performance Rating

CDX Tasksheet Number: H304

☐ 0 ☐ 1 ☐ 2 ☐ 3 ☐ 4

Supervisor/instructor signature ____________________ Date__________

Student/intern information:

Name________________________________ Date__________ Class____________________

Vehicle used for this activity:

Year____________ Make________________________________ Model____________________

Odometer____________________________ VIN ____________________________________

▶ TASK Inspect and test switches, bulbs/LEDs, sockets, connectors, terminals, relays, wires, and control components/modules of parking, clearance, and taillight circuits; repair or replace as needed. **NATEF 5E5**

Time off__________

Time on__________

Total time__________

CDX Tasksheet Number: H305

1. Consult the appropriate service information for the correct wiring diagram information to perform this task.
2. Inspect and test all switches associated with parking, clearance, and taillight circuits by operating them and checking for illumination of all lights in the circuit.
   a. List your observations:

   b. For any circuits that didn't operate, check the switch connections for corrosion and connector tightness. List your observations:

   c. Measure the voltage drop across the switch. List your observations:

   d. Determine any necessary actions:

3. Check all sockets for any water damage or burnt conditions.
   a. Condition of sockets: Good: ______ Bad: ______
4. Check all connectors to sockets, relays and control modules for looseness, cracking and burn marks that may cause the system to malfunction.
   a. Condition of connectors: Good: ______ Bad: ______

   Note: Any burn marks or discoloration of the connectors may indicate excessive amperage running through them.
5. If the connectors are found to be bad, determine any necessary actions:

6. Test all relays, control components, and modules for proper operation.
   a. For any relays, control components, and modules that didn't operate properly, list your observations:
      ____
      ____
      ____

   b. Following the specified procedures, test the malfunctioning components.
      List your tests and results:
      ____
      ____
      ____

   c. Determine any necessary actions:
      ____
      ____
      ____

7. Check all wiring that is present to that circuit for bare spots, cracked insulation, and no connection to connector or component. Perform voltage drop tests to the circuit if necessary.
   a. Condition of wiring: Good: ______ Bad: ______

8. If the wiring is found to be bad, determine any necessary actions:
   ____
   ____
   ____

9. Return the vehicle to its beginning condition, and return any tools to their proper locations.

10. Discuss your findings with your instructor.

Performance Rating

CDX Tasksheet Number: H305

☐	☐	☐	☐	☐
0	1	2	3	4

Supervisor/instructor signature ______________________________ Date______________

Student/intern information:

Name____________________ Date__________ Class________________

Vehicle used for this activity:

Year__________ Make____________________ Model________________

Odometer__________________ VIN ________________________

▶ TASK Inspect and test instrument panel light circuit switches, relays, bulbs/LEDs, sockets, connectors, terminals, wires, and printed circuits/control modules; repair or replace as needed. **NATEF 5E6**

Time off________

Time on________

Total time________

CDX Tasksheet Number: H306

1. Consult the appropriate service information for the correct wiring diagram information to perform this task.
2. Inspect and test all switches associated with the instrument panel light circuits by operating them and checking for illumination of the lights in the circuit.
   a. List your observations:
   b. For any circuits that didn't operate, check the switch connections for corrosion and connector tightness. List your observations:
   c. Measure the voltage drop across the switch. List your observations:
   d. Determine any necessary actions:
3. Check all wiring connections for damage or burnt conditions. Good: ______ Bad: ______
4. Check all connectors to relays and control modules for looseness, cracking and burn marks that may cause the system to malfunction.

   Note: Any burn marks or discoloration of the connectors may indicate excessive amperage running through them.

   a. Condition of connectors: Good: ______ Bad: ______
5. If the connectors are bad, determine any necessary actions:

6. Test relay(s) and modules for proper operation.
   a. For any relays, control components, and modules that didn't operate properly, list your observations:
   ____
   ____
   ____

   b. Following the specified procedures, test the malfunctioning components. List your tests and results:
   ____
   ____
   ____

   c. Determine any necessary actions:
   ____
   ____
   ____

7. Check all wiring that is present to that circuit for bare spots, cracked insulation, and no connection to connector or component. Perform voltage drop tests to the circuit if necessary.
   a. Condition of wiring: Good: ______ Bad: ______

8. If the wiring is found to be bad, determine any necessary actions:
   ____
   ____
   ____

9. Return the vehicle to its beginning condition, and return any tools to their proper locations.

10. Discuss your findings with your instructor.

Performance Rating

CDX Tasksheet Number: H306

☐	☐	☐	☐	☐
0	1	2	3	4

Supervisor/instructor signature ______________________________ Date______________

Student/intern information:

Name______________________ Date__________ Class______________

Vehicle used for this activity:

Year__________ Make______________________ Model______________

Odometer__________________ VIN______________________

Time off________

Time on________

Total time________

▸ TASK Inspect and test interior cab light circuit switches, bulbs/LEDs, sockets, low voltage disconnect (LVD), connectors, terminals, wires, and control components/modules; repair or replace as needed. **NATEF 5E7**

CDX Tasksheet Number: H307

1. Consult the appropriate service information for the correct wiring diagram information to perform this task.

2. Inspect and test all switches associated with interior cab light circuits by operating them and checking for illumination of all lights in the circuit.
   a. Are the switches working? Yes: ______ No: ______
   b. If no, consult the appropriate service information to perform a repair or replacement of the faulty switches. List your observations:

3. Check all switch connections for corrosion and connector tightness. List your observations:

4. Check the LVD (Low Voltage Disconnect) for corrosion and tightness. These may be found in the battery box or inside the cab area. List your observations:

5. Check all sockets for any water damage or burnt conditions.
   a. Condition of sockets: Good: ______ Bad: ______

6. Check all connectors to sockets, relays and control modules for looseness, cracking and burn marks that may cause the system to malfunction.
   a. Condition of connectors: Good: ______ Bad: ______

   Note: Any burn marks or discoloration of the connectors may indicate excessive amperage running through them.

7. If the connectors are found to be bad, determine any necessary actions:

8. Test relay(s) and modules for proper operation.
    a. For any relays and modules that didn't operate properly, list your observations:
    ____
    ____
    ____

    b. Following the specified procedures, test the malfunctioning components. List your tests and results:
    ____
    ____
    ____

    c. Determine any necessary actions:
    ____
    ____
    ____

9. Check all wiring that is present to that circuit for bare spots, cracked insulation, and no connection to connector or component. Perform voltage drop tests to the circuit if necessary.
    a. Condition of wiring: Good: ______ Bad: ______

10. If the wiring is found to be bad, determine any necessary actions:
    ____
    ____
    ____

11. Return the vehicle to its beginning condition, and return any tools to their proper locations.

12. Discuss your findings with your instructor.

Performance Rating

CDX Tasksheet Number: H307

☐	☐	☐	☐	☐
0	1	2	3	4

Supervisor/instructor signature ______________________________ Date______________

Student/intern information:

Name________________________________ Date____________ Class____________________

Vehicle used for this activity:

Year______________ Make______________________________ Model________________

Odometer________________________ VIN ______________________________

Time off________

Time on________

Total time________

▶ TASK Inspect and test tractor-to-trailer multi-wire connector(s); repair or replace as needed.

NATEF 5E8

CDX Tasksheet Number: H308

1. Consult the appropriate service information for the correct wiring diagram information to perform this task.
2. Test the trailer connector/ISO utilizing a DVOM (digital volt-ohmmeter) for continuity throughout each wire in the cable.
   a. Test and record connector continuity for each pin. Highest resistance: ________ Ohms
3. Test and record the voltage at each pin (clockwise from the Ground terminal) with the relevant circuits activated.
   a. ____________________
   b. ____________________
   c. ____________________
   d. ____________________
   e. ____________________
   f. ____________________
   g. ____________________
4. Check that all connector pins are not damaged and that corrosion is not present in the connector indicating water penetration.
5. Damage or corrosion present? Yes: _____ No: _____
   a. If damage is present, consult the appropriate service information on repairing or replacing the connectors or cable and record it below.

   ____

   ____

   ____
6. Determine any necessary actions:

   ____

   ____

   ____
7. Discuss your findings with your instructor.

Performance Rating

CDX Tasksheet Number: H308

☐	☐	☐	☐	☐
0	1	2	3	4

Supervisor/instructor signature ______________________________________ Date____________

Student/intern information:

Name____________________________ Date__________ Class__________________

Vehicle used for this activity:

Year__________ Make____________________________ Model__________________

Odometer__________________________ VIN __________________________________

▸ TASK Inspect, test, and adjust stoplight circuit switches, bulbs/LEDs, sockets, connectors, terminals, wires and control components/modules; repair or replace as needed.

NATEF 5E9

Time off__________

Time on__________

Total time__________

CDX Tasksheet Number: H309

1. Consult the appropriate service information for the correct wiring diagram information to perform this task.

2. Inspect and test all switches associated with the stoplight switch circuits by operating them and checking for illumination of all lights in the circuit.
   a. List your observations:

   b. For any circuits that didn't operate, check the switch connections for corrosion and connector tightness. List your observations:

   c. Measure the voltage drop across the switch. List your observations:

   d. Determine any necessary actions:

3. Check for correct adjustment of the stoplight circuit switch by consulting the manufacturer service information and list your observations:

4. Check all sockets for any water damage or burnt conditions.
   a. Condition of sockets: Good: ______ Bad: ______

5. Check all connectors to sockets, relays and control modules for looseness, cracking and burn marks that may cause the system to malfunction.
   a. Condition of connectors: Good: ______ Bad: ______

   Note: Any burn marks or discoloration of the connectors may indicate excessive amperage running through them.

6. If the connectors are found to be bad, determine any necessary actions:
____
____
____

7. Test relay(s) and modules for proper operation.
    a. For any relays and modules that didn't operate properly, list your observations:
    ____
    ____
    ____

    b. Following the specified procedures, test the malfunctioning components. List your tests and results:
    ____
    ____
    ____

    c. Determine any necessary actions:
    ____
    ____
    ____

8. Check all wiring that is present to that circuit for bare spots, cracked insulation, and no connection to connector or component. Perform voltage drop tests to the circuit if necessary.
    a. Condition of wiring: Good: ______ Bad: ______

9. If the wiring is found to be bad, determine any necessary actions:
____
____
____

10. Return the vehicle to its beginning condition, and return any tools to their proper locations.

11. Discuss your findings with your instructor.

Performance Rating

CDX Tasksheet Number: H309

☐ 0 ☐ 1 ☐ 2 ☐ 3 ☐ 4

Supervisor/instructor signature ______________________________ Date______________

Student/intern information:

Name____________________ Date__________ Class________________

Vehicle used for this activity:

Year__________ Make____________________ Model________________

Odometer____________________ VIN ____________________

▶ TASK Inspect and test turn signal and hazard circuit flasher(s), switches, relays, bulbs/LEDs, sockets, connectors, terminals, wires and control components/modules; repair or replace as needed. **NATEF 5E10**

Time off__________

Time on__________

Total time__________

CDX Tasksheet Number: H310

1. Consult the appropriate service information for the correct wiring diagram information to perform this task.
2. Inspect and test all switches associated with the turn signal and hazard flasher(s) circuits by operating them and checking for illumination of all lights in the circuit.
   a. Are the turn signals and hazard flashers working? Yes: ______ No: ______
   b. If no, consult the appropriate service information to affect a repair or replace faulty switches. This may require the use of a DVOM (digital volt-ohmmeter) to make voltage drop tests. List your observations:
3. Check all switch connections for corrosion and connector tightness. List your observations:
4. Check all sockets for any water damage or burnt conditions.
   a. Condition of sockets: Good: ______ Bad: ______
5. Check all connectors to sockets, relays and control modules for looseness, cracking and burn marks that may cause the system to malfunction.
   a. Condition of connectors: Good: ______ Bad: ______
   Note: Any burn marks or discoloration of the connectors may indicate excessive amperage running through them.
6. If the connectors are found to be bad, determine any necessary actions:
7. Test relay(s) and modules for proper operation.
   a. For any relays and modules that didn't operate properly, list your observations:
   b. Following the specified procedures, test the malfunctioning components. List your tests and results:

c. Determine any necessary actions:

____

____

____

8. Check all wiring that is present to that circuit for bare spots, cracked insulation, and no connection to connector or component. Perform voltage drop tests to the circuit if necessary.
    a. Condition of wiring: Good: ______ Bad: ______

9. If the wiring is found to be bad, determine any necessary actions:

____

____

____

10. Return the vehicle to its beginning condition, and return any tools to their proper locations.

11. Discuss your findings with your instructor.

Performance Rating

CDX Tasksheet Number: H310

☐ 0 ☐ 1 ☐ 2 ☐ 3 ☐ 4

Supervisor/instructor signature ______________________________ Date__________

Student/intern information:

Name_______________ Date_______ Class_______________

Vehicle used for this activity:

Year_______ Make_______________ Model_______________

Odometer_______________ VIN _______________

▸ TASK Inspect and test reverse lights and warning device circuit switches, bulbs/LEDs, sockets, horns, buzzers, connectors, terminals, wires and control components/modules; repair or replace as needed. **NATEF 5E11**

Time off_______

Time on_______

Total time_______

CDX Tasksheet Number: H311

1. Consult the appropriate service information for the correct wiring diagram information to perform this task.

2. Inspect and test all switches associated with the reverse lights and warning device circuits by operating them and checking for illumination of all lights in the circuit.
   a. Are the reverse lights working? Yes: ______ No: ______
   b. If no, consult the appropriate service information to repair or replace faulty switches. List your observations:

3. Check all switch connections for corrosion and connector tightness. List your observations:

4. Check all sockets for any water damage or burnt conditions.
   a. Condition of sockets: Good: ______ Bad: ______

5. Check all horns and buzzers for proper sound levels and decibels.
   a. Are the horn and buzzers working properly? Yes: ______ No: ______
   b. If no, consult the appropriate service information for proper procedures to repair or replace the faulty components. List your observations:

6. Check all connectors to sockets, relays and control modules for looseness, cracking and burn marks that may cause the system to malfunction.
   a. Condition of connectors: Good: ______ Bad: ______

   Note: Any burn marks or discoloration of the connectors may indicate excessive amperage running through them.

7. If the connectors are found to be bad, determine any necessary actions:

8. Test relay(s) and modules for proper operation.
    a. For any relays and modules that didn't operate properly, list your observations:
    ____
    ____
    ____

    b. Following the specified procedures, test the malfunctioning components. List your tests and results:
    ____
    ____
    ____

    c. Determine any necessary actions:
    ____
    ____
    ____

9. Check all wiring that is present to that circuit for bare spots, cracked insulation, and no connection to connector or component. Perform voltage drop tests to the circuit if necessary.
    a. Condition of wiring: Good: ______ Bad: ______

10. If the wiring is found to be bad, determine any necessary actions:
    ____
    ____
    ____

11. Return the vehicle to its beginning condition, and return any tools to their proper locations.

12. Discuss your findings with your instructor.

Performance Rating

CDX Tasksheet Number: H311

☐	☐	☐	☐	☐
0	1	2	3	4

Supervisor/instructor signature ______________________________ Date______________

CDX

Generic automotive diagnostic procedure

Verify vehicle information
Select vehicle-specific scan tool
Select scan tool software for vehicle
Locate scan tool connection on vehicle
Select adaptor plug/device
Use default data link connector
Connect scan tool
Activate scan tool
Select vehicle
Select system to be tested
Legend
Start or End
Process Step
Decision Point
Test System
No code - System OK
Read trouble codes
Look up code in data information source
Interpret code
Locate system identified by code
Check system/ component connection
Connection is in good condition.Test component
Test failed
Connection poor or loose. Rectify connection fault
Test OK
Refer to supervisor
Clear codes on scan tool and retest system
Code reactivates
Replace component
No code - System OK
Ignore code terminate activity

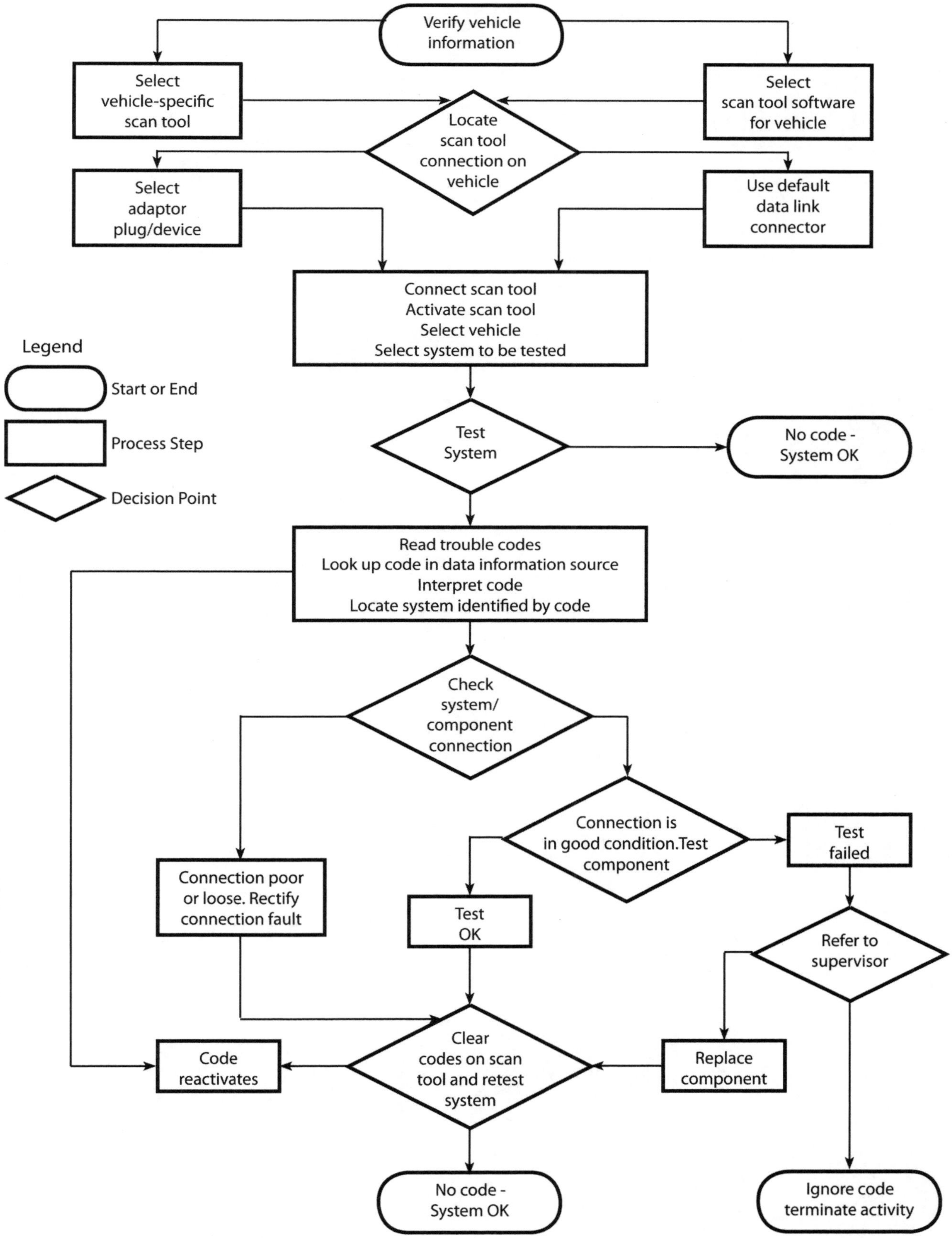

Truck Electrical & Electronics: Gauges and Warning Devices

Student/intern information:

Name_______________ Date_______________ Class_______________

Vehicle used for this activity:

Year_______________ Make_______________ Model_______________

Odometer_______________ VIN_______________

Time off_______________

Time on_______________

Total time_______________

Learning Objective/Task	CDX Tasksheet Number	2014 NATEF Priority Level	2014 NATEF Reference Number
• Interface with vehicle's on-board computer; perform diagnostic procedure, verify instrument cluster operations using recommended electronic service tool(s) (including PC-based software and/or data scan tools); determine needed action.	H312	P-1	5F1
• Identify causes of intermittent, high, low, or no gauge readings; determine needed action.	H313	P-2	5F2
• Identify causes of data bus-driven gauge malfunctions; determine needed action.	H314	P-3	5F3
• Inspect and test gauge circuit sensor/sending units, gauges, connectors, terminals, and wires; repair or replace as needed.	H315	P-2	5F4
• Inspect and test warning devices (lights and audible), circuit sensor/sending units, bulbs/LEDs, sockets, connectors, wires, and control components/modules; repair or replace as needed.	H316	P-1	5F5
• Inspect, test, replace, and calibrate (if applicable) electronic speedometer, odometer, and tachometer systems.	H317	P-2	5F6

Materials Required

- Vehicle or simulator with gauge and warning device concerns
- Vehicle manufacturer's service information including schematic wiring diagrams
- Test lamp, digital volt-ohmmeter (DVOM), PC-based software, and/or data scan tools
- Electrical spare parts, including fuses, circuit breakers, gauges, wire, sender units, sensors, bulbs, sockets, and connectors
- Manufacturer-specific tools depending on the concern
- Refer to the sample Diagnostics Procedure chart at the end of this section.

Some Safety Issues to Consider

- Activities require you to measure electrical values. Always ensure that the instructor/supervisor checks test instrument connections prior to connecting power or taking measurements. High current flows can be dangerous; avoid accidental short circuits or grounding the battery's positive connections.
- Activities may require test driving the vehicle on the school grounds or on a hoist, both of which carry severe risks. Attempt this task only with full permission from your supervisor/instructor, and follow all the guidelines exactly.
- Comply with personal and environmental safety practices associated with clothing; eye protection; hand tools; power equipment; proper ventilation; and the handling, storage, and disposal of chemicals/materials in accordance with federal, state, and local regulations.

- Always wear the correct protective eyewear and clothing, and use the appropriate safety equipment, as well as fender covers, seat protectors, and floor mat protectors.
- Make sure you understand and observe all legislative and personal safety procedures when carrying out practical assignments. If you are unsure of what these are, ask your supervisor/instructor.

Performance Standard

0–No exposure: No information or practice provided during the program; complete training required
1–Exposure only: General information provided with no practice time; close supervision needed; additional training required
2–Limited practice: Has practiced job during training program; additional training required to develop skill
3–Moderately skilled: Has performed job independently during training program; limited additional training may be required
4–Skilled: Can perform job independently with no additional training

Student/intern information:

Name________________ Date________ Class__________

Vehicle used for this activity:

Year________ Make________________ Model__________

Odometer______________ VIN ________________

▸ TASK Interface with vehicle's on-board computer; perform diagnostic procedure, verify instrument cluster operations using recommended electronic service tool(s) (including PC-based software and/or data scan tools); determine needed action. **NATEF 5F1**

Time off________

Time on________

Total time________

CDX Tasksheet Number: H312

1. Describe the customer concern:

2. Research how to interface with the vehicle's on-board computer. List the procedure and type of PC-based software and/or data scan tools that will be used for the vehicle.

3. Connect the PC-based software and/or data scan tool to the vehicle's data link connector (DLC), and retrieve any diagnostic trouble codes (DTCs). List the DTCs:

4. If the computer system has freeze frame capability, copy the data here.

5. Research the DTCs for this vehicle in the appropriate service information.
   a. List the DTC code description(s) for each code stored.

   b. Print out the procedure for diagnosing each code, and attach a copy to this sheet.

6. Have your supervisor/instructor verify satisfactory completion of this section of the procedure. Supervisor/instructor's initials: ________

7. Follow the vehicle service information procedure to diagnose the specific cause of the DTC, and use the PC-based software and/or data scan tool to assist in the diagnosis of the problem. List the data related to this DTC.

8. Compare these data to the service information specifications and list your interpretations.
____
____
____

9. Determine any necessary action(s):
____
____
____

10. Have your supervisor/instructor verify satisfactory completion of this section of the procedure. If instructed, carry out any rectification required.
Supervisor/instructor's initials: ____________

11. Return the vehicle to its beginning condition, and return any tools you used to their proper locations.

12. Discuss the findings with the instructor.

Performance Rating

CDX Tasksheet Number: H312

☐ 0 ☐ 1 ☐ 2 ☐ 3 ☐ 4

Supervisor/instructor signature ______________________________ Date ____________

Student/intern information:

Name__________ Date__________ Class__________

Vehicle used for this activity:

Year__________ Make__________ Model__________

Odometer__________ VIN __________

▶ TASK Identify causes of intermittent, high, low, or no gauge readings; determine needed action. **NATEF 5F2**

Time off__________

Time on__________

Total time__________

CDX Tasksheet Number: H313

1. List the customer concern regarding intermittent, high, low, or no gauge readings.

2. Research the particular concern in the appropriate service information.
   a. List the possible causes:

   b. List any relevant gauge or sending unit specifications:

3. Diagnose the cause of the concern using the service information and wiring diagrams. List your tests and their results:

4. Perform any voltage drop tests necessary to diagnose any causes or concerns in the instrument cluster system. List your tests and their results:

5. List the cause of the concern:

6. Determine any necessary action(s) to correct the fault:
____
____
____

7. Discuss your findings with your instructor.

Performance Rating

CDX Tasksheet Number: H313

☐ 0 ☐ 1 ☐ 2 ☐ 3 ☐ 4

Supervisor/instructor signature _______________________________ Date_____________

Student/intern information:

Name__________________ Date________ Class____________

Vehicle used for this activity:

Year________ Make__________________ Model____________

Odometer________________ VIN __________________

▶ TASK Identify causes of data bus-driven gauge malfunctions; determine needed action.

NATEF 5F3

Time off________

Time on________

Total time________

CDX Tasksheet Number: H314

1. Identify customer concern in the data bus-driven gauge malfunctions.
2. Interface with the vehicles on-board computer and determine if there are any malfunctions or codes present. List them below:
   a. Code #1: ________
   b. Code #2: ________
   c. Code #3: ________
   d. Code #4: ________
3. List any manufacturer-specific procedures to diagnose any codes present:
4. Perform the diagnosis listing any tests you performed and their results:
5. Determine any necessary actions:
6. Discuss the findings with your instructor.

Performance Rating

CDX Tasksheet Number: H314

☐ 0 ☐ 1 ☐ 2 ☐ 3 ☐ 4

Supervisor/instructor signature ____________________ Date________

Student/intern information:

Name________________________ Date__________ Class__________________

Vehicle used for this activity:

Year__________ Make__________________________ Model__________________

Odometer______________________ VIN ______________________________

▶ TASK Inspect and test gauge circuit sensor/sending units, gauges, connectors, terminals, and wires; repair or replace as needed. NATEF 5F4

Time off________

Time on________

Total time________

CDX Tasksheet Number: H315

1. List the customer concern regarding abnormal gauge readings:

2. Research the particular concern in the appropriate service information. List the possible causes:

   a. List any relevant gauge or sending unit specifications:

3. Diagnose the cause of the concern using the appropriate service information and wiring diagrams. List your tests and their results:

4. Check the conditions of all wiring, connectors, and terminals in the circuit.
   a. Condition of wiring: Good: _____ Bad: _____
   b. Condition of connectors: Good: _____ Bad: _____
   c. Condition of terminals: Good: _____ Bad: _____

5. Determine and record any necessary action(s) to correct any faults in the circuit:

6. Discuss your findings with your instructor.

Performance Rating

CDX Tasksheet Number: H315

☐	☐	☐	☐	☐
0	1	2	3	4

Supervisor/instructor signature ______________________________ Date__________

Student/intern information:

Name____________________ Date__________ Class____________

Vehicle used for this activity:

Year__________ Make____________________ Model____________

Odometer__________________ VIN ____________________

▶ TASK Inspect and test warning devices (lights and audible) circuit sensor/sending units, bulbs/LEDs, sockets, connectors, wires, and control components/modules; repair or replace as needed.

NATEF 5F5

Time off________

Time on________

Total time________

CDX Tasksheet Number: H316

1. Consult the appropriate service information for the correct wiring diagram information to perform this task.

2. Inspect and test all warning devices (lights and audible) sensor circuits by operating them and checking for illumination of all lights in the circuit.
   a. Are the warning devices working? Yes: _____ No: _____
   b. If no, consult the appropriate service information to repair or replace the faulty components. List your tests and results:

3. Check all switch connections for corrosion and connector tightness. List your observations:

4. Check all connectors to sockets and control modules for looseness, cracking, and burn marks that may cause the system to malfunction.
   a. Condition of connectors: Good: _____ Bad: _____

      Note: Any burn marks or discoloration of the connectors may indicate excessive amperage running through them.

5. If the connectors are found to be bad, determine any necessary actions:

6. Test all modules for proper operation.
   a. For any modules that didn't operate properly, list your observations:
   b. Following the specified procedures, test the malfunctioning components. List your tests and results:
   c. Determine any necessary actions:

7. Check all wiring that is present to the circuit for bare spots, cracked insulation, and no connection to connector or component. Perform voltage drop tests to the circuit if necessary.
   a. Condition of wiring: Good: _____ Bad: _____

8. If the wiring is found to be bad, determine any necessary actions:
   ____
   ____
   ____

9. Return the vehicle to its beginning condition, and return any tools to their proper locations.

10. Discuss your findings with your instructor.

Performance Rating

CDX Tasksheet Number: H316

☐	☐	☐	☐	☐
0	1	2	3	4

Supervisor/instructor signature ______________________ Date __________

Student/intern information:

Name________________ Date________ Class____________

Vehicle used for this activity:

Year________ Make________________ Model____________

Odometer________________ VIN ________________

▶ TASK Inspect, test, replace, and calibrate (if applicable) electronic speedometer, odometer, and tachometer systems. **NATEF 5F6**

Time off________

Time on________

Total time________

CDX Tasksheet Number: H317

Note: This is usually done by a state recognized specialty repair shop for these!

1. Describe the customer concern:

2. Research the particular concern in the appropriate service information; list the possible causes, and identify tests to be performed:

3. Inspect the vehicle systems fitted with electronic speedometer, odometer, and tachometer systems to determine the cause of the concern. List your tests and results:

4. List the cause of the concern:

5. Determine any necessary actions:

6. Have your supervisor/instructor verify your answers.
   Supervisor/instructor's initials: ________

7. Repair, replace, or calibrate electronic speedometer, odometer, and tachometer systems as outlined in the appropriate service information. List your observations:

____

____

____

____

8. Have your supervisor/instructor check your work.
Supervisor/instructor's initials: ____________

9. Return the vehicle to its beginning condition, and return any tools you used to their proper locations.

10. Discuss the findings with the instructor.

Performance Rating

CDX Tasksheet Number: H317

☐ 0 ☐ 1 ☐ 2 ☐ 3 ☐ 4

Supervisor/instructor signature ______________________ Date__________

CDX Generic automotive diagnostic procedure

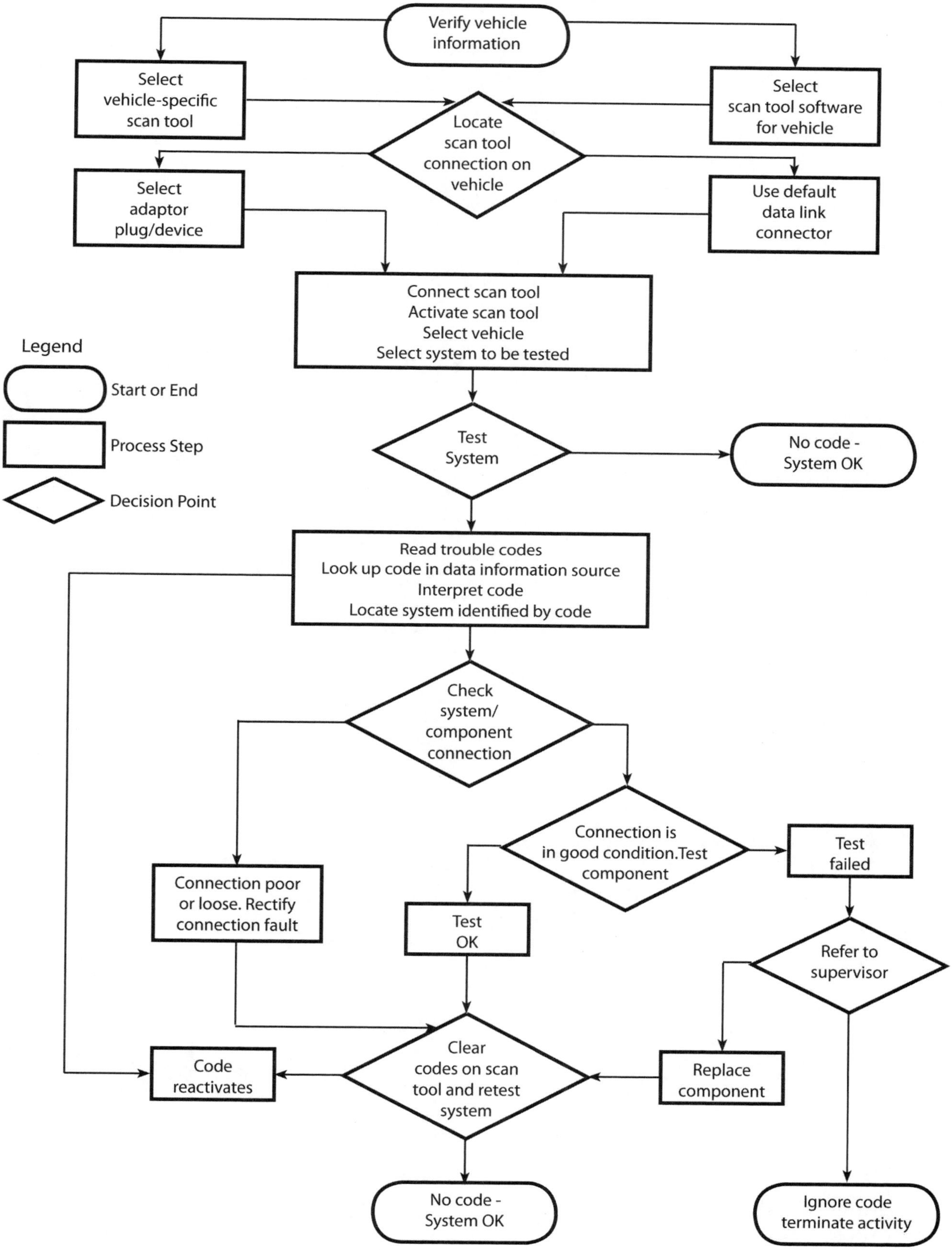

Verify vehicle information

Select vehicle-specific scan tool

Select scan tool software for vehicle

Locate scan tool connection on vehicle

Select adaptor plug/device

Use default data link connector

Connect scan tool
Activate scan tool
Select vehicle
Select system to be tested

Legend

Start or End

Process Step

Decision Point

Test System

No code - System OK

Read trouble codes
Look up code in data information source
Interpret code
Locate system identified by code

Check system/ component connection

Connection is in good condition.Test component

Test failed

Connection poor or loose. Rectify connection fault

Test OK

Refer to supervisor

Clear codes on scan tool and retest system

Code reactivates

Replace component

No code - System OK

Ignore code terminate activity

Truck Electrical & Electronics: Related Electronic Systems

Student/intern information:

Name__________ Date__________ Class__________

Vehicle used for this activity:

Year__________ Make__________ Model__________

Odometer__________ VIN __________

Time off__________

Time on__________

Total time__________

Learning Objective/Task	CDX Tasksheet Number	2014 NATEF Priority Level	2014 NATEF Reference Number
• Interface with vehicle's on-board computer; perform diagnostic procedures using recommended electronic service tool(s) (including PC-based software and/or data scan tools); determine needed action.	H318	P-1	5G1
• Identify causes of constant, intermittent, or no horn operation; determine needed action.	H319	P-2	5G2
• Inspect and test horn circuit relays, horns, switches, connectors, wires, clock springs, and control components/modules; repair or replace as needed.	H320	P-2	5G3
• Identify causes of constant, intermittent, or no wiper operation; diagnose the cause of wiper speed control and/or park problems; determine needed action.	H321	P-2	5G4
• Inspect and test wiper motor, resistors, park switch, relays, switches, connectors, wires, and control components/modules; repair or replace as needed.	H322	P-2	5G5
• Inspect wiper motor transmission linkage, arms, and blades; adjust or replace as needed.	H323	P-2	5G6
• Inspect and test windshield washer motor or pump/relay assembly, switches, connectors, terminals, wires, and control components/modules; repair or replace as needed.	H324	P-3	5G7
• Inspect and test side view mirror motors, heater circuit grids, relays, switches, connectors, terminals, wires, and control components/modules; repair or replace as needed.	H325	P-3	5G8
• Inspect and test heater and A/C electrical components including: A/C clutches, motors, resistors, relays, switches, connectors, terminals, wires, and control components/modules; repair or replace as needed.	H326	P-3	5G9
• Inspect and test auxiliary power outlet, integral fuse, connectors, terminals, wires, and control components/modules; repair or replace as needed.	H327	P-3	5G10
• Identify causes of slow, intermittent, or no power side window operation; determine needed action.	H328	P-3	5G11
• Inspect and test motors, switches, relays, connectors, terminals, wires, and control components/modules of power side window circuits; repair or replace as needed.	H329	P-3	5G12
• Inspect and test block heaters; determine needed repairs.	H330	P-2	5G13
• Inspect and test cruise control electrical components; repair or replace as needed.	H331	P-3	5G14
• Inspect and test switches, relays, controllers, actuator/solenoids, connectors, terminals, and wires of electric door lock circuits.	H332	P-3	5G15

Learning Objective/Task	CDX Tasksheet Number	2014 NATEF Priority Level	2014 NATEF Reference Number
• Check operation of keyless and remote lock/unlock devices; determine needed action.	H333	P-3	5G16
• Inspect and test engine cooling fan electrical control components/modules; repair or replace as needed.	H334	P-2	5G17
• Identify causes of data bus communication problems; determine needed action.	H335	P-2	5G18

Materials Required

- Vehicles or simulators with on-board computer systems and related electrical faults such as horn, wiper, windshield washer, heated mirrors, air conditioning, auxiliary power outlets, electric windows, block heaters, cruise control, electric door locks, keyless remotes, engine cooling fan, data bus communications problems
- Vehicle manufacturer's service information including schematic wiring diagrams
- Digital volt-ohmmeter (DVOM), ammeter, current clamp, PC-based software, and/or data scan tools
- Electrical spare parts, including fuses, circuit breakers, relays, wires, connectors
- Manufacturer-specific tools depending on the concern
- Vehicle-lifting equipment if applicable
- Refer to the sample Diagnostics Procedure chart at the end of this section.

Some Safety Issues to Consider

- Activities require you to measure electrical values. Always ensure that the instructor/supervisor checks test instrument connections prior to connecting power or taking measurements. High current flows can be dangerous; avoid accidental short circuits or grounding the battery's positive connections.
- Air-conditioning systems have refrigerant gas within the system. When the system is running, high-pressure gas and liquid refrigerant will be circulating in the system. Use extreme caution working around high-pressure hoses.
- This activity may require you to work with solenoid actuators. Actuators may create a crush injury hazard; keep fingers away from mechanisms.
- Electric motors may start up when you least expect it; keep fingers and clothing away from the mechanism.
- Activities may require test driving the vehicle on the school grounds or on a hoist, both of which carry severe risks. Attempt this task only with full permission from your supervisor/instructor, and follow all the guidelines exactly.
- Comply with personal and environmental safety practices associated with clothing; eye protection; hand tools; power equipment; proper ventilation; and the handling, storage, and disposal of chemicals/materials in accordance with federal, state, and local regulations.
- Always wear the correct protective eyewear and clothing, and use the appropriate safety equipment, as well as fender covers, seat protectors, and floor mat protectors.
- Make sure you understand and observe all legislative and personal safety procedures when carrying out practical assignments. If you are unsure of what these are, ask your supervisor/instructor.

Performance Standard

0–No exposure: No information or practice provided during the program; complete training required
1–Exposure only: General information provided with no practice time; close supervision needed; additional training required
2–Limited practice: Has practiced job during training program; additional training required to develop skill
3–Moderately skilled: Has performed job independently during training program; limited additional training may be required
4–Skilled: Can perform job independently with no additional training

Student/intern information:

Name________________ Date________ Class________________

Vehicle used for this activity:

Year________ Make________________ Model________________

Odometer________________ VIN ________________

▶ TASK Interface with vehicle's on-board computer; perform diagnostic procedures using recommended electronic diagnostic service tool(s) (including PC-based software and/or data scan tools); determine needed action. **NATEF 5G1**

Time off________

Time on________

Total time________

CDX Tasksheet Number: H318

1. Describe the customer concern.

____

2. Research how to interface with the vehicle's on-board computer. List the procedure and type of PC-based software and/or data scan tools that will be used for the vehicle.

____

3. Connect the PC-based software and/or data scan tool to the vehicle's data link connector (DLC), and retrieve any diagnostic trouble codes (DTCs). List any DTCs:

____

4. If the computer system has freeze-frame capability, copy the data here:

____

5. Research the DTCs for this vehicle in the appropriate service information.
   a. List the DTC code description(s) for each code stored.

   ____

   b. Print out the procedure for diagnosing each code, and attach a copy to this sheet.

6. Have your supervisor/instructor verify satisfactory completion of this section of the procedure. Supervisor/instructor's initials: ________

7. Follow the vehicle service information procedure to diagnose the specific cause of the DTC, and use the PC-based software and/or data scan tool to assist in the diagnosis of the problem. List the data related to this DTC.

____
____
____
____

8. Compare the data to the service information specifications and list your interpretations.

____
____
____
____

9. Determine any necessary action(s):

____
____
____
____

10. Have your supervisor/instructor verify satisfactory completion of this section of the procedure. If instructed, carry out any rectification required.
Supervisor/instructor's initials: _______________

11. Return the vehicle to its beginning condition, and return any tools you used to their proper locations.

12. Discuss the findings with the instructor.

Performance Rating

CDX Tasksheet Number: H318

☐	☐	☐	☐	☐
0	1	2	3	4

Supervisor/instructor signature _______________ Date_______________

Student/intern information:

Name__________ Date__________ Class__________

Vehicle used for this activity:

Year__________ Make__________ Model__________

Odometer__________ VIN __________

▶ TASK Identify causes of constant, intermittent, or no horn operation; determine needed action. **NATEF 5G2**

Time off__________

Time on__________

Total time__________

CDX Tasksheet Number: H319

1. Locate information about the diagnosis of vehicle horn and the wiring diagram in the appropriate service information for the vehicle you are working on.
   a. List the procedure for diagnosing the vehicle's horn circuit.

2. Following the specified procedure, diagnose any faults in the vehicle horn circuit.
   a. List the tests you performed and their results:

3. If a vehicle with a fault is not available, utilizing a DVOM (digital volt-ohmmeter) and an instructor designated vehicle, measure the voltage in the horn circuit according to manufacturer guidelines. Record your findings:

4. List the cause of the concern:

5. Determine any necessary actions:

6. Discuss your findings with your instructor.

Performance Rating

CDX Tasksheet Number: H319

☐ 0 ☐ 1 ☐ 2 ☐ 3 ☐ 4

Supervisor/instructor signature __________ Date__________

Student/intern information:

Name________________________________ Date____________ Class____________________

Vehicle used for this activity:

Year____________ Make______________________________ Model____________________

Odometer____________________________ VIN ______________________________________

▶ TASK Inspect and test horn circuit relays, horns, switches, connectors, wires, clock springs, and control components/modules; repair or replace as needed. **NATEF 5G3**

Time off____________

Time on____________

Total time____________

CDX Tasksheet Number: H320

1. Consult the appropriate service information for the correct wiring diagram information to perform this task.
2. Inspect and test all switches associated with the horn circuits by operating them and checking for audible sounds in the circuit.
   a. Are the horn circuits working? Yes: _____ No: _____
   b. If no, consult the appropriate service information to repair or replace the faulty instrument panel components.
3. Test clock spring operation by engaging the horn in different steering wheel positions.
4. Check all horn circuit connections for corrosion and connector tightness.
5. Check all wiring connections for damage or burnt conditions.
   a. Condition of wiring connections: Good: _____ Bad: _____
   b. Check all connectors to relays and control modules for looseness, cracking, and burn marks that may cause the system to malfunction.
   c. Condition of connectors: Good: _____ Bad: _____

   Note: Any burn marks or discoloration of the connectors may indicate excessive amperage running through them.
6. If the connectors are found to be bad, determine any necessary actions:

   ____

   ____

   ____

   ____
7. Test relay(s) and modules for proper operation.
   a. List your observations:

   ____

   ____

   ____
8. Check all wiring that is present to that circuit for bare spots, cracked insulation, and no connection to connector or component. Perform voltage drop tests to the circuit if necessary.
   a. Condition of wiring: Good: _____ Bad: _____

9. If the wiring is found to be bad, determine any necessary actions:

____

____

____

____

10. Return the vehicle to its beginning condition, and return any tools to their proper locations.

11. Discuss your findings with your instructor.

Performance Rating

CDX Tasksheet Number: H320

☐ 0 ☐ 1 ☐ 2 ☐ 3 ☐ 4

Supervisor/instructor signature _______________________ Date___________

Student/intern information:

Name__________ Date__________ Class__________

Vehicle used for this activity:

Year__________ Make__________ Model__________

Odometer__________ VIN __________

▶ TASK Identify causes of constant, intermittent, or no wiper operation; diagnose the cause of wiper speed control and/or park problems; determine needed action. **NATEF 5G4**

Time off__________

Time on__________

Total time__________

CDX Tasksheet Number: H321

1. Using appropriate service information for the vehicle you are working on, research the causes of constant, intermittent, or no wiper operation. List the potential causes:

2. Locate "diagnosis of vehicle wiper systems" in the appropriate service information for the vehicle you are working on.

3. List the diagnostic procedures for vehicle wiper systems, including speed control and park problems.

4. Check your documented procedures with your supervisor/instructor.
   Supervisor/instructor's initials: __________

5. Using the appropriate service information, diagnose faults in the vehicle wiper system.
   a. List your tests and their results:

6. Determine any necessary action(s):

7. Check corrective actions with your supervisor/instructor.
   Supervisor/instructor's initials: __________

8. Perform the necessary corrective action(s). List your observations:
____
____
____
____

9. Return the vehicle to its beginning condition, and return any tools you used to their proper locations.

10. Discuss the findings with the instructor.

Performance Rating

CDX Tasksheet Number: H321

☐ 0 ☐ 1 ☐ 2 ☐ 3 ☐ 4

Supervisor/instructor signature _______________________________ Date_______________

Student/intern information:

Name____________________ Date__________ Class____________________

Vehicle used for this activity:

Year__________ Make____________________ Model____________________

Odometer____________________ VIN ______________________________

▸ TASK Inspect and test wiper motor, resistors, park switch, relays, switches, connectors, wires and control components/modules; repair or replace as needed. **NATEF 5G5**

Time off__________

Time on__________

Total time__________

CDX Tasksheet Number: H322

1. Understanding how components are designed to operate within a circuit will make problems easier to diagnose.

2. Locate the wiring diagram for the wiper motor circuit that you are testing. Determine purpose and operation of the components. Knowledge of how to read a wiring diagram is critical in diagnosing malfunctions in any given circuit.

3. Test the wiper motor switch by moving the switch through all of its positions to make sure it is operating as it should.
   a. Operation of the switch: Pass _____ Fail _____
   b. Do the wipers park correctly when turned off? Yes: _____ No: _____

4. If the switch fails to operate as designed, you will need to diagnose the circuit. List your tests and results:

   ____
   ____
   ____
   ____
   ____

5. Check all connectors to relays and control modules for looseness, cracking, and burn marks that may cause the system to malfunction.
   a. Condition of connectors: Good: _____ Bad: _____

      Note: Any burn marks or discoloration of the connectors may indicate excessive amperage running through them.

6. If the connectors are bad, determine any necessary actions:

   ____
   ____
   ____

7. Test relay(s) and modules for proper operation.
   a. Consult the service information and test them for proper operation. List your observations:

      ____
      ____
      ____
      ____
      ____

8. Check all wiring that is present to that circuit for bare spots, cracked insulation, and no connection to connector or component. Perform voltage drop tests to the circuit if necessary.
   a. Condition of wiring: Good: _____ Bad: _____

9. If the wiring is bad, determine any necessary actions:
   ____
   ____
   ____

10. Return the vehicle to its beginning condition, and return any tools to their proper locations.

11. Discuss your findings with your instructor.

Performance Rating

CDX Tasksheet Number: H322

☐ 0   ☐ 1   ☐ 2   ☐ 3   ☐ 4

Supervisor/instructor signature ______________________________ Date ____________

Student/intern information:

Name____________________ Date__________ Class________________

Vehicle used for this activity:

Year__________ Make____________________ Model________________

Odometer____________________ VIN ____________________

▶ TASK Inspect wiper motor transmission linkage, arms, and blades; adjust or replace as needed.

NATEF 5G6

Time off__________

Time on__________

Total time__________

CDX Tasksheet Number: H323

1. Inspect wiper motor transmission linkage:
   a. Check for linkage connections that have cracked or dry rotted bushings.
      i. Condition of bushings: Pass _____ Fail _____
   b. Check for elongated linkage ends from loose or worn bushings.
      i. Are the linkage ends damaged? Yes: _____ No: _____
   c. Check for bent linkage arms.
      i. Are the linkage arms bent or damaged? Yes: _____ No: _____
2. Inspect wiper blades for dry rot, torn rubber, and/or smearing.
   a. Condition of blades: Good: _____ Bad: _____
3. Consult the appropriate service information for instructions on replacing and adjusting the wiper assemblies. Record the procedures below:

   ____

   ____

   ____
4. Place a fender cover between the wiper blade and windshield to reduce the chance of breaking the windshield. Remove the wiper blade.
5. Have your instructor verify removal of the wiper blade.
   Supervisor/instructor's initials: ________________
6. Reinstall the wiper blade. List your observations:

   ____

   ____

   ____
7. Discuss your findings with your instructor.

Performance Rating

CDX Tasksheet Number: H323

☐ 0 ☐ 1 ☐ 2 ☐ 3 ☐ 4

Supervisor/instructor signature ______________________________ Date__________

Student/intern information:

Name________________________ Date__________ Class________________

Vehicle used for this activity:

Year__________ Make________________________ Model________________

Odometer____________________ VIN ________________________________

▶ TASK Inspect and test windshield washer motor or pump/relay assembly, switches, connectors, terminals, wires, and control components/modules; repair or replace as needed.

NATEF 5G7

Time off________

Time on________

Total time________

CDX Tasksheet Number: H324

1. Locate the wiring diagram for the wiper motor circuit that you are testing. Determine purpose and operation of the components. Knowledge of how to read a wiring diagram is critical in diagnosing malfunctions in any given circuit. Understanding how components are designed to operate within a circuit will make problems easier to diagnose.

2. Test the windshield washer motor or pump/relay assembly switch through all of its positions to make sure it is operating as it should.
   a. Operation of the switch: Pass _____ Fail _____
   b. Check operation of pump for windshield fluid distribution. Pass _____ Fail _____

      Note: Most windshield washer pump switches are incorporated into the turn signal switch. Consult the appropriate service information for locations of these switches. Locations can also be found in the owner's manual found in most glove compartments.

3. If the switch fails to operate as designed, determine any necessary actions:

   ____

   ____

   ____

4. Check all connectors to relays and control modules for looseness, cracking, and burn marks that may cause the system to malfunction.
   a. Condition of connectors: Good: _____ Bad: _____

      Note: Any burn marks or discoloration of the connectors may indicate excessive amperage running through them.

   b. If the connectors are bad, make recommendations for repairing or replacing the connectors.

      ____

      ____

      ____

5. Test relay(s) and modules for proper operation.
   a. Consult the service information and test them for proper operation. List your observations:

      ____

      ____

      ____

6. Check all wiring that is present to that circuit for bare spots, cracked insulation, and no connection to connector or component. Perform voltage drop tests to the circuit if necessary.
   a. Condition of wiring: Good: _____ Bad: _____

7. If the wiring is bad, determine any necessary actions:

____

____

____

8. Return the vehicle to its beginning condition, and return any tools to their proper locations.

9. Discuss your findings with your instructor.

Performance Rating

CDX Tasksheet Number: H324

☐ 0 ☐ 1 ☐ 2 ☐ 3 ☐ 4

Supervisor/instructor signature _______________________ Date_____________

Student/intern information:

Name________________ Date________ Class____________

Vehicle used for this activity:

Year________ Make________________ Model____________

Odometer________________ VIN ________________

▶ TASK Inspect and test side view mirror motors, heater circuit grids, relays, switches, connectors, terminals, wires and control components/modules; repair or replace as needed.

NATEF 5G8

Time off________

Time on________

Total time________

CDX Tasksheet Number: H325

1. Locate the wiring diagram for the side view mirror motors and heater circuit grids that you are testing. Determine purpose and operation of the components. Knowledge of how to read a wiring diagram is critical in diagnosing malfunctions in any given circuit. Understanding how components are designed to operate within a circuit will make problems easier to diagnose.

2. Test the side view mirror motors and heater switch through all of its positions to make sure it is operating as it should.
   a. Operation of the switch: Pass _____ Fail _____
   b. Check operation of side view mirror heater. Pass _____ Fail _____

3. If the switch fails to operate as designed, consult the appropriate service information for proper procedures for testing. Determine any necessary actions:

4. Check all connectors to relays and control modules for looseness, cracking, and burn marks that may cause the system to malfunction.
   a. Condition of connectors: Good: _____ Bad: _____

   Note: Any burn marks or discoloration of the connectors may indicate excessive amperage running through them.

5. If the connectors are bad, determine any necessary actions:

6. Test relay(s) and modules for proper operation.
   a. Consult the service information and test them for proper operation. List your observations:

7. Check all wiring that is present to that circuit for bare spots, cracked insulation, and no connection to connector or component. Perform voltage drop tests to the circuit if necessary.
   a. Condition of wiring: Good: _____ Bad: _____

8. If the wiring is bad, determine any necessary actions:
   ____
   ____
   ____

9. Return the vehicle to its beginning condition, and return any tools to their proper locations.

10. Discuss your findings with your instructor.

Performance Rating

CDX Tasksheet Number: H325

☐ 0 ☐ 1 ☐ 2 ☐ 3 ☐ 4

Supervisor/instructor signature ______________________ Date__________

Student/intern information:

Name____________________ Date__________ Class________________

Vehicle used for this activity:

Year__________ Make____________________ Model________________

Odometer____________________ VIN ____________________

▶ TASK Inspect and test heater and A/C electrical components including: A/C clutches, motors, resistors, relays, switches, connectors, terminals, wires and control components/modules; repair or replace as needed. **NATEF 5G9**

Time off________

Time on________

Total time________

CDX Tasksheet Number: H326

1. Locate the wiring diagram for the heater and A/C electrical components you are testing. Knowledge of how to read a wiring diagram is critical in diagnosing malfunctions in any given circuit. Understanding how components are designed to operate within a circuit will make problems easier to diagnose.

2. Test the heater and A/C electrical components switch through all of its positions to make sure it is operating as it should.
   a. Operation of the switch: Pass _____ Fail _____

   b. Check operation of the A/C clutch by engaging the A/C circuit. Check under the hood to see if the clutch on the compressor is turning.
      i. Operation of A/C clutch: Pass _____ Fail ______
      ii. If there is no clutch engagement, consult and record manufacturer procedures to test, repair, or replace the A/C clutch.

   c. Check the operation of the resistors. If the resistors are functioning, the blower motor will be able to be operated in all speeds available.
      i. Operation of resistors: Pass _____ Fail _____
      ii. Check the appropriate service information for correct resistor values.
         • Specified resistor values: ____________________ ohms
         • Actual resistor values: ____________________ ohms

   d. Check to make sure the A/C blower motor is functioning properly.
      i. Operation of A/C blower motor: Pass _____ Fail _____
      ii. If blower motor will not operate, consult and record manufacturer procedures to test, repair or replace the blower motor.

3. If the switch fails to operate as designed, consult the appropriate service information for proper procedures for testing, repair, or replacement. Determine any necessary actions:

4. Check all connectors to relays and control modules for looseness, cracking, and burn marks that may cause the system to malfunction.

   Note: Any burn marks or discoloration of the connectors may indicate excessive amperage running through them.

   a. Condition of connectors: Good: _____ Bad: _____

5. If the connectors are found to be bad, make recommendations for repairing or replacing the connections.

   ____
   ____
   ____

6. Test relay(s) and modules for proper operation.
   a. Consult the service information and test them for proper operation. List your observations:

      ____
      ____
      ____

7. Check all wiring that is present to that circuit for bare spots, cracked insulation, and no connection to connector or component. Perform voltage drop tests to the circuit if necessary.
   a. Condition of wiring: Good: _____ Bad: _____

8. If the wiring is found to be bad, determine any necessary actions:

   ____
   ____
   ____

9. Return the vehicle to its beginning condition, and return any tools to their proper locations.

10. Discuss your findings with your instructor.

Performance Rating

CDX Tasksheet Number: H326

☐	☐	☐	☐	☐
0	1	2	3	4

Supervisor/instructor signature ______________________________ Date______________

Student/intern information:

Name____________________ Date________ Class________________

Vehicle used for this activity:

Year________ Make____________________ Model______________

Odometer__________________ VIN ________________________

▶ TASK Inspect and test auxiliary power outlet, integral fuse, connectors, terminals, wires, and control components/modules; repair or replace as needed. **NATEF 5G10**

Time off________

Time on________

Total time________

CDX Tasksheet Number: H327

1. Locate the wiring diagram for the auxiliary power outlet circuit that you are testing. Determine purpose and operation of the components. Knowledge of how to read a wiring diagram is critical in diagnosing malfunctions in any given circuit. Understanding how components are designed to operate within a circuit will make problems easier to diagnose.

   Note: The auxiliary power outlet or inverter can be used to power some convenient appliances like TVs, microwaves, and toaster ovens that operate on 110 volts.

2. Test the auxiliary power outlet with a DVOM (digital volt-ohmmeter) to make sure it has the proper operating voltage required.
   a. Operation of the auxiliary power outlet: Pass _____ Fail _____
   b. Voltage applied to the outlet: ____________ volts

3. Check the mounting hardware for tightness.

4. If the outlet fails to operate as designed, consult the appropriate service information for proper procedures for testing. Determine any necessary actions:

   ____

   ____

   ____

5. Check all connectors and terminals on control modules for looseness, cracking, and burn marks that may cause the system to malfunction.
   a. Condition of connectors: Good: _____ Bad: _____

      Note: Any burn marks or discoloration of the connectors may indicate excessive amperage running through them.

6. If connectors and/or terminals are bad, determine any necessary actions:

   ____

   ____

   ____

7. Test modules for proper operation.
   a. Consult the service information and test them for proper operation. List your tests and observations:

      ____

      ____

      ____

8. Check all wiring that is present to that circuit for bare spots, cracked insulation, and no connection to connector or component. Perform voltage drop tests to the circuit if necessary.
    a. Condition of wiring: Good: _____ Bad: _____

9. If the condition of the wiring is bad, determine any necessary actions:
    ____
    ____
    ____

10. Return the vehicle to its beginning condition, and return any tools to their proper locations.

11. Discuss your findings with your instructor.

Performance Rating

CDX Tasksheet Number: H327

☐	☐	☐	☐	☐
0	1	2	3	4

Supervisor/instructor signature ______________________________ Date__________

Student/intern information:

Name__________ Date__________ Class__________

Vehicle used for this activity:

Year__________ Make__________ Model__________

Odometer__________ VIN __________

▶ TASK Identify causes of slow, intermittent, or no power side window operation; determine needed action. **NATEF 5G11**

Time off__________

Time on__________

Total time__________

CDX Tasksheet Number: H328

1. Research causes of slow, intermittent, or no power side window operation and list them.
   a. Slow power side window operation:

   b. Intermittent power side window operation:

   c. No power side window operation:

2. Examine the vehicle/simulator and determine fault(s) with power side window operation.
3. Describe the customer concern.

4. Using the appropriate service information, determine the steps necessary for testing the component(s).

5. Write a short description of the purpose and operation of the suspected component(s).

6. Following the specified procedure, diagnose the fault. List your tests and their results:

7. List the cause of the concern:

8. Determine any necessary actions:

9. Return the vehicle to its beginning condition, and return any tools you used to their proper locations.

10. Discuss the findings with the instructor.

Performance Rating

CDX Tasksheet Number: H328

☐ 0 ☐ 1 ☐ 2 ☐ 3 ☐ 4

Supervisor/instructor signature ____________________ Date __________

Student/intern information:

Name____________________ Date__________ Class________________

Vehicle used for this activity:

Year__________ Make____________________ Model________________

Odometer____________________ VIN ____________________

TASK Inspect and test motors, switches, relays, connectors, terminals, wires, and control components/modules of power side window circuits; repair or replace as needed.

NATEF 5G12

Time off__________

Time on__________

Total time__________

CDX Tasksheet Number: H329

1. Using appropriate service information for the vehicle you are working on, research how to inspect and test motors, switches, relays, connectors, terminals, wires, and control components/modules of power side window circuits. List the results.
    a. Motors:
    b. Switches, relays, connectors, terminals, and wires:
    c. Control components/modules:
2. Check your documented procedures with your supervisor/instructor. Supervisor/instructor's initials: __________
3. Using the appropriate service information, inspect and test motors, switches, relays, connectors, terminals, wires, and control components/modules.
4. List the tests you performed and their results:
5. List the cause of the fault:
6. Determine any necessary action(s):

7. Have your supervisor/instructor verify satisfactory completion of this section of the procedure. If instructed, carry out any rectification required.
Supervisor/instructor's initials: ____________

8. Return the vehicle to its beginning condition, and return any tools you used to their proper locations.

9. Discuss the findings with the instructor.

Performance Rating

CDX Tasksheet Number: H329

☐	☐	☐	☐	☐
0	1	2	3	4

Supervisor/instructor signature ________________________________ Date____________

Student/intern information:

Name________________ Date________ Class____________

Vehicle used for this activity:

Year________ Make________________ Model____________

Odometer________________ VIN ____________________

▶ TASK Inspect and test block heaters; determine needed repairs. **NATEF 5G13**

Time off________

Time on________

Total time________

CDX Tasksheet Number: H330

1. Using appropriate service information for the vehicle you are working on, research how to inspect and test block heaters. List the steps you will need to perform:

2. Check your documented procedures with your supervisor/instructor.
   Supervisor/instructor's initials: ________

3. Using the appropriate service information, inspect and test block heaters.

4. List the tests and their results:

5. List the cause of the fault:

6. Determine any necessary action(s):

7. Have your supervisor/instructor verify satisfactory completion of this section of the procedure. If instructed, carry out any rectification required.
   Supervisor/instructor's initials: ________

8. Return the vehicle to its beginning condition, and return any tools you used to their proper locations.

9. Discuss the findings with the instructor.

Performance Rating

CDX Tasksheet Number: H330

☐	☐	☐	☐	☐
0	1	2	3	4

Supervisor/instructor signature ________________ Date________

Student/intern information:

Name_______________ Date_______ Class_______________

Vehicle used for this activity:

Year_______ Make_______________ Model_______________

Odometer_______________ VIN _______________

▶ TASK Inspect and test cruise control electrical components; repair or replace as needed.

NATEF 5G14

Time off_______

Time on_______

Total time_______

CDX Tasksheet Number: H331

1. Using appropriate service information for the vehicle you are working on, research how to inspect and test cruise control electrical components. List the steps you will need to perform:

2. Check your documented procedures with your supervisor/instructor.
Supervisor/instructor's initials: _______

3. Using the appropriate service information, inspect and test cruise control electrical components.

4. List the tests and their results:

5. List the cause of the fault:

6. Determine any necessary action(s):

7. Have your supervisor/instructor verify satisfactory completion of this section of the procedure. If instructed, carry out any rectification required.
Supervisor/instructor's initials: _______

8. Return the vehicle to its beginning condition, and return any tools you used to their proper locations.

9. Discuss the findings with the instructor.

Performance Rating

CDX Tasksheet Number: H331

☐ 0 ☐ 1 ☐ 2 ☐ 3 ☐ 4

Supervisor/instructor signature _______________ Date_______

Student/intern information:

Name________________ Date________ Class____________

Vehicle used for this activity:

Year________ Make________________ Model____________

Odometer________________ VIN ________________

▶ TASK Inspect and test switches, relays, controllers, actuator/solenoids, connectors, terminals, and wires of electric door lock circuits. **NATEF 5G15**

Time off________

Time on________

Total time________

CDX Tasksheet Number: H332

1. Using appropriate service information for the vehicle you are working on, research how to inspect and test switches, relays, connectors, terminals, wires, control components/modules, and actuator/solenoids of electric door lock circuits. List the steps you will need to perform:
   a. Controllers:
   b. Switches, relays, connectors, terminals, and wires:
   c. Actuator/soleniods:
2. Check your documented procedures with your supervisor/instructor.
   Supervisor/instructor's initials: ________
3. Using the appropriate service information, inspect and test switches, relays, controllers, actuator/solenoids, connectors, terminals, and wires of electric door lock circuits.
4. List the tests and their results:
5. List the cause of the fault:
6. Determine any necessary action(s):

7. Have your supervisor/instructor verify satisfactory completion of this section of the procedure. If instructed, carry out any rectification required.
Supervisor/instructor's initials: ___________

8. Return the vehicle to its beginning condition, and return any tools you used to their proper locations.

9. Discuss the findings with the instructor.

Performance Rating

CDX Tasksheet Number: H332

☐ 0 ☐ 1 ☐ 2 ☐ 3 ☐ 4

Supervisor/instructor signature ___________________________ Date___________

Student/intern information:

Name____________________ Date__________ Class________________

Vehicle used for this activity:

Year__________ Make____________________ Model______________

Odometer________________ VIN ____________________

▶ TASK Check operation of keyless and remote lock/unlock devices; determine needed action.

NATEF 5G16

Time off__________

Time on__________

Total time__________

CDX Tasksheet Number: H333

1. Using appropriate service information for the vehicle you are working, research how to check the operation of keyless and remote lock/unlock devices. List the steps you will need to perform:
2. Check your documented procedures with your supervisor/instructor.
   Supervisor/instructor's initials: __________
3. Using the appropriate service information, check the operation of keyless and remote lock/unlock devices.
4. List the tests and their results:
5. List the cause of the fault:
6. Determine any necessary action(s):
7. Have your supervisor/instructor verify satisfactory completion of this section of the procedure. If instructed, carry out any rectification required.
   Supervisor/instructor's initials: __________
8. Return the vehicle to its beginning condition, and return any tools you used to their proper locations.
9. Discuss the findings with the instructor.

Performance Rating

CDX Tasksheet Number: H333

☐	☐	☐	☐	☐
0	1	2	3	4

Supervisor/instructor signature ____________________ Date__________

Student/intern information:

Name____________________ Date__________ Class________________

Vehicle used for this activity:

Year__________ Make____________________ Model________________

Odometer____________________ VIN ________________________

▶ TASK Inspect and test engine cooling fan electrical control components/modules, wiring; repair or replace as needed. **NATEF 5G17**

Time off__________

Time on__________

Total time__________

CDX Tasksheet Number: H334

1. Using appropriate service information for the vehicle you are working on, research how to inspect and test engine cooling fan electrical control components/modules. List the steps you will need to perform:
2. Check your documented procedures with your supervisor/instructor.
   Supervisor/instructor's initials: __________
3. Using the appropriate service information, inspect and test engine cooling fan electrical control components/modules.
4. List the tests and their results:
5. List the cause of the fault:
6. Determine any necessary action(s):
7. Have your supervisor/instructor verify satisfactory completion of this section of the procedure. If instructed, carry out any rectification required.
   Supervisor/instructor's initials: __________
8. Return the vehicle to its beginning condition, and return any tools you used to their proper locations.
9. Discuss the findings with the instructor.

Performance Rating

CDX Tasksheet Number: H334

☐	☐	☐	☐	☐
0	1	2	3	4

Supervisor/instructor signature ________________________ Date__________

Student/intern information:

Name____________________ Date__________ Class________________

Vehicle used for this activity:

Year__________ Make____________________ Model________________

Odometer____________________ VIN ____________________

▶ TASK Identify causes of data bus communication problems; determine needed action.

NATEF 5G18

Time off__________

Time on__________

Total time__________

CDX Tasksheet Number: H335

1. Research causes of data bus-driven communication problems and list them.
2. Examine the vehicle/simulator and determine fault(s) with data bus-driven communication.
3. Describe the customer concern.
4. Using the appropriate service information, determine the steps and service tool and equipment necessary for testing the data bus-driven communications.
5. Diagnose the system. List the tests and their results:
6. Determine any necessary action(s):
7. Return the vehicle to its beginning condition, and return any tools you used to their proper locations.
8. Discuss the findings with the instructor.

Performance Rating

CDX Tasksheet Number: H335

☐ 0 ☐ 1 ☐ 2 ☐ 3 ☐ 4

Supervisor/instructor signature ____________________ Date__________

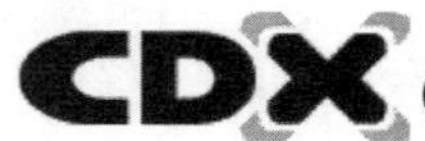

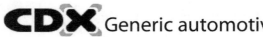

Generic automotive diagnostic procedure

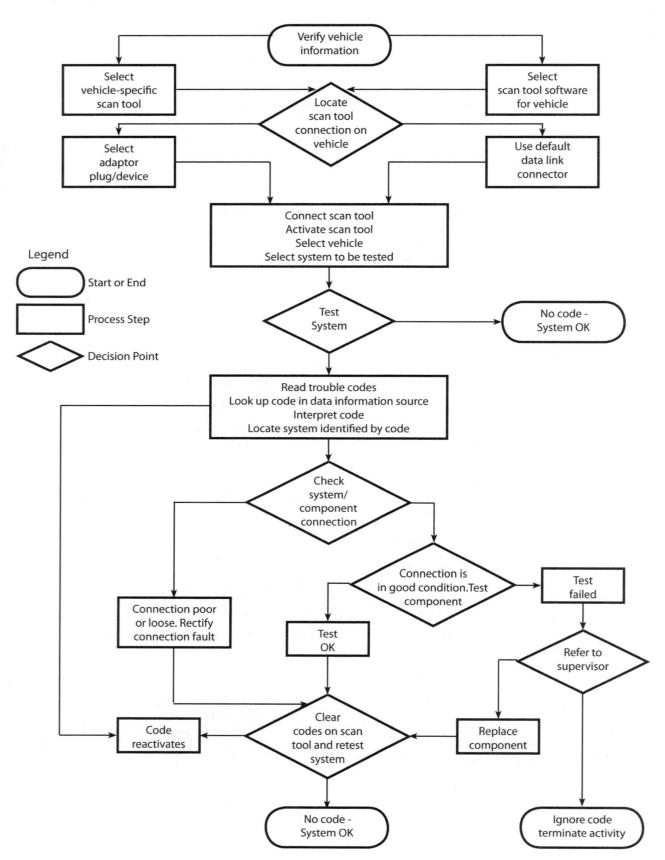

Appendix

CDX Tasksheet Number	NATEF 2014 Medium/Heavy Truck Tasksheet Title	2014 NATEF Reference number	2014 NATEF Priority Level	Page
	Diesel Engines, DT101			
A. General				**3**
H026	Inspect fuel, oil, Diesel Exhaust Fluid (DEF) and coolant levels, and condition; determine needed action.	1A1	P-1	5
H027	Identify engine fuel, oil, coolant, air, and other leaks; determine needed action.	1A2	P-1	7
H028	Listen for engine noises; determine needed action.	1A3	P-3	9
H029	Observe engine exhaust smoke color and quantity; determine needed action.	1A4	P-2	11
H030	Identify causes of no cranking, cranks but fails to start, hard starting, and starts but does not continue to run problems; determine needed action.	1A5	P-1	15
H032	Identify engine vibration problems.	1A7	P-2	17
B. Cylinder Head and Valve Train				**19**
MHT01	Remove, clean, inspect for visible damage and replace cylinder head(s) assembly.	N/A	N/A	21
MHT02	Clean and inspect threaded holes, studs and bolts for serviceability; determine needed action.	N/A	N/A	23
H034	Inspect cylinder head for cracks/damage; check mating surfaces for warpage; check condition of passages; inspect core/expansion and gallery plugs; determine needed action.	1B1	P-2	25
H035	Disassemble head and inspect valves, guides, seats, springs, retainers, rotators, locks and seals; determine needed action.	1B2	P-3	27
H036	Measure valve head height relative to deck and valve face-to-seat contact; determine needed action.	1B3	P-3	29
H037	Inspect injector sleeves and seals; measure injector tip or nozzle protrusion; perform needed action.	1B4	P-3	31
H038	Inspect valve train components; determine needed action.	1B5	P-1	33
H039	Reassemble cylinder head.	1B6	P-3	37
H040	Inspect measure and replace/reinstall overhead camshaft; measure/adjust end play and backlash.	1B7	P-3	41
H041	Inspect electronic wiring harness and brackets for wear, bending, cracks, and looseness; determine needed action.	1B8	P-1	43
H042	Adjust valve bridges (crossheads); adjust valve clearances and injector settings.	1B9	P-2	45
C. Engine Block				**47**
H043	Perform crankcase pressure test; determine needed action.	1C1	P-1	49
H044	Remove, inspect, service, and install pans, covers, vents, gaskets, seals, wear rings, and crankcase ventilation components.	1C2	P-2	51
H045	Disassemble, clean and inspect engine block for cracks/damage; measure mating surfaces for warpage; check condition of passages, core/expansion and gallery plugs; inspect threaded holes, studs, dowel pins and bolts for serviceability; determine needed action.	1C3	P-2	53

CDX Tasksheet Number	NATEF 2014 Medium/Heavy Truck Tasksheet Title	2014 NATEF Reference number	2014 NATEF Priority Level	Page
H046	Inspect cylinder sleeve counterbore lower bore; check bore distortion; determine needed action.	1C4	P-2	57
H047	Clean, inspect and measure cylinder walls or liners for wear and damage; determine needed action.	1C5	P-2	59
H048	Replace/reinstall cylinder liners and seal; check and adjust liner height (protrusion).	1C6	P-2	63
H049	Inspect in-block camshaft bearings for wear and damage; determine needed action.	1C7	P-3	65
H050	Inspect, measure, and replace/reinstall in-block camshaft; measure/adjust end play.	1C8	P-3	67
H051	Clean and inspect crankshaft for surface cracks and journal damage; check condition of oil passages; check passage plugs; measure journal diameter; determine needed action.	1C9	P-2	69
H052	Inspect main bearings for wear patterns and damage; replace as needed; check bearing clearances; check and correct crankshaft end play.	1C10	P-2	71
H053	Inspect, install and time gear train; measure gear backlash; determine needed action.	1C11	P-2	73
H054	Inspect connecting rod bearings for wear patterns; measure pistons, pins, retainers and bushings; perform needed action.	1C12	P-3	77
H055	Determine piston-to-cylinder wall clearance; check ring-to-groove clearance and end gap; install rings on pistons.	1C13	P-3	79
H056	Assemble pistons and connecting rods; install in block; install rod bearings and check clearances.	1C14	P-2	81
H057	Check condition of piston cooling jets (nozzles); determine needed action.	1C15	P-2	85
H058	Inspect and measure crankshaft vibration damper; determine needed action.	1C16	P-3	87
H059	Install and align flywheel housing; inspect flywheel housing(s) to transmission housing/engine mating surface(s) and measure flywheel housing face and bore runout; determine needed action.	1C17	P-3	89
H060	Inspect flywheel/flexplate (including ring gear) and mounting surfaces for cracks and wear; measure runout; determine needed action.	1C18	P-2	91
D. Lubrication Systems Diagnosis and Repair				**93**
H061	Test engine oil pressure and check operation of pressure sensor, gauge and/or sending unit; test engine oil temperature and check operation of temperature sensor; determine needed action.	1D1	P-1	95
H062	Check engine oil level, condition and consumption; determine needed action.	1D2	P-1	97
H063	Inspect and measure oil pump, drives, inlet pipes, and pick-up screens; check drive gear clearance; determine needed action.	1D3	P-3	99
H064	Inspect oil pressure regulator valve(s), by-pass and pressure relief valve(s), oil thermostat, and filters; determine needed action.	1D4	P-3	101
H065	Inspect, clean and test oil cooler and components; determine needed action.	1D5	P-3	103
H066	Inspect turbocharger lubrication and cooling systems; determine needed action.	1D6	P-2	105
H067	Determine proper lubricant and perform oil and filter change.	1D7	P-1	107

CDX Tasksheet Number	NATEF 2014 Medium/Heavy Truck Tasksheet Title	2014 NATEF Reference number	2014 NATEF Priority Level	Page
E. Cooling System				**109**
H068	Check engine coolant type, level, condition and consumption; test coolant for freeze protection and additive package concentration; determine needed action.	1E1	P-1	111
H069	Test coolant temperature and check operation of temperature and level sensors, gauge and/or sending unit; determine needed action.	1E2	P-1	113
H070	Inspect and reinstall/replace pulleys, tensioners and drive belts; adjust drive belts and check alignment.	1E3	P-1	115
H071	Inspect thermostat(s), by passes, housing(s) and seals; replace as needed.	1E4	P-2	117
H072	Recover coolant, flush and refill with recommended coolant/additive package; bleed cooling system.	1E5	P-1	119
H073	Inspect coolant conditioner/filter assembly for leaks; inspect valves, lines and fittings; replace as needed.	1E6	P-1	123
H074	Inspect water pump and hoses, replace as needed.	1E7	P-1	125
H075	Inspect, clean and pressure test radiator, pressure cap, tank(s) and recovery systems; determine needed action.	1E8	P-1	127
H076	Inspect thermostatic cooling fan system (hydraulic, pneumatic and electronic) and fan shroud; replace as needed.	1E9	P-1	129
H077	Inspect turbo charger cooling systems; determine needed action.	1E10	P-2	131
F. Air Induction and Exhaust Systems				**133**
H078	Perform air intake system restriction and leakage tests; determine needed action.	1F1	P-1	135
H079	Perform intake manifold pressure (boost) test; determine needed action.	1F2	P-3	137
H080	Perform exhaust back pressure test; determine needed action.	1F3	P-3	139
H081	Inspect turbocharger(s), wastegate, and piping systems; determine needed action.	1F4	P-2	141
H083	Check air induction system: piping, hoses, clamps, and mounting; service or replace air filter as needed.	1F6	P-1	143
H084	Remove and reinstall turbocharger/wastegate assembly.	1F7	P-3	145
H085	Inspect intake manifold, gaskets, and connections; replace as needed.	1F8	P-3	149
H086	Inspect, clean, and test charge air cooler assemblies; inspect aftercooler assemblies; replace as needed.	1F9	P-2	151
H087	Inspect exhaust manifold, piping, mufflers, and mounting hardware; repair or replace as needed.	1F10	P-2	153
H088	Inspect exhaust after treatment devices; determine necessary action.	1F11	P-2	155
Diesel Fuel System, DT102				
A. General				**159**
H030	Check engine no cranking, cranks but fails to start, hard starting, and starts but does not continue to run problems; determine needed action.	1A5	P-1	161
H031	Identify causes of surging, rough operation, misfiring, low power, slow deceleration, slow acceleration, and shutdown problems; determine needed action.	1A6	P-2	163

CDX Tasksheet Number	NATEF 2014 Medium/Heavy Truck Tasksheet Title	2014 NATEF Reference number	2014 NATEF Priority Level	Page
H033	Check and record electronic diagnostic codes.	1A8	P-1	167
B. Air Induction and Exhaust Systems				**169**
H082	Inspect and test turbocharger(s) (variable ratio/geometry VGT), pneumatic, hydraulic, electronic controls, and actuators.	1F5	P-2	171
H088	Inspect exhaust after treatment devices; determine necessary action.	1F11	P-2	173
H089	Inspect and test preheater/inlet air heater, or glow plug system and controls; perform needed action.	1F12	P-2	175
H090	Inspect and test exhaust gas recirculation (EGR) system including EGR valve, cooler, piping, filter, electronic sensors, controls, and wiring; determine needed action.	1F13	P-2	177
C. Fuel Supply System				**179**
H091	Check fuel level and condition; determine needed action.	1G1.1	P-1	181
H092	Perform fuel supply and return system tests; determine needed action.	1G1.2	P-1	183
H093	Inspect fuel tanks, vents, caps, mounts, valves, screens, crossover system, supply and return lines and fittings; determine needed action.	1G1.3	P-1	185
H094	Inspect, clean and test fuel transfer (lift) pump, pump drives, screens, fuel/water separators/indicators, filters, heaters, coolers, ECM cooling plates and mounting hardware; determine needed action.	1G1.4	P-1	187
H095	Inspect and test pressure regulator systems (check valves, pressure regulator valves, and restrictive fittings); determine needed action.	1G1.5	P-1	189
H096	Check fuel system for air; determine needed action.; prime and bleed fuel system; check primer pump.	1G1.6	P-1	191
D. Electronic Fuel Management System				**193**
H097	Inspect and test power and ground circuits and connections; measure and interpret voltage, voltage drop, amperage, and resistance readings using a digital multimeter (DMM); determine needed action.	1G2.1	P-1	195
H098	Interface with vehicle's on-board computer; perform diagnostic procedures using recommended electronic diagnostic equipment and tools (to include PC based software and/or data scan tools); determine needed action.	1G2.2	P-1	197
H099	Check and record electronic diagnostic codes and trip/operational data; monitor electronic data; clear codes; determine further diagnosis.	1G2.3	P-1	199
H100	Locate and use relevant service information (to include diagnostic procedures, flow charts, and wiring diagrams).	1G2.4	P-1	201
H101	Inspect and replace electrical connector terminals, seals and locks.	1G2.5	P-1	203
H102	Inspect and test switches, sensors, controls, actuator components and circuits; adjust or replace as needed.	1G2.6	P-1	205
H103	Using electronic service tool(s) access and interpret customer programmable parameters.	1G2.7	P-1	207
H104	Perform on-engine inspections and tests on electronic unit injector (EUI) high pressure oil supply and control systems; determine needed action.	1G2.8	P-2	211
H105	Remove and install electronic unit injectors (EUI) and related components; recalibrate ECM (if applicable).	1G2.9	P-2	213

CDX Tasksheet Number	NATEF 2014 Medium/Heavy Truck Tasksheet Title	2014 NATEF Reference number	2014 NATEF Priority Level	Page
H106	Perform cylinder contribution test utilizing recommended electronic service tools.	1G2.10	P-1	215
H107	Perform on-engine inspections and tests on hydraulic electronic unit injectors (HEUI) and system electronic controls; determine needed action.	1G2.11	P-2	217
H108	Perform on-engine inspections and tests on hydraulic electronic unit injector (HEUI) high pressure oil supply and control systems; determine needed action.	1G2.12	P-2	219
H109	Perform on-engine inspections and tests on high pressure common rail type injection (HPCR) type systems; determine needed action.	1G2.13	P-2	221
H110	Inspect high pressure injection lines, hold downs, fittings and seals; determine needed action.	1G2.14	P-2	223
E. Engine Brakes				**225**
H111	Inspect and adjust engine compression/exhaust brakes; determine needed action.	1H1	P-2	227
H112	Inspect, test and adjust engine compression/exhaust brake control circuits, switches and solenoids; repair or replace as needed.	1H2	P-3	229
H113	Inspect engine compression/exhaust brake housing, valves, seals, lines and fittings; repair or replace as needed.	1H3	P-3	231
Heavy Duty Drive Trains, DT103				
A. Clutch Diagnosis and Repair				**235**
H114	Identify causes of clutch noise, binding, slippage, pulsation, vibration, grabbing, dragging, and chatter problems; determine needed action.	2A1	P-1	237
H115	Inspect and adjust clutch linkage, cables, levers, brackets, bushings, pivots, springs and clutch safety switch (includes push and pull-type assemblies; check pedal height and travel; perform needed action.	2A2	P-1	239
H116	Inspect, adjust, repair or replace hydraulic clutch slave and master cylinders, lines and hoses and bleed system.	2A3	P-2	241
H117	Inspect adjust, lubricate or replace release (throw-out) bearing, sleeve, bushings, springs, housing, levers, release fork, fork pads, rollers, shafts and seals.	2A4	P-1	243
H118	Inspect, adjust and replace single-disc clutch pressure plate and clutch disc.	2A5	P-1	247
H119	Inspect, adjust and replace two-plate clutch pressure plate, clutch discs, intermediate plate and drive pins/lugs.	2A6	P-1	249
H120	Inspect and/or replace clutch brake assembly; inspect input shaft and bearing retainer; perform needed action.	2A7	P-2	251
H121	Inspect, adjust and replace self-adjusting/continuous-adjusting clutch mechanisms.	2A8	P-1	253
H122	Inspect and replace pilot bearing.	2A9	P-1	255
H123	Remove and reinstall flywheel, inspect flywheel mounting area on crankshaft, rear main oil seal and measure crankshaft end play; determine needed action.	2A10	P-1	257
H124	Inspect flywheel, starter ring gear and measure flywheel face and pilot bore; determine needed action.	2A11	P-1	259

CDX Tasksheet Number	NATEF 2014 Medium/Heavy Truck Tasksheet Title	2014 NATEF Reference number	2014 NATEF Priority Level	Page
H125	Inspect flywheel housing(s) to transmission housing/engine mating surface(s) and measure flywheel housing face and bore runout; determine needed action.	2A12	P-2	261
B. Transmission/Transaxle Diagnosis and Repair				**263**
H126	Identify causes of transmission noise, shifting, lockup, jumping-out-of-gear, overheating, and vibration problems; determine needed action.	2B1	P-1	265
H127	Inspect, test, repair or replace air shift controls, lines, hoses, valves, regulators, filters and cylinder assemblies.	2B2	P-2	267
H128	Inspect and replace transmission mounts, insulators, and mounting bolts.	2B3	P-1	269
H129	Inspect for leakage and replace transmission cover plates, gaskets, seals, and cap bolts; inspect seal surfaces and vents; repair as needed.	2B4	P-1	271
H130	Check transmission fluid level and condition; determine needed service; add proper type of lubricant.	2B5	P-1	273
H131	Inspect, adjust and replace transmission shift lever, cover, rails, forks, levers, bushings, sleeves, detents, interlocks, springs and lock bolts/safety wires.	2B6	P-2	277
H132	Remove and reinstall transmission.	2B7	P-1	279
H133	Inspect input shaft, gear, spacers, bearings, retainers and slingers; determine needed action.	2B8	P-3	281
H134	Inspect transmission oil filters and coolers; replace as needed.	2B9	P-2	283
H135	Inspect speedometer components; determine needed action.	2B10	P-2	285
H136	Inspect and adjust power take-off (P.T.O.) assemblies, controls, and shafts; determine needed action.	2B11	P-3	289
H137	Inspect and test function of reverse light, neutral start and warning device circuits; determine needed action.	2B12	P-1	291
H138	Inspect and test transmission temperature gauge and sensor/sending unit; determine needed action.	2B13	P-2	293
H139	Inspect and test operation of automated mechanical transmission and manual electronic shift controls, shift, range and splitter solenoids, shift motors, indicators, speed and range sensors, electronic/transmission control unit (ECU/TCU), neutral/in gear and reverse switches, and wiring harnesses; determine needed action.	2B14	P-2	295
H140	Inspect and test operation of automated mechanical transmission electronic shift selectors, air and electrical switches, displays and indicators, wiring harnesses, and air lines; determine needed action.	2B15	P-2	299
H141	Use appropriate electronic service tool(s) and procedures to diagnose automated mechanical transmission problems; check and record diagnostic codes, clear codes, and interpret digital multimeter (DMM) readings; determine needed action.	2B16	P-1	301
H142	Inspect and test operation of automatic transmission electronic shift controls, shift solenoids, shift motors, indicators, speed and range sensors, electronic/transmission control units (ECU/TCU), neutral/in gear and reverse switches, and wiring harnesses.	2B17	P-2	303
H143	Inspect and test operation of automatic transmission electronic shift selectors, switches, displays and indicators, wiring harnesses.	2B18	P-2	305

CDX Tasksheet Number	NATEF 2014 Medium/Heavy Truck Tasksheet Title	2014 NATEF Reference number	2014 NATEF Priority Level	Page
H144	Use appropriate electronic service tool(s) and procedures to diagnose automatic transmission problems; check and record diagnostic codes, clear codes and interpret digital multimeter (DMM) readings; determine needed action.	2B19	P-3	307
C. Drive Shaft and Universal Joint				**309**
H145	Identify cause of driveshaft and universal joint noise and vibration problems; determine needed action.	2C1	P-1	311
H146	Inspect, service, or replace driveshaft, slip joint, yokes, drive flanges, and universal joints, driveshaft boots and seals, and retaining hardware; check phasing of all shafts.	2C2	P-1	313
H147	Inspect driveshaft center support bearings and mounts; determine needed action.	2C3	P-1	315
H148	Measure driveline angles; determine needed action.	2C4	P-1	317
D. Axle				**321**
H149	Identify cause of drive axle(s) drive unit noise and overheating problems; determine needed action.	2D1	P-2	323
H150	Check and repair fluid leaks; inspect and replace drive axle housing cover plates, gaskets, sealants, vents, magnetic plugs and seals.	2D2	P-1	325
H151	Check drive axle fluid level and condition; determine needed service; add proper type of lubricant.	2D3	P-1	327
H152	Remove and replace differential carrier assembly.	2D4	P-2	329
H153	Inspect and replace differential case assembly including spider gears, cross shaft, side gears, thrust washers, case halves and bearings.	2D5	P-3	331
H154	Inspect and replace components of locking differential case assembly.	2D6	P-3	333
H155	Inspect differential carrier housing and caps, side bearings bores, and pilot (spigot, pocket) bearing bore; determine needed action.	2D7	P-3	335
H156	Measure ring gear runout; determine needed action.	2D8	P-2	339
H157	Inspect and replace ring and drive pinion gears, spacers, sleeves, bearing cages and bearings.	2D9	P-3	341
H158	Measure and adjust drive pinion bearing preload.	2D10	P-3	343
H159	Measure and adjust drive pinion depth.	2D11	P-3	345
H160	Measure and adjust side bearing preload and ring gear backlash.	2D12	P-2	347
H161	Check and interpret ring rear and pinion tooth contact pattern; determine needed action.	2D13	P-2	349
H162	Inspect, adjust or replace ring gear thrust block/screw.	2D14	P-3	351
H163	Inspect power divider (inter-axle differential) assembly; determine needed action.	2D15	P-3	353
H164	Inspect, adjust, repair or replace air operated power divider (inter-axle differential) lockout assembly including diaphragms, seals, springs, yokes, pins, lines, hoses, fittings and controls.	2D16	P-2	357
H165	Inspect, repair or replace drive axle lubrication system; pump, troughs, collectors, slingers, tubes, and filters.	2D17	P-3	359
H166	Inspect and replace drive axle shafts.	2D18	P-1	361
H167	Remove and replace wheel assembly; check rear wheel seal and axle flange gasket for leaks; perform needed action.	2D19	P-1	363

CDX Tasksheet Number	NATEF 2014 Medium/Heavy Truck Tasksheet Title	2014 NATEF Reference number	2014 NATEF Priority Level	Page
H168	Identify cause of drive axle for wheel bearing noise and check for damage; perform needed action.	2D20	P-1	367
H169	Inspect and test drive axle temperature gauge, wiring harnesses, and sending unit/sensor; determine needed action.	2D21	P-2	369
H170	Clean, inspect, lubricate and replace wheel bearings; replace seals and wear rings; inspect and replace retaining hardware; adjust drive axle wheel bearings.	2D22	P-1	371
Truck Electrical & Electronics, DT108				
A. General Electric Systems				**375**
H271	Read, interpret, and diagnose electrical/electronic circuits using wiring diagrams.	5A1	P-1	377
H272	Check continuity in electrical/electronic circuits using appropriate test equipment.	5A2	P-1	379
H273	Check applied voltages, circuit voltages and voltage drops in electrical/electronic circuits using appropriate test equipment.	5A3	P-1	381
H274	Check current flow in electrical/electronic circuits and components using appropriate test equipment.	5A4	P-1	383
H275	Check resistance in electrical/electronic circuits and components using appropriate test equipment.	5A5	P-1	385
H276	Locate shorts, grounds and opens in electrical/electronic circuits.	5A6	P-1	387
H277	Identify parasitic (key-off) battery drain problems; perform tests; determine needed action.	5A7	P-1	389
H278	Inspect and test fusible links, circuit breakers, relays, solenoids, and fuses; replace as needed.	5A8	P-1	391
H279	Inspect and test spike suppression devices; replace as needed.	5A9	P-3	393
H280	Check frequency and pulse width; in electrical/electronic circuits using appropriate test equipment.	5A10	P-3	395
B. Battery				**397**
H281	Identify battery type; perform appropriate battery load test; determine needed action.	5B1	P-1	399
H282	Determine battery state of charge using an open circuit voltage test.	5B2	P-1	401
H283	Inspect, clean, and service battery; replace as needed.	5B3	P-1	403
H284	Inspect and clean battery boxes, mounts, and hold downs; repair or replace as needed.	5B4	P-1	405
H285	Charge battery using slow or fast charge method as appropriate.	5B5	P-1	407
H286	Inspect, test and clean battery cables and connectors; repair or replace as needed.	5B6	P-1	409
H287	Jump start a vehicle using jumper cables and a booster battery or appropriate auxiliary power supply using proper safety procedures.	5B7	P-1	411
H288	Perform battery capacitance test; determine needed action.	5B8	P-2	413
H289	Identify and test low voltage disconnect (LVD) systems; determine needed repair.	5B9	P-2	415

CDX Tasksheet Number	NATEF 2014 Medium/Heavy Truck Tasksheet Title	2014 NATEF Reference number	2014 NATEF Priority Level	Page
C. Starting System				**417**
H290	Perform starter circuit cranking voltage and voltage drop tests; determine needed action.	5C1	P-1	419
H291	Inspect and test components (key switch, push button and/or magnetic switch) and wires in the starter control circuit; replace as needed.	5C2	P-2	423
H292	Inspect and test, starter relays and solenoids/switches; replace as needed.	5C3	P-1	425
H293	Remove and replace starter; inspect flywheel ring gear or flex plate.	5C4	P-1	427
D. Charging System Diagnosis and Repair				**429**
H294	Test instrument panel mounted volt meters and/or indicator lamps; determine needed action.	5D1	P-1	431
H295	Identify cause of a no charge, low charge or overcharge problems; determine needed action.	5D2	P-1	433
H296	Inspect and replace alternator drive belts, pulleys, fans, tensioners, and mounting brackets; adjust drive belts and check alignment.	5D3	P-1	435
H297	Perform charging system voltage and amperage output test; perform AC ripple test; determine needed action.	5D4	P-1	437
H298	Perform charging circuit voltage drop tests; determine needed action.	5D5	P-1	439
H299	Remove and replace alternator.	5D6	P-1	441
H300	Inspect, repair, or replace cables, wires, and connectors in the charging circuit.	5D7	P-1	443
E. Lighting Systems				**445**
H301	Interface with vehicle's on-board computer; perform diagnostic procedures using recommended electronic diagnostic equipment and tools (including PC based software and/or data scan tools); determine needed action.	5E1	P-1	447
H302	Identify causes of brighter than normal, intermittent, dim or no headlight and daytime running light (DRL) operation.	5E2	P-1	449
H303	Test, aim, and replace headlights.	5E3	P-1	451
H304	Test headlight and dimmer circuit switches relays, wires, terminals, connectors, sockets, and control components/modules; repair or replace as needed.	5E4	P-1	453
H305	Inspect and test switches, bulbs/LEDs, sockets, connectors, terminals, relays, and wires, and control components/modules of parking, clearance and taillight circuits; repair or replace as needed.	5E5	P-1	455
H306	Inspect and test instrument panel light circuit switches, relays, bulbs/LED's, sockets, connectors, terminals, wires and printed circuits/control modules; repair or replace as needed.	5E6	P-2	457
H307	Inspect and test interior cab light circuit switches, bulbs, sockets, connectors, terminals, wires, and control component/modules; repair or replace as needed.	5E7	P-2	459
H308	Inspect and test tractor-to-trailer multi-wire connector(s); repair or replace as needed.	5E8	P-1	461

CDX Tasksheet Number	NATEF 2014 Medium/Heavy Truck Tasksheet Title	2014 NATEF Reference number	2014 NATEF Priority Level	Page
H309	Inspect, test and adjust stoplight circuit switches, bulbs/LEDs, sockets, connectors, terminals, wires and control components/modules; replace or repair as needed.	5E9	P-1	463
H310	Inspect and test turn signal and hazard circuit flasher(s), switched, relays, bulbs/LEDs, sockets, connectors, terminals, wires and control components/modules; repair or replace as needed.	5E10	P-2	465
H311	Inspect and test reverse lights and warning device circuit switches, bulbs/LEDs, sockets, horns, buzzers, connectors, terminals, wires and control components/modules; repair or replace as needed.	5E11	P-1	467
F. Gauges and Warning Devices				**471**
H312	Interface with vehicle's on-board computer; perform diagnostic procedure using recommended electronic diagnostic equipment and tools (including PC based software and/or data scan tools); determine needed action.	5F1	P-1	473
H313	Identify causes of intermittent, high, low, or no gauge readings; determine needed action.	5F2	P-2	475
H314	Identify causes of data bus-driven gauge malfunctions; determine needed action.	5F3	P-3	477
H315	Inspect and test gauge circuit sensor/sending units, gauges, connectors, terminals, and wires; repair or replace as needed.	5F4	P-2	479
H316	Inspect and test warning devices (lights and audible) circuit sensor/sending units, bulbs/LEDs, sockets, connectors, wires, and control components/modules; repair or replace as needed.	5F5	P-1	481
H317	Inspect, test, replace, and calibrate (if applicable) electronic speedometer, odometer, and tachometer systems.	5F6	P-2	483
G. Related Electronic Systems				**487**
H318	Interface with vehicle's on-board computer; perform diagnostic procedures using recommended electronic diagnostic equipment and tools (including PC based software and/or data scan tools); determine needed action.	5G1	P-1	489
H319	Identify causes of constant, intermittent, or no horn operation; determine needed action.	5G2	P-2	491
H320	Inspect and test horn circuit relays, horns, switches, connectors, wires and control components/modules; repair or replace as needed.	5G3	P-2	493
H321	Identify causes of constant, intermittent, or no wiper operation; diagnose the cause of wiper speed control and/or park problems; determine needed action.	5G4	P-2	495
H322	Inspect and test wiper motor, resistors, park switch, relays, switches, connectors, wires and control components/modules; repair or replace as needed.	5G5	P-2	497
H323	Inspect wiper motor transmission linkage, arms, and blades; adjust or replace as needed.	5G6	P-2	499
H324	Inspect and test windshield washer motor or pump/relay assembly, switches, connectors, terminals, wires, and control components/modules; repair or replace as needed.	5G7	P-3	501
H325	Inspect and test side view mirror motors, heater circuit grids, relays, switches, connectors, terminals, wires, and control components/modules; repair or replace as needed.	5G8	P-3	503

CDX Tasksheet Number	NATEF 2014 Medium/Heavy Truck Tasksheet Title	2014 NATEF Reference number	2014 NATEF Priority Level	Page
H326	Inspect and test heater and A/C electrical components including: A/C clutches, motors, resistors, relays, switches, connectors, terminals, wires, and control components/modules; repair or replace as needed.	5G9	P-3	505
H327	Inspect and test auxiliary power outlet, integral fuse, connectors, terminals, wires, and control components/modules; repair or replace as needed.	5G10	P-3	507
H328	Identify causes of slow, intermittent, or no power side window operation; determine needed action.	5G11	P-3	509
H329	Inspect and test motors, switches, relays, connectors, terminals, wires, and control components/modules of power side window circuits; repair or replace as needed.	5G12	P-3	511
H330	Inspect and test block heaters; determine needed repairs.	5G13	P-3	513
H331	Inspect and test cruise control electrical components; repair or replace as needed.	5G14	P-3	515
H332	Inspect and test switches, relays, controllers, actuator/solenoids, connectors, terminals, and wires of electric door lock circuits.	5G15	P-3	517
H333	Check operation of keyless and remote lock/unlock devices; determine needed action.	5G16	P-3	519
H334	Inspect and test engine cooling fan electrical control components/ modules; repair or replace as needed.	5G17	P-2	521
H335	Identify causes of data bus communication problems; determine needed action.	5G18	P-2	523